Direct-current Machinery

The quality of the materials used in the manufacture of this book is governed by continued postwar shortages.

DIRECT-CURRENT
MACHINERY

By GROVER C. BLALOCK, E. E.

Professor of Electrical Engineering
Purdue University

First Edition
Second Impression

McGRAW-HILL BOOK COMPANY, Inc.

NEW YORK AND LONDON

1947

DIRECT-CURRENT MACHINERY

Preface

Some ten or twelve years ago it was generally assumed by engineers and educators that the use of d-c machinery in the industries was declining and would ultimately reach the vanishing point, and in this belief the semester hours devoted to d-c machinery were reduced in order to make room in the crowded curriculum for other subjects, such as electronics, that were clamoring for time and space as required subjects. Subsequent sales and applications have disproved the accuracy of this assumption; in fact, the sales volume of d-c machinery, as compared with the sales volume of a-c machinery, has shown a decided gain within recent years. In view of this, it has become necessary in many schools to find room for additional hours to be devoted to d-c machinery and controls. The practice of tailoring machines and their controls to meet the needs of specific applications is growing rapidly; and, unless students are given some insight into the matters of specialized d-c machinery and specialized control equipment, they will find themselves seriously handicapped in attempting to fit themselves into jobs calling for applications of d-c machinery to specific industrial drives.

In line with the above conclusions, the author has endeavored in this text to present a concise but balanced picture, including basic and specialized d-c machines and their controls. Free use has been made of practical illustrative examples, problems, and illustrations, in an attempt to give the student a real conception of the practical significance of the theory studied. It is presumed that the student will have covered the principles of electric and magnetic circuits in a previous course and will have covered the necessary mathematics for understanding the derivations of essential equations.

Since the text is intended for relatively brief courses, the treatment is neither exhaustive nor highly theoretical. Fundamental derivations are supplied for most of the equations, with suitable discussion for justification of the equation and examples

v

to show its application to practical conditions. Operating characteristics of generators and motors, with moderate emphasis upon design features, are presented with the idea of giving the student a reasonably good background of theory upon which to base judgment in making selections of machines for specific applications. The problems following each chapter have been carefully selected, and it is believed that their analysis and solution by the student will be of material aid in digesting the text material.

A chapter on batteries is included because storage batteries are definitely linked with d-c machinery in that they are so generally used in conjunction with it.

GROVER C. BLALOCK

WEST LAFAYETTE, IND.,
July, 1947.

Contents

Chapter IV, COMMUTATION, ARMATURE REACTION

Art.

Chapter V, OPERATION OF GENERATORS

Chapter VI, GENERATOR CHARACTERISTICS

CHAPTER VII, DIRECT-CURRENT MOTORS

CHAPTER VIII, MOTOR CONTROL

CHAPTER IX, LOSSES, EFFICIENCIES

Chapter XIII, BATTERIES

CHAPTER I

ELECTROMAGNETIC INDUCTION

1. Electromotive Force.—In order that current may flow over the wires of an electric circuit, an electromotive force must be established and maintained between the two ends of the circuit, or a difference of potential must be maintained between the terminal points. This may be accomplished in any one of several ways, but essentially the system must include a battery or a dynamo type of electric generator as the source from which electrical energy is supplied to the circuit. It should be understood, however, that these so-called primary sources of electricity are not, in themselves, sources of energy but merely transform energy from a chemical or mechanical form to an electrical form so that it may be more conveniently transferred from one location to another and may be more effectively applied to its final task of lighting lamps, operating machinery, etc. Thus the energy of burning coal or falling water may be transferred many miles at moderate cost to light our homes and operate our factories. Battery sources of electrical energy, though useful in many ways and for many purposes, are too limited in power and energy capacity to be depended upon for the operation of lighting and motor circuits of any considerable size. For such circuits, generating stations using the energy of coal or falling water for the operation of turbines and electric generators must be provided.

The experiments of Michael Faraday (1830–1831) resulted, among other things, in the discovery that an electromotive force may be established between the ends of a conductor in three principal ways and that, when the ends of the conductor are joined, an electric current will flow as long as the difference in potential between the two ends is maintained.

Methods of establishing a difference in electric potential between the ends of conductors, as determined by Faraday, are

a. By a conductor moving or cutting across a stationary magnetic field.

b. By a moving magnetic field cutting across a stationary conductor.

c. By a change in the number of magnetic lines enclosed by a stationary loop or coil.

Direct-current electric generators are usually designed to operate by the first method, and alternating-current generators usually operate by the second method. This difference between the two machines is necessary because of the need for rectification, after generation, of the emf in the d-c machine and because of the higher values of emf, with a consequent need for better insulation, in the a-c generator.

The third method of establishing an emf is utilized in the design and operation of induction coils and transformers and finds little direct application in connection with d-c circuits and machinery.

2. Laws of Induction.—The following laws, relating to induced electromotive forces, were first discovered by Faraday and later studied and summarized by Lenz. They are the basic laws governing the actions of generators, motors, and transformers, the first being commonly referred to as *Lenz's law* and the second as *Faraday's law.*

First Law.—A change in the magnetic flux passing through, or linking with, a loop or coil causes emf to be induced in a direction to oppose any change in circuit conditions, this opposition being produced magnetically when current flows in response to the induced emf.

Second Law.—The emf induced between the ends of a loop or coil is proportional to the *rate of change* of magnetic flux enclosed by the coil; or the emf induced between the ends of a bar conductor is proportional to the time rate at which magnetic flux is cut by the conductor.

The first law is one of reaction and has its basis in the fundamental principle of energy conservation. The second law emphasizes rate of change, or rate of flux cutting, rather than density or extent of the magnetic field. Thus movement of either the conductor or the magnetic flux lines may induce a voltage, the value of which may be altered by variation in the rate of movement. But movement of either the conductor or the flux lines is not essential, since a change in the number of lines threading a stationary coil likewise results in voltage induction. Both these laws are of importance in connection with all electrical machinery and circuits. The final statement of the second law has perhaps the most obvious and direct application to d-c machinery, since all d-c motors and generators operate with conductors moving across the flux lines of a magnetic field.

3. Polarities of Induced Electromotive Forces.—The polarities of the emfs induced by methods a and b (Art. 1) are definite and are always the same for a given direction of the magnetic flux field in combination with a given direction of motion of the conductor relative to the field. Basically the direction of the induced emf in any coil or conductor follows Lenz's law and may be determined by reasoning upon this basis, when the directions of field and movement are known. A convenient conventional method, with no basic reasoning back of it, is known as Fleming's *right-hand rule* and is applied by extending the thumb, forefinger, and middle finger of the right hand, perpendicular to one another, in such a position that the thumb indicates the direction of motion of the conductor relative to the magnetic field and the forefinger points in the direction of the magnetic field, the middle finger then indicating the direction of the induced emf. If any two of the three factors here involved—direction of movement of conductor relative to the magnetic field, direction of the magnetic field, and direction of the induced emf—are known, the other may be determined by this method.

Another convenient means of determining the direction of the induced voltage in a conductor, when the directions of the flux field and of the conductor movement are known, is to consider the direction of the flux lines when they are bent to encircle the conductor as it presses through the elastic medium. The direction of these encircling flux lines will indicate the direction of current flow in the conductor, since there is a definite relation between the direction of current flow and the direction of the flux lines surrounding the conductor.[1]

[1] Ampere's right-hand-rule: Consider that the right hand grasps the conductor with the thumb pointing in the direction of current flow; the fingers then point in the direction that the magnetic flux lines encircle the conductor.

The direction of the emf induced by method *c* is such that, if a conducting path is established between the ends of the loop or coil, the current that flows through the circuit thus established sets up a magnetic field in opposition to the change in flux that induces the emf—as stated in Lenz's law. When the induction of emf results from a collapsing magnetic field, the induced emf will be in the direction to cause current flow and magnetism in a direction to strengthen the collapsing magnetic field; but, if the induction of emf results from increasing magnetic field, the induced emf will be in the opposite direction relatively, the resulting current flow being in a direction to set up a magnetic field in opposition to the original field.

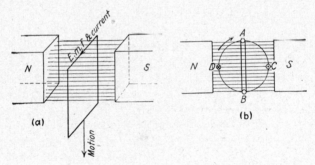

FIG. 1.—Generation of electromotive force.

In diagram *a* of Fig. 1, one side of the coil is shown cutting across the magnetic flux, and the amount of flux enclosed by the loop is decreasing. The direction of current flow in the loop is therefore, according to Lenz's law, such as to set up a magnetic field in the same direction as the causative, or primary, field. If the direction of movement and position of the wire loop were such as to cause an increase in amount of flux enclosed by the loop, the current would reverse and set up a magnetic field in opposition to the primary field. Thus a reversal in direction of motion of the loop will result in reversal of current in the loop each time the direction is changed if—and this is essential—a change is made from decreasing to increasing amount of flux enclosed by the loop, or vice versa.

In diagram *b* of Fig. 1, the coil encloses a maximum amount of magnetic flux when it occupies position *AB*. The amount of enclosed flux grows less as the coil moves toward position *CD*, becomes zero when it reaches *CD*, since the plane of the coil is now parallel with the magnetic field, then begins to increase *in the opposite direction* after position *CD* is passed, reaching a negative maximum when position *BA* is reached, diminishing again to zero at position *DC*, and reversing and increasing again in the original direction to a maximum as it again reaches position *AB*.

Since the induced emf depends upon *rate of change* in magnetic flux threading the coil, or *rate of cutting* lines of magnetic flux, the induced emf will be maximum as the coil passes positions *CD* and

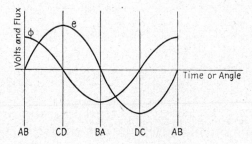

Fig. 2.—Sine wave of voltage, produced by rotation of a coil at uniform speed in a flux field of uniform density.

DC but will be zero as the coil passes positions *AB* and *BA*, although the *quantity* of magnetic flux threading the coil will be maximum at positions *AB* and *BA* and zero at positions *CD* and *DC*. It should also be noted that the *rate of cutting* by the coil sides is maximum at positions *CD* and *DC* and zero at positions *AB* and *BA*. Such a coil, rotated at uniform speed in a magnetic field of uniform density, will generate emfs, that when plotted against time or angle, will form a sine curve—commonly known as a *sine wave*. Figure 2 illustrates a sine wave of voltage values in conjunction with a similar wave of flux values, the changes in which cause the induction of voltage. The time relationships between these waves bear out the statements previously made as to dependency of induced voltage upon rate of change in flux threading the coil, the lettered points upon the figure corresponding with the lettered positions of the coil in Fig. 1.

The sine wave of induced voltage values is the ideal form sought by the designer of a-c generators, and the usual a-c voltage wave approximates this form.

4. Value of Induced Voltage.—The cgs unit of emf, or induced voltage, called the *abvolt*, is defined as that value induced, in a coil of one turn, when the flux linking with the coil is changing at the rate of one line, or maxwell, per second; or as that value induced when magnetic flux is being cut by the conductor at the rate of 1 maxwell per second.

The abvolt is a very small unit, much too small for practical use. The volt, equal to 10^8 abvolts, is the practical unit commonly used. Also, for checking purposes, working standards are provided by certain standard cells having quite definite and constant voltage.

Since emf is proportional to the rate of change of flux, or to the rate at which a conductor cuts across a magnetic field, its instantaneous value is expressed as a derivative

$$e = N\frac{d\phi}{dt} \qquad \text{abvolts} \tag{1}$$

or

$$e = N\frac{d\phi}{dt} \times 10^{-8} \qquad \text{volts} \tag{2}$$

where N = number of series turns in the coil or conductor.

However, we are frequently concerned with the average value over a definite interval of time, and this is obtained by dividing the total change in magnetic flux, or the total lines cut, by the time consumed; therefore

$$E = N\frac{\phi}{T} \times 10^{-8} \qquad \text{volts} \tag{3}$$

where ϕ is expressed in maxwells. The factor 10^8 drops out if ϕ is expressed in webers, as in the mks system, recently adopted but not yet in general use.

For movement of a conductor at constant velocity through a uniform field, the voltage may also be calculated as

$$E = Blv \sin \theta \times 10^{-8} \qquad \text{volts} \tag{4}$$

where B is magnetic flux density, l is length of conductor, v is velocity, and θ is the angle made by the conductor with the flux field. If the conductor moves directly across the field at right angles to it, then $\theta = 90$ deg and $\sin \theta = 1$. If there are N conductors in series, as in a coil, moving directly across and at right angles to the flux field,

$$E = NBlv \times 10^{-8} \qquad \text{volts} \qquad (5)$$

The units must be consistent as, for instance, if B is given in gausses—flux lines per square centimeter—l must be in centimeters and v in centimeters per second in order that the product may be the total lines cut by the conductor per second; or, if B is given in flux lines per square inch, l must be in inches and v in inches per second. It should be noted that Eqs. (4) and (5) are special forms of the basic rule as stated by Eqs. (1) and (2). The rule is convenient for use in calculation of generated voltages in d-c machinery but is not universally applicable to all possible cases involving relative motion of conductors and magnetic fields.[1]

5. Self-induction.—Since every conductor, when carrying current, is surrounded by magnetic flux that increases and decreases in amount and extent as the current through the conductor increases and decreases in value, the flux emanating from each turn on a coil must cut across other turns of the coil, in one direction when current and flux are increasing and in the opposite direction when they are decreasing; or, as sometimes stated, the direction of flux cutting across the turns of the coil depends upon whether the magnetic field is expanding or collapsing. Accordingly, a counter emf of self-induction is induced in the turns of the coil, the direction of this emf being such as to oppose change in value of the current flowing in the coil, in accordance with Lenz's law (Art. 2). To denote the oppositional character of the emf induced in this manner, the negative sign is used in conjunction with Eqs. (1) and (2). thus

$$e = -N\frac{d\phi}{dt} \times 10^{-8} \qquad \text{volts} \qquad (6)$$

[1] For further discussion of the limitations of this rule, see George V. Mueller, "Introduction to Electrical Engineering," Art. 95, McGraw-Hill Book Company, Inc., 1940.

The voltage of self-induction may also be expressed as

$$e = -L\frac{di}{dt} \quad \text{volts} \tag{7}$$

where

$$L = N\frac{d\phi}{di} \times 10^{-8} \quad \text{henrys} \tag{8}$$

L being the symbol used for inductance, the unit of which is called the *henry.*

If the magnetic circuit is not being operated near the region of saturation, or if the core is of nonmagnetic material, the magnetic flux will be directly proportional to the current, and

$$L = N\frac{\phi}{I} \times 10^{-8} \quad \text{henrys} \tag{9}$$

In this case, the inductance may be said to equal the number of linkages[1] per unit current divided by 10^8.

Following this, it will be evident that a circuit in which a change of 1 amp causes a change of 10^8 linkages will have an inductance of 1 henry and also that application of 1 volt in a circuit of 1 henry inductance and negligible resistance will cause current to accelerate in the circuit at the rate of 1 amp per sec. From this, the deduction may be made that the inductance of a circuit, in henrys, is equal to the emf in volts required to cause a current to accelerate in that circuit at the rate of 1 amp per sec.

Since, for a coil with N turns on a magnetic circuit of length l, cross section A, and permeability μ, the magnetic flux

$$\phi = \frac{\text{mmf}}{R} = \frac{0.4\pi NI}{l/A\mu} = \frac{0.4\pi NIA\mu}{l} \tag{10}$$

therefore, from Eq. (9),

$$L = \frac{N\phi}{I} \times 10^{-8} = \frac{4\pi N^2 A\mu}{l} \times 10^{-9} \tag{11}$$

thus showing that, for a coil having a magnetic circuit of constant permeability, the inductance varies as the square of the number of turns.

---

[1] The product of conductor turns or loops, and the flux lines cutting or linking with these turns, is usually referred to as *linkages.*

Equation (9) offers a convenient means of calculating the inductance of circuits in which the value of magnetic flux for a given current is known or can be calculated, as in the case of circuits or coils without iron or other magnetic material in their flux paths.

Example.—A transmission line is calculated to have a magnetic flux of 37.5×10^6 maxwells passing between the parallel wires per mile of line when a current of 100 amp is flowing. What is the inductance per mile of line?

Solution:

$$L = \frac{\phi}{I} \times 10^{-8} = \frac{37.5 \times 10^6}{100 \times 10^8}$$
$$0.00375 \text{ henry } = 3.75 \text{ milhenrys}$$

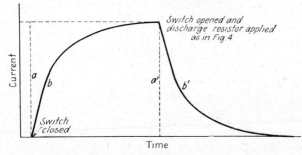

FIG. 3.—Effect of self-induction upon the time required to establish or interrupt current flow.

One result of self-induction, or inductance, in the d-c circuit is the requirement of a time interval for the building up of current in the circuit, the time required being dependent upon the number of coils in the circuit and their disposition, the nature of the core on which the coil is wound, and the value of the circuit resistance. The establishment of a magnetic field requires an expenditure of energy and therefore involves the time element. When the current decreases, the same amount of energy must be returned to the circuit or expended in some other way. Flashing at the switch points when current in an inductive circuit is being interrupted indicates that a portion of the stored energy is being used up as heat at this point.

6. Energy Stored in a Magnetic Field.—Since an opposing voltage must be overcome in setting up a magnetic field about the turns of a coil, work is done and energy is stored in the field when the exciting current is brought up from zero to any stated value. Maintaining the field at a constant value requires no expenditure of energy, but the energy expended in building up the field—the energy stored in the field and remaining there as long as the current is maintained at a steady value—is released when the circuit is interrupted and the current reduced to zero. Energy is required, also, to supply the heat losses in coils and core due to resistance, eddy currents, and hysteresis, and this energy is dissipated as waste heat to the surrounding air.

The power required at any instant in setting up a magnetic field may be stated as

$$p = ei \tag{12}$$

and the energy for the time dt

$$dw = pdt = eidt \tag{13}$$

or, substituting the value of e from Eq. (7), with a positive sign to represent the applied voltage necessary to overcome the counter emf of self-induction,

$$dw = Lidi \tag{14}$$

The total energy required to set up the field is represented by the integrated energy between zero current and current I, or

$$W = L \int_0^I idi = L\frac{I^2}{2} \tag{15}$$

W being in joules when L is in henrys and I in amperes.

Thus it is seen that the stored energy in a magnetic field is directly proportional to the square of the current. This applies, however, only to circuits of constant permeability, such as coils with nonmagnetic cores and transmission lines. For coils wound on iron or steel cores, where the permeability varies to a considerable degree with current changes, the inductance has no constant value and must be included as an additional variable in the equations.

The energy supplied to a circuit during a time interval beginning at time t_1 and ending at time t_2 becomes

$$W = \int_{t_1}^{t_2} eidt = \int_{I_1}^{I_2} Lidi \qquad \text{joules} \qquad (16)$$

where

$$i = I_1 \quad \text{when } t = t_1$$

and

$$i = I_2 \quad \text{when } t = t_2$$

The energy change then becomes

$$W = \tfrac{1}{2} L(I_2^2 - I_1^2) \qquad \text{joules} \qquad (17)$$

this representing energy added to the circuit when I_2 is greater than I_1 or representing energy supplied by the circuit when I_2 is less than I_1. Such changes in energy are independent of the intermediate values of I during the time interval represented by t_2—t_1 and depend only upon the final and beginning values as represented by I_2 and I_1.

7. Inertia Effects of Inductance.—Referring to Eq. (8), the positive form of this equation represents the voltage applied to balance or overcome the emf of self-induction, and it will be observed that this bears a close relationship in its form and significance to an equation in mechanics involving force, mass, and acceleration,

$$F = M \frac{dv}{dt} \qquad (18)$$

Considering voltage in the electric circuit to be analogous to force in mechanics and remembering that current is a rate of transfer of electricity and may be considered analogous to a velocity, it is evident that the positive form of Eq. (7) may be considered analogous to Eq. (18) if inductance may be likened to mass. Actually the effect of inductance in the electric circuit closely resembles that of inertia in mechanics, and mechanical models may be constructed that demonstrate very accurately the effects of inductance through its analogy to mass. The inertia effect of inductance causes an appreciable lapse of time between the instant of voltage application to a circuit and the attainment of full value of current flow in the circuit, as indicated by Fig. 3, while sudden stoppage of current flow is accompanied by the same dangerous possibilities that attend the sudden stoppage of moving bodies. With sudden stoppage of current flow, high voltages may be set up in the inductive circuit in which the current is being interrupted and appear at its terminals. Thus, in the reduction of a current of 100 amp to 0 in 1 sec, for example, through cutting of conductors by the collapsing field, the generation of 500 volts may result. If the time is shortened to 0.1 sec, the resulting voltage becomes 5000; and, if the time is 0.01 sec, the voltage reaches the comparatively enormous value of 50,000 volts. This explains the breakdown of insulation sometimes experienced when highly inductive field circuits are suddenly opened; also the loss of life sometimes caused when an operator accidentally establishes contact across the switch terminals at the instant of opening an inductive circuit.

 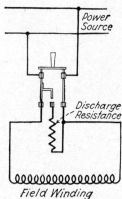

Fig. 4.—Field discharge switch and connection.

In order to limit this "inductive kick" to a safe value, a path of relatively low resistance must be provided for a current flow in response to the voltage set up by the collapsing magnetic field in circuits of high inductance. Special switches, as shown in Fig. 4, may be provided for such circuits as, for instance, the field circuits of large generators. Such switches establish a low-resistance path across the field terminals at the instant, or slightly before, the line voltage breaks contact with the circuit, thus providing for a gradual and harmless dissipation of the energy stored in the magnetic field. The same end may be achieved by use of special resistors made of *Thyrite*, a substance that has the unusual quality of offering high resistance to current flow at normal voltages but allows current flow to a much greater extent when the voltage reaches values markedly above normal or rated value. A properly designed resistor of this material may therefore be connected permanently across the field-circuit terminals, without noticeable effect at normal voltage, to serve as a safety valve by allowing harmless dissipation of the energy stored in the field coils when the supply-circuit switch is suddenly opened.

8. Mutual Induction.—Turns of wire on a neighboring circuit will be affected by an expanding and receding magnetic field due to current changes as well as to adjacent turns on the same circuit. Thus we find that a coil of wire placed around any portion of a coil, or core, in which the flux is changing will have a voltage induced in it; and, if the circuit is closed, a current will flow, the direction of

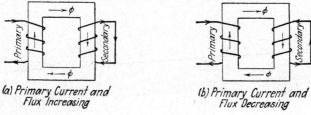

(a) Primary Current and Flux Increasing   (b) Primary Current and Flux Decreasing

Fig. 5.—Mutual induction as exemplified in the transformer.

the current being dependent upon whether the flux is increasing because of increasing current in the first, or primary, coil or decreasing because of decreasing current in the primary coil. The current in the secondary coil will, in compliance with Lenz's law and as indicated in Fig. 5, flow in a direction to oppose the change of current in the primary coil. With increasing primary current and flux, the secondary current sets up an opposing flux; with decreasing primary current and flux, the secondary current reverses and sets up an assisting flux.

Not all the flux set up by current in one coil will interlink with the other coil, a portion—the so-called leakage flux—completing its circuit by some other path. The amount of effective flux, as contrasted with leakage flux, will depend upon the relative positions of the coils.   The ratio of total flux produced by one coil to the flux interlinking the other coil is called the *coefficient of coupling*. Close-coupled coils are those which are so disposed relative to one another that the leakage flux is reduced to a small value.   The emf induced in the second coil may be varied by shifting its position relative to the first, thereby changing the coupling.

The henry is also the unit of mutual inductance.   Two circuits have a mutual inductance of 1 henry when a change of 1 amp in the first causes a change of 10^8 flux interlinkages in the second.

Problems

1. If a conductor 12 in. long is moved through a uniform magnetic field of 6000 gausses at a velocity of 50 fps at right angles to the field, what will be the value of the emf generated?

2. Twenty straight insulated wires, each 25 cm long, are assembled in a bundle or coil and connected end to end in such manner that the voltages generated by them will be additive.   They are then made to cut directly across a field having a flux density of 10,000 gausses at a rate of 4000 fpm.   What voltage should appear at the ends of the coil?

3. A six-pole generator is driven at a speed of 1500 rpm.   The flux per pole is 5×10^6 maxwells.   How many conductors in series are necessary to induce a voltage of 125 volts?

4. How many conductors must be connected in series on an armature 10 in. long in order that 250 volts may be generated while the conductors are cutting across a field having a density of 12,000 gausses at a speed of 3000 fpm?

5. The conductors on the armature of a generator are located 6 in. from the shaft, and the length of conductor under the pole is 8 in.   The armature is rotating at a speed of 1200 rpm, and the flux density in the air gap is 6000 gausses.   What will be the voltage generated by each conductor while crossing the pole face?

6. A six-pole generator has an armature 10 in. in diameter and an active length of 12 in.   The pole faces cover three-fourths of the armature, and the flux density in the air gap is 60,000 lines per sq in.   The speed is 1800 rpm. (a) What will be the emf induced in each conductor while it is underneath a pole and cutting flux?   (b) What will be the average emf per conductor for one complete revolution?

7. If the generator of Prob. 6 has a total of 60 conductors connected in series for each circuit, or path, through the armature, what will be its terminal voltage when operated without load at normal speed and excitation?

8. A generator field circuit consists of 10 pole coils in series, each coil having 800 turns.   Each pole normally supplies a flux of 2,500,000 maxwells.   (a) If, when the field circuit is interrupted, the flux is decreased to zero in 2 sec, what average emf will be induced in the field circuit and appear at the switch terminals? (b) If the flux is reduced to zero in 0.1 sec, what will be the induced emf?

9. If, in Prob. 8, the field circuit requires a current of 5 amp to produce the required flux of 2,500,000 maxwells per pole, find (a) the inductance of the field circuit, assuming that flux is proportional to field current, and (b) the energy stored in the field circuit with normal current flow.

10. A coil having inductance of 0.2 henry but negligible resistance and a rheostat with 10 ohms resistance but negligible inductance are connected in series to a 120-volt d-c circuit. (a) What will be the voltages across the coil and rheostat at the instant the switch is closed? (b) What will be the voltage across each when the current has reached a steady value?

11. Following closure of the switch upon the circuit of Prob 10, the current is observed at a given instant to be 4 amp. (a) What will be the voltage across each section of the circuit at the instant of observation? (b) What will be the final or steady value of current flowing in the circuit?

12. The rotation of a coil of 90 turns causes the flux linking it to vary according to the equation $\phi = 3 \times 10^5 \cos 377t$. Determine the equation of emf that will be generated.

13. Referring to Fig. 1b, assume data as follows: pole faces 12 in. square, coil AB has 30 turns and is 12 in. long and has a mean diameter of 10 in. The flux is uniformly distributed between the pole faces and has a value of 6×10^6 maxwells. Speed of rotation 10 rps. (a) Find the maximum voltage generated per revolution of the coil. (b) Find the average voltage generated as the coil passes from position AB to position BA.

14. Assuming that flux threading a coil could be made to follow the straight-line variations shown in the adjoining figure, (a) show by sketch the manner in which the induced emf will vary, and (b) choose values of turns, flux, and time, and calculate the voltages that would be induced in the coil when subjected to this form of flux variation.

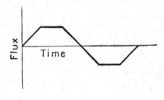

15. Show by sketch the manner in which the voltage induced in a coil would vary if the flux variation could be made to follow the semicircular form shown in the adjoining figure.

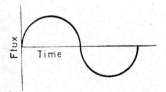

CHAPTER II

THE DYNAMO

9. Principle of Operation.—The dynamoelectric machine, or dynamo, may be designed for converting mechanical energy into electrical energy, in which case it is called a *generator*, or it may be designed for converting electrical energy into mechanical energy, in which case it is called a *motor*. · For either purpose, motor or generator operation, the dynamo may be defined as a rotational machine, functioning through the production of a relative motion between electrical conductors and a magnetic field. In d-c dynamos, the magnetic field is stationary and the armature conductors rotate through it, since it is necessary to interpose a commutator as a reversing device between the conductors on the armature and that portion of the electrical circuit external to the machine itself, the commutator being built onto the end of the armature and revolving with it.

Operation of the dynamo is based upon *Faraday's law of induced voltage*, which states that the emf induced between the ends of a loop or coil is proportional to the *rate of change* of magnetic flux enclosed by the coil; or the emf induced between the ends of a bar conductor is proportional to the time rate at which magnetic flux is cut by the conductor.

If a conductor is moved across a magnetic field, a voltage is induced, the direction of which depends upon the direction of the field and the direction of motion, and the value of which is constant as long as the rate of cutting is constant. If the conductor is bent into the form of a coil and rotated in a uniform field, as in Fig. 6, at constant speed, the rate of cutting will vary from a maximum when the

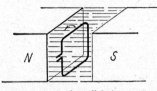

FIG. 6.—A single coil being rotated in a uniform magnetic field.

plane of the coil is in line with the field to zero when the plane of the coil is at right angles to the field. This results in an alternat-

16

ing voltage; and, in order to make this voltage available for use in an external circuit, slip rings and brushes must be provided, as illustrated in Fig. 7. If it is de-sired that the voltage and current be continuously in the same direction insofar as the external circuit is con-cerned, a commutator and brushes must be provided, as illustrated in Fig. 8.

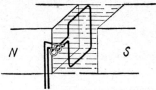

Fig. 7.—Slip rings and brushes provide connection between coil and outer circuit for an alternating current.

With a single coil and a two-ele-ment commutator, the current in the external circuit would be unidirectional but varying in value. In order to produce a uniform current of constant value, a com-

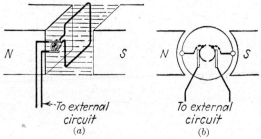

To external circuit
(a)

To external circuit
(b)

Fig. 8.—A commutator and brushes are necessary in order that unidirectional currents be supplied to the external circuit.

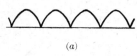

(a)

Fig. 9(a).—Unidirectional but varying current produced by single-coil and two-segment commutator.

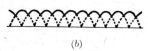

(b)

Fig. 9(b).—Effect of in-creasing the number of coils and commutator segments.

paratively large number of coils and com-mutator segments must be provided. With a large number of coils in series between brushes, distributed uniformly over the surface of the armature, the resulting voltage becomes sufficiently near uniform that for all practical pur-poses it may be considered constant in value.

10. General Construction.—A d-c gen-erator or motor of conventional type is made up of the following parts:

a. Outer frame or yoke.　　　*e.* Armature windings.
b. Pole cores.　　　　　　　*f.* Commutator.
c. Pole coils. ·　　　　　　 *g.* Brushes.
d. Armature core.　　　　　 *h.* Bearings.

Of these, the yoke, pole cores, armature core, and the air gap between armature and pole cores form the magnetic circuit; and the pole coils, armature windings, commutator, and brushes form the electric circuits.

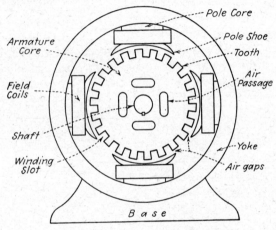

Fig. 10.—Transverse section through a four-pole dynamo. Armature coils not shown.

The frame, or yoke, answers the double purpose of providing a mechanical support for the poles and the end bells, which carry the bearings and brush rigging, and of providing a path for the magnetic flux between poles. The projecting feet that support the machine in its normal position upon the floor, shelf, or other foundation may be riveted or welded to the field yoke, or a casting may include the feet as an integral part of the frame.

Early dynamos made use of cast-iron frames, but cast steel was later adopted because of its higher magnetic permeability. Some manufacturers now prefer the use of rolled steel, bent into shape and welded, because of its higher permeability and greater uniformity.

The pole cores may be cast solid with the yoke but are more commonly made of sheet-steel laminations, riveted together and bolted into place in the yoke. The pole coils are first wound to the correct dimensions upon a form, then slipped into place upon the core. They may be composed of many turns of insulated wire of relatively small cross section, creating a so-called *shunt* winding; they may be composed of a few turns of relatively heavy wire, to create a *series* winding; or the same pole coil may contain both types of winding with electrical connections to different terminals, but creating magnetic flux for the common magnetic circuit through the pole cores, armature core, air gaps and yoke. In any case, all turns are carefully insulated from each other, and the whole assembly is taped together, impregnated with insulating compound, and baked thoroughly to form a compact moistureproof unit that may be placed in position on the core before it is bolted

Fig. 11.—Field-pole core, built up of thin sheet-steel laminations.

to the frame. The outer ends of the pole core are usually extended in the manner illustrated in Fig. 10, to form a pole shoe in order to increase the cross-sectional area of the air gap and decrease its magnetic reluctance.

The armature core is made up of thin sheet-steel laminations, punched to proper size in large presses and so shaped that, in the assembly, slots are provided for the armature coils. In all but the smallest machines, provision is made for ventilation of the core and windings by openings lengthwise of the shaft and by radial ducts through the body of the core. These, with fan vanes, riveted to the ends of the core, provide an effective means of cooling the core and coils during operation of the machine (see Fig. 21).

Bearings are commonly of the sleeve type, with babbitted wearing surfaces, although many motors of industrial sizes are now equipped with ball or roller bearings. Lubrication for the sleeve type of bearing is provided by ring oilers, supplying oil from a reservoir in the bearing bracket or pedestal, while the ball and roller bearings are grease-packed.

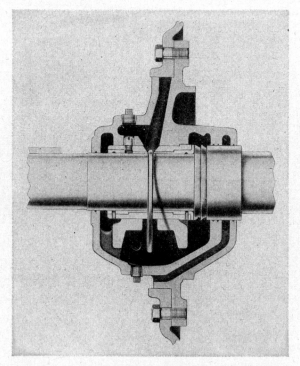

Fig. 12.—Sleeve-type bearing. (*General Electric Company.*)

Figure 12 illustrates the sleeve type of bearing, showing the oil ring, oil reservoir, and the oil throwers designed to prevent oil creepage along the shaft into the machine proper. Figure 13 illustrates the ball type of bearing, showing the hard steel balls, the ball raceway, and the grease chamber.

11. Magnetic Circuits.—The path of the magnetic flux through the field yoke, pole cores, armature core, and air gap is indicated in Fig. 14. The pole coils are so placed as to form alternate north and south poles, as illustrated, for machines having more than two

poles. Thus the flux leaving a north pole will divide, half of the
flux going to each adjacent south pole, where it is joined by a like
amount of flux from the next adjacent north pole. Thus there will

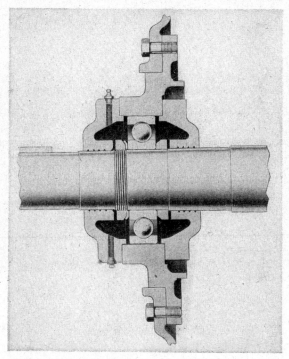

FIG. 13.—Ball-type bearing. (*General Electric Company.*)

be twice the number of flux lines in each pole core as exist in any
section of the armature core or in any section of the field yoke.
Actually less than half the pole flux will be found to exist in the
armature paths because of losses due to leakage across the air
path between pole tips, allowance for this loss being a necessary
part of the design.

Since the magnetic reluctance of the air gap is large compared
with the metal portions of the magnetic circuit, it is necessary to
restrict air-gap lengths to relatively small values in a direction

perpendicular to the armature surface and also to expand the pole
ends to form tips or shoes of enlarged area that follow closely the
curvature of the armature.

In order to reduce further the reluctance of the magnetic circuit,
as well as to provide mechanical security for the armature conductors, slots are provided for the
conductors, the intervening
teeth serving as a flux path of
lowered reluctance compared
with the slots themselves. Because of this lower reluctance
of the teeth, the flux has a tendency to follow the teeth as
they traverse the pole face, thus
creating a varying flux across
the pole face and introducing
another design problem because of the eddy currents set
up in the lower end of the pole
core. The pole core is usually
made of laminated soft steel,
which is of material assistance
in keeping the pole-face losses to a minimum.

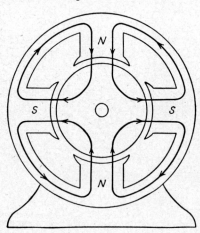

Fig. 14.—Mean paths of magnetic flux in
a four-pole dynamo.

12. Excitation.—The setting up of flux lines across the air gap
between the pole shoes and armature core, referred to as *field
excitation,* is brought about by the passage of current through coils
of wire around the pole cores, these being wound in such a manner
as to make the polarities alternately north and south. Field windings are of two types. One type is composed of a large number of
turns of relatively light wire, designed for parallel connection with
the armature or machine terminals and therefore capable of carrying the currents set up by application of the terminal voltage to
the field terminals. A second type is composed of a small number
of turns of relatively heavy wire, designed for connection in series
with the armature or line and therefore capable of carrying the full
armature or line current.

The first type of field winding, the so-called shunt winding, may be connected to an outside source of power, as shown in Fig. 15c, in which case the term *separate excitation*, or separately excited, is used to distinguish it from the self- or shunt-excited machine

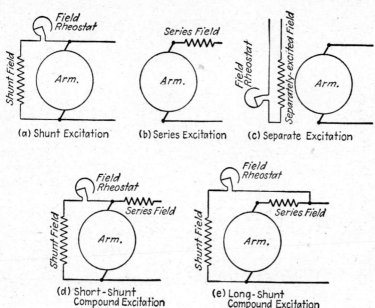

Fig. 15.—Methods of providing and controlling excitation of magnetic fields in direct-current machines.

(Fig. 15a) in which the field connections are made to the armature or machine terminals.

When, as is frequently done, both methods are utilized in the same machine, the term *compound excitation* is used. A compound motor or generator therefore utilizes both the series and the shunt type of field winding for its excitation. The term *short shunt* is used to indicate the particular type of connection shown in Fig. 15d, where the shunt field is connected across the armature alone; and the term *long shunt* is used to indicate the connection shown in Fig. 15e, where the shunt-field connection is across both armature and series field. There is little difference in the operation of the machine by reason of short-shunt or long-shunt connections being used, but there is considerable difference in the operating characteristics of the compound generator or motor as compared with

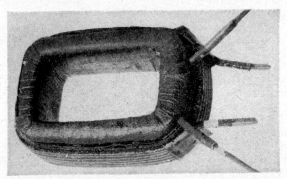

Fig. 16.—A field coil with both shunt and series windings. (*General Electric Company.*)

the corresponding machine when shunt or separately excited. The differences will be discussed in detail in later chapters.

Fig. 17.—Stator assembly, showing main poles and interpoles, with exciting coils in place. (*General Electric Company.*)

Besides the main poles, a certain number of smaller auxiliary poles called *interpoles* or *commutating poles* are usually provided. Their function is to control the commutation and prevent sparking at the brush tips. The exciting coils for these are designed to carry the armature current and are therefore made of relatively heavy material. Figure 17 shows the position of the interpoles between the main poles of the stator.

13. The Commutator.—If a coil, formed of conducting material, is rotated in a magnetic field, as illustrated in Fig. 6, a voltage is induced the value of which is proportional to the rate at which flux is cut and the direction of which is determined by the direction of movement of the conductor relative to the field. The polarity of the coil ends will therefore reverse as the coil passes through the neutral zone midway between the poles. With slip rings and brushes provided, as indicated in Fig. 7, the induced voltage may be imposed upon an external circuit, in which case an alternating voltage and current flows through the coil and the external circuit in series. In d-c machines, however, it is desired that voltage and current external to the machine be unidirectional in character, thus necessitating the use of a *commutator* instead of slip rings. In its simplest form, such a commutator would consist of two segments, as illustrated in Fig. 8, attached to opposite ends of a single coil. This would result in a unidirectional, but varying voltage and current, which would not usually be satisfactory. A large number of coils and a commutator composed of a like number of segments is necessary to produce comparative uniformity in the voltage and current.

If magnetic flux could be confined to a definite path, so that the flux field could be sharply defined and limited, with no fringing of flux at the edges, a coil traversing the field at a constant rate of flux cutting—constant density of flux and constant rate of travel—would generate a wave form of voltage like that shown in Fig. 18a. For uniform flux underneath the poles but with some fringing effect, the wave form shown in Fig. 18b might be obtained, which, when rectified by the commutator, would have the appearance of Fig. 19. With a con-

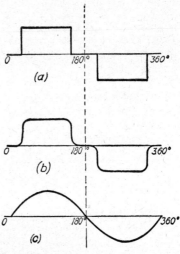

Fig. 18.—Alternating voltage waves, as produced by a coil rotating in a magnetic field.

siderable number of coils, distributed uniformly over the surface of the armature, the resulting voltage applied to the outer circuit be-

comes sufficiently uniform so that for all ordinary purposes it may
be considered constant in value.

As ordinarily constructed, the ends of the armature coils are
brought out and connected to commutator bars shaped as shown in

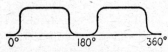

Fig. 20 and held together by a circular clamp fitting into the V-shaped
ends of the bars in a manner designed to draw the bars inward,
forming a rigid assembly of the bars
and the intervening strips of mica

Fig. 19.—Voltage wave as rectified
by a commutator.

or other insulation separating them. This assembly assures that
no movement of bars will take place during rotation of the armature yet keeps all bars and connect-
ing conductors insulated from each
other except through the medium of the
brushes. The insulating strips between
the bars, as well as the V rings of insulation between the bars and end
clamps, are commonly made from built-
up mica sheets.

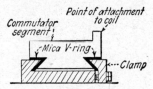

Fig. 20.—Method employed in
assembling a commutator.

After assembly of all parts of the armature and connection of the
coils to the commutator bars, the commutator is given a smoothing
cut in a lathe. Following this, the mica strips between bars are
usually "undercut," with special tools, to prevent the roughening

Fig. 21.—Complete armature assembly, with fan for ventilation. Note air pas-
sages through the teeth of the metal core, between the conductors. (*Century Electric
Co.*)

of the commutator that results when the bars wear faster than the insulating strips, leaving the latter projecting above the copper.

Modern machines, fitted with brushes of the proper quality, require no lubrication of the commutator other than that furnished by the graphitic content of the brush.

Fig. 22.—Armature core and commutator of a 3500-hp, 600-volt, steel-mill motor, showing teeth, slots, ventilation spacers, and risers from the commutator for connection with the coils. (*Allis-Chalmers Manufacturing Company.*)

The number of bars in a given commutator is limited by design features, chief among which is the voltage between bars. In order that the machine will operate without risk of flashovers on the commutator, the voltage between bars should be kept to a fairly low value, being ordinarily less than 15 volts, with a possibility of 20 volts as the upper limit of conservative design. This limitation renders it impracticable to design d-c generators for voltage ratings as high as those for a-c generators.

14. Brushes and Brush Rigging.—Brushes are made in varying degrees of hardness, of various shapes, and in various styles to meet

the requirements of different machines. Usually a holder in the form of a metal box of rectangular section is provided, this holder being adjustable in distance from the commutator and of such dimensions that the brush is allowed a close sliding fit. This, with a spring whose tension can be adjusted, provides for holding the brush in close contact with the commutator but allow-

Fig. 23.—Typical brush holder, with flexible connector and adjustable spring tension.

for inequalities on the commutator surface. The fit of the brush to the box and the angle at which it is held against the commutator should be such as to prevent chattering.

It has been found poor practice to depend upon the brush holder and spring for conducting current between brush and external circuit. Instead, except in very small machines, flexible copper connectors are provided, these being riveted to the brush at one end and secured at the other end by set screw or bolt to the portion of the brush rigging forming the conducting path to the external circuit. The brush holder and its mounting stud are insulated from the metal of the machine frame. The entire brush

Fig. 24.—Brush rigging for a four-pole motor. (*General Electric Company.*)

rigging is made movable as a unit about the commutator in order to allow for adjustment. In modern machines, provided with auxiliary commutating poles, whose special function will be described later, usually little or no adjustment of brushes is necessary after the machine leaves the factory.   Ordinarily the brush tension should be maintained at about 1.5 lb per sq in. of contact area, but it may need to be somewhat higher for high-speed machines or machines having commutators that tend to become roughened in service.

Fig. 25.—Brush assembly, showing springs for adjusting tension and flexible "pigtail" connectors for carrying current between brush and brush rigging, which is insulated from the machine frame. (*Century Electric Company.*)

15. The Dynamo as a Generator.—In general, the dynamo machine, as described in the preceding paragraphs, may be used as either a motor or a generator. Usually, however, a given machine is designed for normal operation in only one capacity and may not perform with equal satisfaction in the other capacity; although, if it is designed with both ends in view, satisfactory operation in either capacity may be obtained, though not necessarily at the same voltage and speed ratings. For example, with some types of application, it is quite feasible to utilize the driving motor in the capacity of generator for obtaining braking action. With some types of motor, this requires special switching devices. With other types, all that is necessary for the reversal in function is to have the speed exceed a certain value.

As a generator, the dynamo produces a voltage in accordance ith the fundamental equation

$$e = -N\frac{d\phi}{dt} \times 10^{-8} \qquad \text{volts} \qquad (6)$$

which is an expression of Faraday's law.

If it is desired to determine the average value of volts induced over a definite interval of time, Eq. (6) reduces to the form

$$E = N\frac{(\phi_2 - \phi_1)}{t_2 - t_1} \times 10^{-8} \qquad \text{volts} \qquad (19)$$

N being the number of turns in the coil threaded by the changing flux ϕ and $t_2 - t_1$ being the time in seconds within which the change in flux from value ϕ_1 to value ϕ_2 takes place.

For the movement of a conductor at constant velocity through a uniform field at right angles to the field, the voltage may also be calculated as

$$E = Blv \times 10^{-8} \qquad \text{volts} \qquad (20)$$

where B is flux density, l is total active length of conductor, and v is velocity. The units in which the quantities B, l, and v are expressed may be in any convenient system of units so long as consistency is maintained. Thus, if B represents the number of flux lines per square inch, l must be expressed in inches, and v in inches per second. And similarly for any other system of units.

A study of armature windings will emphasize the fact that there are always at least two similar paths in parallel through the windings of an armature, equal voltages being generated in each path; and, since it is usually the average voltage with which we are most concerned in connection with d-c machines, the following equation will be found most convenient for calculating the voltage generated by the armature windings of such machines.

$$E = \frac{Z}{\text{paths}} \times \phi \times \text{poles} \times \frac{\text{rpm}}{60} \times 10^{-8} \qquad \text{volts} \qquad (21)$$

where Z is total number of conductor crossings of the armature, referred to later as inductors, and ϕ is magnetic flux lines per pole.

The derivation of this equation should be obvious, since it represents a summing up of the magnetic lines cut by one inductor in 1

sec, multiplied by the number of inductors per path of the armature, and divided by 10^8, the rate of flux cutting that defines the
volt.   It gives the average voltage generated, since the inductors
are not cutting flux during the entire revolution, nor is the density
of the flux likely to be constant underneath the field poles.

The above equation may be further simplified for a machine in
service, since for such machines all factors in the equation except
flux and speed may be considered constant.   The equation thus
reduces to the form

$$E = K_1 \phi S \qquad \text{volts} \tag{22}$$

where ϕ is flux per pole, S is speed in rpm, and K_1 includes all other
factors in Eq. (21).

16. The Dynamo as a Motor.—As a motor, the dynamo electric
machine is supplied with electric power from an outside source,
current flows through the armature and field coils, and the conductors are forced into movement in accordance with the principle that
a current-carrying conductor is acted upon by a force tending to
move it aside when it is placed in a magnetic field.

The force exerted upon a current-carrying conductor is dependent upon the density of the magnetic field, the length of conductor
in the field, and the value of the current flowing in the conductor.
Assuming that the conductor is located in the flux field at right
angles to the field, the force developed may be expressed in equation
form as follows:

$$F = Bli = BL\frac{I}{10} \tag{23}$$

When B, the flux density at the conductor, is expressed in gausses,
or lines per square centimeter, l, the length of conductor, is in
centimeters, and i is the current in cgs units or I is the current in
amperes, the force F will be in dynes.   If the conductor makes an
angle θ, other than a right angle with the flux field, the effective
length to be used in the above equation is the component of the
total length that is perpendicular to the field.   This necessitates
multiplication by the sine of the angle the conductor makes with
the flux field, and Eq. (23) therefore becomes

$$F = BL\frac{I}{10}\sin\theta \tag{24}$$

Since the conductors under a given pole all carry current in the same direction, the turning force, or torque, is continuous and is translated into rotary motion.   At the same time, the conductors, obviously, are cutting flux lines beneath the poles and are therefore generating a voltage.   This voltage is in opposition to the voltage that causes current flow through the armature and hence is re-

Fig. 26.—Commutator and brush rigging on a 4500 hp, 600-volt, steel mill motor. (*Allis-Chalmers Manufacturing Company.*)

ferred to as a *countervoltage* or *back emf*, the value of the current flowing through the armature being dependent upon the difference between the applied voltage and the countervoltage.

Considerable difference will usually be encountered in the mechanical construction of dynamos intended for use as motors as contrasted with those intended for use as generators, since generators can usually be located in clean, well-kept rooms, separate from industrial dirt and debris; but motors must of necessity be located conveniently adjacent to the equipment to be operated by them and hence may need greater protection from dirt, chips, fumes, etc., and also, because of their tighter enclosure for mechanical protection, may require that facilities be provided for forced circulation of cooling air.

17. Rheostats.—In connection with operation of the dynamo, as either motor or generator, it is usually necessary to provide control of the current through the shunt-field coils in order to allow for a controlled variation of the air-gap flux. This permits the induced voltage to be adjusted over a considerable range, which in the generator can be used to compensate for speed and load

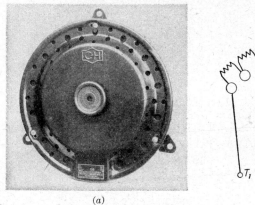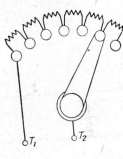

(a)   (b)

Fig. 27.—Field rheostat, as used for control of motor and generator field currents. (*Cutler-Hammer, Inc.*)

changes and in the motor can be used to provide manual control of motor speed to meet varying load conditions.

Such control can be obtained through variation of circuit resistance by means of *rheostats*, which are made in various forms and of several different materials. The form of rheostat specifically intended for application to field circuits of small motors and generators is illustrated in Fig. 27. The resistance material is an alloy of high specific resistance, made up with a varying section, such that at one end of the range the allowable current capacity is appreciably higher than at the other end. Two ratings are accordingly placed upon the name plate, one applying to the "out" end of the rheostat and the other to the "in" end, both being maximum permissible current that can safely be put through the rheostat.

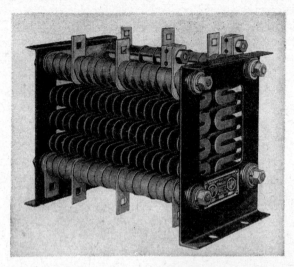

Fig. 28.—Example of the grid type of rheostat. (*The Electric Controller & Manufacturing Company.*)

For larger machines and for other resistance purposes, such as providing artificial loads for generators, iron wire or grids made of various alloys are used. Such materials are made up in convenient form and provided with suitable switching arrangements for varying the amount of resistance in the circuit. Figure 28 illustrates

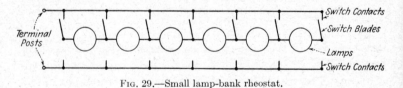

Fig. 29.—Small lamp-bank rheostat.

a common "grid" form of rheostat, the purpose of the assembly being to provide a long path of relatively small cross section, separated to allow the free circulation of air that is necessary to carry away the heat generated by the energy put into the rheostat.

Fans are sometimes used to increase the air flow, thus carrying away the heat at a greater rate.

Lamp-bank rheostats are sometimes convenient for use in "loading" small generators or for controlling the current flow in other circuits of relatively low power capacity. A convenient switching arrangement is illustrated in Fig. 29, which provides a

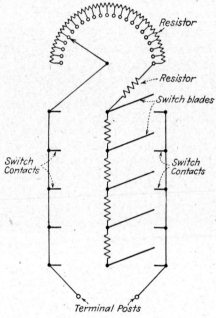

Fig. 30.—Heavy-duty load rheostat. (As used in dynamo laboratory at Purdue University.)

range of resistance values extending from that obtained by connecting all the lamps in series to that obtained by connecting all the lamps in parallel.   The range of resistance values attainable by this means is reduced materially, however, by the lowering of the resistance per lamp, due to lowered currents and cooler filaments, when lamps are connected in series.   In the rheostat shown, there will be 21 steps of resistance in going from one extreme to the other, obtainable by various series, series-parallel, and parallel

combinations. A convenient form of rheostat for current values
higher than those which can be obtained with the small lamp bank
described above is shown in Fig. 30. Various series, series-parallel,
and parallel combinations are obtainable that, with the many low-
resistance steps provided by movement of the top lever, provide a
wide range of closely adjustable resistance values. The actual
resistance and current capacity will depend, of course, upon the
resistance and cross section of the unit resistors used, also to some
extent upon the means of ventilation that is provided.

Problems

1. A field rheostat having 75 ohms resistance is rated 2 amp when its resistance is all in series with the circuit and 4 amp at the other extreme when all
the resistance is out of the rheostat. If connected in series with a field coil of
75 ohms resistance across a 240-volt supply line, will the rheostat be safe from
damage at any point within its range? What will be the value of current flowing in the circuit at each extreme of the rheostat arm? What will be the minimum field-coil resistance with which this rheostat could safely be used with
240 volts applied to the circuit? With 120 volts applied to the circuit?

2. A certain field rheostat has ratings of 60 ohms, 5 amp max with resistance
out and 2.5 amp max with resistance in.

(a) Determine the minimum resistance of shunt-field winding with which
this rheostat may safely be used if the terminal voltage of the machine is 250
volts.

(b) Through what range of values could the voltage and current of the field
be varied by the use of this rheostat in series with the field calculated in (a)?

(c) If the above rheostat has 21 contact buttons and is designed to give an
equal change in current for each step when used in series with a field coil as
calculated in (a), determine the values of resistance between the first two and
the last two contact buttons.

3. (a) Make a tabulation of resistance values for the lamp-bank rheostat
of Fig. 29, assuming the use of 100-watt 115-volt lamps of constant resistance,
in going by consecutive steps from maximum resistance, with all lamps in
series, to minimum resistance, with all lamps in parallel. (Actually the resistance of such lamps is not constant but varies with current, by reason of changes
in temperature of the filament.)

(b) What current range would be attainable by the above rheostat with 115
volts applied to the rheostat terminals? Why would it be safe to do this,
without other resistance in series, as with the field rheostat?

4. Tabulate the resistance values obtainable with the load rheostat of Fig.
30, assuming each resistance unit to have 4 ohms resistance—the entire upper-
arm set of contacts being classed as one resistance unit, listing the values in an

unbroken range from maximum, with the six units in series, to minimum, with five units in parallel, and omitting the small adjustment values obtainable by use of the upper arm but including the in and out positions of this arm. (Note that the range may be made continuous with no overlapping except for a small break near the low-resistance end of the series.)

5. A conductor, located in a magnetic field, perpendicular to the field, carries a current of 20 amp. If the length of conductor is 10 in. and the field has a uniform density of 50,000 lines per sq in., what is the force in pounds acting upon the conductor? What will be the force if the conductor is shifted in position so that it makes an angle of 60 deg with the field?

6. A conductor moves through a magnetic field at such a rate that 1000 kilolines of flux are cut by it in a time 0.02 sec. What is the average value of voltage induced in the conductor?

7. The armature of a four-pole generator rotates at a speed of 1200 rpm. A magnetic flux equal to 2×10^6 lines crosses the air gap to the armature at each pole. Determine (*a*) the average rate at which lines are being cut by a conductor at the surface of the armature, and (*b*) the average voltage induced in the conductor during one revolution.

8. How many inductors, or conductor crossings of the armature, will be required *per path* in a four-pole dynamo that is to generate 50 volts when operating at a speed of 1500 rpm, the magnetic flux per pole being 9×10^5 maxwells?

9. If a given machine generates 500 volts at a speed of 1000 rpm, what voltage will be generated if the speed is raised to 1250 rpm (*a*) with the field flux unchanged and (*b*) with the field flux reduced to 80 per cent of its previous value?

10. A generator has six poles and runs at a speed of 1800 rpm. The winding is of a type that provides four paths through the armature. The magnetic flux per pole is equal to 3×10^6 lines.

(*a*) If the machine is to generate 250 volts when operating at rated speed, how many inductors must be utilized in winding the armature?

(*b*) If with the number of inductors determined in (*a*) the speed is decreased to 1500 rpm, to what value must the magnetic flux be changed in order that the same voltage may be generated?

(*c*) With the magnetic flux per pole remaining as in (*a*) and with the number of inductors determined, assume that the number of paths through the winding is changed to two. What will be the effect upon the generated voltage, with the same speed as before?

CHAPTER III

ARMATURE WINDINGS

18. Principles.—An early form of armature winding, known as the *Gramme ring*, is pictured in Figs. 31 and 32. Because of certain inherent disadvantages, it is no longer used but has been superseded by the drum-wound type of armature. The Gramme ring is frequently utilized, however, as a means of studying the paths followed by the current through the winding, the various circuits being more evident in this form of winding than in the drum type.

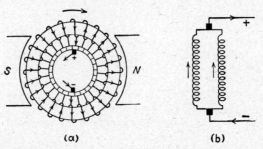

(a) (b)

Fig. 31.—Two-pole Gramme-ring winding and equivalent circuit.

Referring to Fig. 31, representing a two-pole two-path winding, it will be seen that, between the negative and positive brushes, there are an equal number of voltage-generating conductors on each side of the armature and that the coil voltages are additive from bottom to top on either side. The voltage per path then becomes the generated voltage of the machine. And, although the winding is closed upon itself, there will be no local current flow around the armature because the equal voltages generated in the two halves of the winding are in opposition to each other. They unite in parallel, however, at the brushes; and, when an external circuit is connected, beginning at one brush and termininating at the other, each side of the armature forms a path for current flow. Thus, if 20 amp is being supplied by the dynamo, operating as a generator, each section of the armature carries 10 amp. Therefore, the conductor size need be only that necessary for a current equal to half the current rating of the machine.

In the four-pole four-path armature represented in Fig. 32, the opposite pairs of brushes are connected by a conductor before connection to the external circuit, thus forming four circuits, or paths, through the armature. If the path of the current is traced from negative brush to positive brush, it will be found that only one-fourth the total winding will be traversed and that there are four such paths between the two points of connection to the external circuit. Thus each path must generate a value of voltage

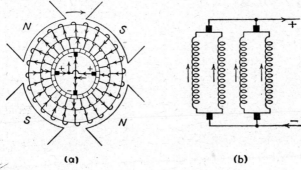

(a)   (b)

Fig. 32.—Four-pole Gramme-ring winding and equivalent circuit.

equal to that for which the generator is designed, and the total current flow is divided equally among the four paths.

19. Drum Windings.—The winding unit, or element, for the drum-wound type of armature, is a coil of the form illustrated in Fig. 33. The straight portions of such a coil, the parts that cut through the magnetic field and in which voltage is induced, are called *face conductors*, or *inductors*. The remaining portions, acting as connecting links between inductors or between inductors and commutator, are called *end connections*.

Drum windings should be so designed that they form closed circuits, *i.e.*, so connected that, by starting at a given point and moving from coil to coil consecutively, the entire winding is traversed and the starting point is again reached without a break in continuity having been encountered. The spacing of the coil sides should be approximately that of the pole span, in order that the

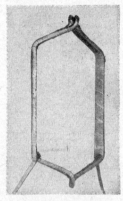

emfs induced in the two sides of the coil may be additive in their effect; and, lastly, the disposition of windings must be such that no local, or short-circuit, currents will flow.

Drum windings are divided into two classes, in accordance with the number of paths by which current can flow through the armature from the negative to the positive side of the line, this difference being effected by the manner in which the coils are connected to the commutator. With the end connections brought to adjacent bars, as illustrated in Fig. 34a, the parallel, or lap, winding is formed, with as many

Fig. 33.—Armature coil or winding element.

paths through the armature as there are poles on the machine. With the method illustrated in Fig. 34b, the coil ends are spread apart, and a type of winding called the *series*, or *wave, winding* is produced, which provides only two paths through the armature regardless of the number of poles. Since these windings close on themselves, they are said to be *reentrant*; and, where a single set of coils is used to complete the winding, the result is called a *simplex winding*, as distinguished from the *multiplex winding* described later. A further characteristic of these windings is that the lap winding requires as many brushes as poles, in

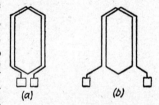

Fig. 34.—Methods of connecting coils to commutator bars (a) for lap winding and (b) for wave winding.

order that the full armature winding may be utilized, whereas the wave winding requires only two brushes but can utilize as many brushes as poles. Alternate brush sets are connected electrically, by flexible leads or otherwise, to each other and to the positive side of the external circuit, and the intermediate brush sets are similarly connected to one another and to the negative side of the circuit.

The appearance of finished drum-wound armatures may be seen
by reference to Figs. 21 and 35. It is sometimes possible to judge
from external appearance of the armature whether it is wave-
wound or lap-wound, but the overlying band wires may render
close inspection of coil ends difficult.

FIG. 35.—Completed armature. Note wedges and band wires for holding the coils
in place. (*Fairbanks, Morse & Company.*)

A number of limiting factors in the choice of number of inductors,
pitch, etc., must be taken into account by the designer in order
that the winding may close properly and that it may be balanced
and symmetrical. In order to check the choices made and determine the workability of the design, it is usual to make a "layout"
of the winding in one of two forms, the circular form illustrated
in Figs. 36 and 37 or the development form illustrated in Fig. 38.

In the circular form of diagram, the inductors, or flux-cutting
portions of the conductors, are shown as straight lines radiating
from the center, numbered serially for convenience in connecting
or checking the circuits. The outermost connecting lines represent
the end connections on the back of the armature, and the inner
connecting lines represent the connections on the front, or commutator, end of the armature, the commutator and brushes being
shown at the center of the diagram. This forms a convenient way

of checking the electrical connections formed by the winding and may be expanded to show the slot arrangement also by closely grouping the inductors, or coil sides, that are to go in each slot. Figures 36 and 37 represent the simplest form of winding, each coil having but a single turn. A similarly simple slot arrangement

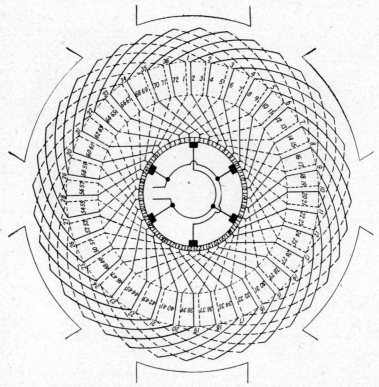

FIG. 36.—Simplex lap winding with 36 slots and 72 coil sides.

would require half as many slots as coil sides, each slot containing two coil sides, one side of each coil being at the top of a slot and the other at the bottom of a slot. The solid lines in the drawing represent the top coil sides, and the dotted lines represent the bottom coil sides.

The development form of winding diagram represents the armature as being cut lengthwise of the shaft and rolled flat. It is somewhat simpler to make but has the disadvantage of a break in continuity of the winding that must be compensated for by repetitions in inductors at the two sides of the diagram or by marking the broken ends.

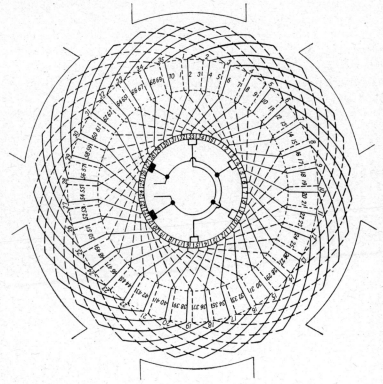

FIG. 37.—Simplex wave winding with 35 slots and 70 coil sides.

20. Slots and Coil Sides.—Since the surface of the armature core is provided with slots for accommodation of the inductors crossing the armature lengthwise of the shaft, it is essential that the number and size of slots and intervening teeth be given careful attention by the designer in order that sufficient space may be provided for both conductor and insulating material, while leaving ample metal in the teeth for the necessary magnetic flux, which the inductors cut to produce the voltage.

Armature coils may consist of a single turn, giving two inductors per coil, as in Figs. 36 to 38, or of two or more turns (Fig. 34), giving a correspondingly greater number of inductors per coil. Where more than one turn is used, the insulated inductors on each side of the coil are taped together, and the coil sides thus formed are inserted into the armature slots (Figs. 22 and 40), the slots having previously been lined with protective insulating material. Usually at least two coil sides are inserted in each slot, and a large but even number, such as four or six coil sides per slot may be utilized where

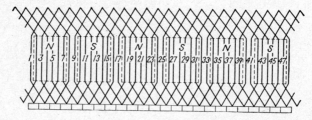

Fig. 38.—Development form of winding diagram.

conditions are such as to make larger numbers necessary or desirable. In any case, the coils must be symmetrically placed on and around the armature in order to preserve its mechanical balance and general appearance. The coils are held in the slots by fiber wedges and further reinforced by band wires wrapped tightly about the armature, as shown in Figs. 26 and 35.

Since all coils will be uniform in shape and dimensions, a symmetrical pattern must be followed in placing the coil sides in the slots. For an arrangement with two coil sides per slot, one side of each coil—the corresponding side in all cases—will be placed at the bottom of a slot and the other side always in the top slot position. A typical arrangement of coil sides and slots is illustrated in Fig. 39. For more than two coil sides per slot, a similar arrangement would be followed, one that would permit all coils to have identical dimensions, for manufacturing reasons and in order that the finished armature may be symmetrical and well balanced.

21. Winding and Commutator Pitch.—In connection with wiring layouts, the winding *pitch* may be given in terms of coil sides or in terms of slots. The term refers to the number of coil sides, or the number of slots, between the point at which a given conductor leaves the armature core and that at which it reenters. The commutator end is usually referred to as the *front* of the armature.

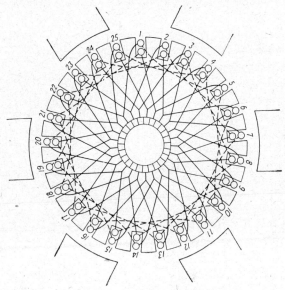

Fig. 39.—Disposition of coil sides in armature slots. Solid lines represent front-end connections and dotted lines represent back-end connections.

The pitch is best found by numbering the coil sides, or slots, serially, the difference between the numbers representing the point of exit and the point of entry being the pitch of the winding, front or rear as the case may be. For instance, in Figs. 36 and 37, the front pitch, in terms of coil sides, is 11 and the back pitch is 13. These values are obtained by taking the difference between the serially numbered coil sides at the point of entry and those at the point of departure from the armature core. These figures represent the armature as having two coil sides per slot, the outer circle of numbers applying to the slots. The front and back pitches of these windings in terms of slots are obtained similarly by finding the difference between point of entry and point of departure. With this in mind, it may be seen that in Fig. 36 the front pitch would be six slots and the back pitch seven slots [1] and that in Fig. 37 the front pitch is five and the back pitch seven slots. [1]

The commutator pitch in bars is determined by finding the difference between the serially numbered bars at opposite ends of a complete coil. In Fig. 36, the commutator pitch is therefore one bar, since the coil ends connect to adjacent bars. In Fig. 37, it is 12, this being the sum of the front and back slot pitches.

In choosing the pitches for a given winding, the back pitch, determined within rather close limits by the pole span, must be chosen first, since the back pitch determines the width of the coil and the sides of a coil must occupy approximately similar positions with respect to adjacent poles, one side cutting flux under a north pole while the other side cuts flux under a south pole, etc. The back pitch may sometimes be somewhat *less* than the pole span, for reasons to be explained later, but it should never be made greater, because of the greater length of material required for the end connections.

The front pitch is determined by the back pitch and the type of winding to be employed, and the commutator pitch is definitely related to the front and back pitches, though stated in different units. Definite rules for determination of all pitches will be set up in succeeding articles.

The total number of commutator bars is determined by the number of winding elements or coils, one bar per coil being necessary. With two coil sides in each slot, the number of commutator bars will therefore be equal to the number of slots. With four coil sides per slot, the number of commutator bars will be double the number of slots, etc.

---

[1] A back pitch of six slots, or even one of five slots, would probably yield better operating results (see Art. 26) besides taking somewhat less weight of material because of shorter end connections. However, the choice of seven slots back pitch was made in order to obtain a greater spread of the connecting leads, making the coil circuits more easily traced.

22. Lap Windings.—For this type of winding, the coil ends are, in the simplest form of winding, brought to adjacent commutator bars. Tracing through the winding diagram shown in Fig. 36 discloses that connections to succeeding coils double, or *lap*, back and that all connections are made and all slots filled as the winding progresses. It is further evident that, in passing from contact with a brush of one polarity to contact with a brush of opposite polarity, a portion of the winding equal to $1/p$, or one-sixth in this case, will have been traversed, thus providing a number of paths through the armature, from positive to negative sides of the external circuit, equal to the number of poles.

By *paths* is meant the routes by which current can travel through the armature. In a two-path winding, for example, with a total current capacity of 20 amp, the current in each path will be 10 amp. This will also be the current per conductor, since all conductors in one path are in series. If the armature has a four-path winding and still has a total current capacity of 20 amp, the current per path and per conductor will be 5 amp.

A study of the circuits, or paths, through the armature will disclose that, if the full winding is to be utilized, there must be as many brushes—or sets of brushes—as there are poles, alternate sets being connected together and to one side of the outgoing circuit. Thus half the total number of brushes will be positive brushes and carry current away from the machine, assuming it to be a generator, and the other half will be negative brushes and carry the incoming current.

The lap winding is particularly applicable to armatures having low-voltage high-current ratings, since such machines require a relatively small number of inductors per path but must have a relatively large number of paths in parallel in order to handle the large currents without the use of bulky conductors. It offers greater freedom of choice in selection of coils and slots and is simpler to lay out and connect up than the wave winding. It is likely to require a greater number of coils, however, than does the wave winding. It has the disadvantage also that, if the generated voltages in the various paths become unbalanced, as may happen by reason of bearing wear or other factors causing unequal reluctances in the several magnetic paths, local currents will circulate and cause the armature to heat even when there is no load on the machine. This tendency, however, may be counteracted through the use of special connections, called *equalizers*.

Fig. 40.—Armature for a 250-hp motor in process of assembly, showing insulation and insertion of coils. (*Allis-Chalmers Manufacturing Company.*)

23. Wave Windings.—A study of the winding diagram shown in Fig. 37 will disclose that the connections to the armature do not lap back toward the coil but go forward. Thus the next coil is located at a considerable distance around the armature. The back pitch is approximately equal to the distance between pole centers, as in the lap winding, and the corresponding sides of succeeding coils occupy similar positions with reference to poles of like polarity. Thus the coil voltages are cumulative, but it is necessary to travel several times around the armature and to traverse half the total winding in order to trace the path between succeeding brushes. The winding, therefore, has only two paths regardless of the number of poles and requires only two brushes. As many brushes as poles may be provided, if desired, in which case the brushes of corresponding polarity are interconnected by coils lying in the neutral zone between poles insofar as the armature winding is concerned, as well as being interconnected externally. Thus there will be but two paths through the armature between positive and negative sides of the circuit, despite the use of the larger number of brushes.

The wave winding is especially well adapted for use on armatures having high-voltage low-current ratings. Since it has but two paths through the armature, fewer inductors are required than for a lap winding of more than two poles, and this usually results in a more economical design. The smaller number of inductors will also require less insulation space in the slots, which in turn should provide better heat transfer and allow the armature to operate at somewhat lower temperature. Since the inductors per path are distributed under all poles alike, any inequalities in flux affect both paths in the same way, and there is no tendency for local circulation of current like that which exists in the lap-wound armature. The fact that only one pair of brushes is essential for the wave winding is sometimes an advantage, in motors or generators, for example, where it is difficult to provide access to all sides of the commutator.

24. Multiplex Windings.—If the windings described in the preceding articles are so placed upon the armature that alternate slots are left open and alternate commutator bars left free, these being filled by the coils and connections of a second winding of the same type, a duplex winding is formed, the effect being to double the number of paths between brushes. If the two windings are entirely distinct, having no electrical connection except through the medium of the brushes, the completed armature is said to have a doubly reentrant winding; but, if the second winding is closed through the first, *i.e.*, if the finish of the first is the beginning of the second and the finish of the second the beginning of the first, the completed winding is said to be singly reentrant.

Three sets of coils may be similarly arranged to form a triplex winding, etc., the advantages of multiplex windings being, in general, the provision of a larger number of paths and reduction in the tendency to spark at the brushes. The larger number of paths makes possible an armature of high current capacity without the use of coils of excessive weight or cross section, since for a given size of conductor the current rating of the armature varies directly with the number of paths.

Multiplex windings, regardless of reentrancy, multiply the number of paths through the armature by the order of the multiplicity, two for duplex, three for triplex, etc., provided that brushes are used of sufficient thickness to bridge the bars connecting the several sets of coils. Duplex windings are sometimes used to provide a greater current capacity than could otherwise be conveniently obtained, but triplex and windings of greater multiplicity are rarely found justifiable.

25. Winding Rules and Calculations.—In deciding upon the type of winding to be used for an armature, the designer is guided first of all by the voltage and current requirements, since the voltage rating for a given speed, excitation, and number of poles depends upon the inductors per path while the current rating depends upon the current capacity per inductor and the number of paths through the armature.

When the type of winding has been decided upon, or if it is desired to investigate the possibilities of one or more types of winding, certain rules must be followed in order to make sure, first, that the winding will close upon itself, or be reentrant, and, second, that the physical dimensions of all coils are the same, for manufacturing reasons. The designer may elect to choose his pitches in terms of coil edges, or coil sides, proceeding afterward to determine the slots required to contain the winding properly; or he may elect to choose the number of slots first; or possibly he may be required to fit his winding to an armature punching of a given number of slots. The rules to be followed are similar for the two cases but should not be confused.

The back pitch must be chosen first of all, since it determines the span of the coil. It will be considered here that full pitch windings are to be used, though exceptions to this will be noted later. In terms of coil edges, therefore, the back pitch will be approximately equal to the total number of coil edges divided by the number of poles, and it must be an odd number because of the manner in which the coils are to be fitted into the slots. In terms of slots, the back pitch will be approximately equal to the total number of slots divided by the number of poles, but it may be even or odd. In neither case may there be a fractional number representing the back pitch.

Lap Windings.—The front pitch for lap windings must be such as will satisfy the following equation, where Y_b represents back pitch, Y_f represents front pitch, and m represents multiplicity, the pitches being in terms of coil sides.

$$Y_f = Y_b \pm 2m \tag{25}$$

Assuming that the number of coils, slots, and bars are equal, the equation for pitches in terms of slots becomes

$$Y_f = Y_b \pm m \tag{26}$$

In either case, the winding will be *progressive* if $Y_b > Y_f$ and *retrogressive* if $Y_b < Y_f$, these terms referring to the direction of travel from the starting point as one follows the circuit through successive coils on a winding diagram.

The commutator pitch Y_c for lap-wound armatures will be numerically equal to the multiplicity of the windings, since each coil returns to an adjacent bar in simplex windings, to the second bar in duplex windings, etc.

The number of paths through a lap winding will be equal to the product of multiplicity and poles; and, because of the few limitations upon choice of pitch, it is always possible to fit an armature with a lap winding without the use of *dummy coils*, such as are sometimes necessary in connection with wave windings.

Example 1.—A six-pole dynamo, with interpoles, requires 360 inductors on its armature, with three turns per coil and two coil sides per slot. (*a*) Determine the number of coils, slots, and commutator bars. (*b*) Select suitable pitches for a simplex lap winding.

Solution:

3 turns = 6 inductors per coil
360 ÷ 6 = 60 coils = 120 coil sides
60 coils requires 60 commutator bars
2 coil sides per slot requires 60 slots

Therefore coils = bars = slots = 60

60 slots ÷ 6 poles = 10 slots, back pitch

Therefore front pitch = 9 slots for progressive and 11 slots for retrogressive winding and

Commutator pitch = 1 bar

Wave Windings.—For wave windings, the choice of front pitch is somewhat more restricted. Again assuming that coils, slots, and bars are equal in number, the choice of front pitch in terms of coil sides must be such as will satisfy the equation

$$\frac{P}{2}(Y_b + Y_f) = Z_1 \pm 2m \qquad (27)$$

where P represents the poles on the machine and Z_1 represents coil sides; whereas, for pitches in terms of slots, the equation

$$\frac{P}{2}(Y_b + Y_f) = B \pm m \qquad (28)$$

must be satisfied, B representing the number of commutator bars.

The commutator pitch, for wave-wound armatures, is equal to one-half the sum of the front and back pitches in terms of coil sides and is equal to the *sum* of front and back pitches in terms of slots. The commutator pitch Y_c may therefore be substituted for $Y_b + Y_f$ in Eq. (28) and used in the form

$$Y_c = \frac{B \pm m}{P/2} \qquad (29)$$

Since Y_c must be a whole number, it is easy to find whether the chosen number of coils—equal to the number of bars—is capable of being formed into a wave winding. If Eq. (29) does not yield a whole number for Y_c, with one or the other of the two signs indicated, then it will not be possible to fill all the slots with active coils. In this case, it may be necessary to use fewer active coils and fill the remaining slot spaces with dummies to preserve the mechanical balance. This results, of course, in some waste of space and material and should be avoided if it is possible to accomplish the desired result more effectively by changes elsewhere in the design.

The wave winding will be progressive in form if a choice is made for commutator pitch that results in the use of a plus sign in Eq. (29); or the winding will be retrogressive if the sign is minus.

The final proof that a given winding will close upon itself and fill all slots properly lies in the drawing of a winding diagram and the connection of all conductors.

Example 2.—Assuming that it is decided to connect the winding of the armature in Example 1 as a simplex wave winding, what changes, if any, in coils, slots, bars, and pitches will be necessary?

Solution: For a first trial, assuming that the same number of coils may be used, the coils, bars, and slots will each be 60 as before. Also the back pitch Y_b will be 10 slots as before. But application of Eq. (29) reveals that this number of coils cannot be used, since neither $60 + 1$ nor $60 - 1$ is divisible by 3 to yield a whole number. For a second trial, therefore, we shall drop one coil and try 59. This yields a whole number, 20, for the commutator pitch when $59 + 1$ is divided by 3. Since $Y_f = Y_c - Y_b$, the front pitch will be $20 - 10$, or 10, slots. This leaves a blank space in the top of one slot and the bottom of another, at a distance apart equal to the back pitch, which must be filled by the two sides of a dummy coil.

Example 3.—Using the same armature as in Examples 1 and 2, tabulate all data relating to coils, bars, slots, and pitches for simplex, duplex, and triplex lap and wave windings, with front and back pitches in terms of slots.

Solution:

Type of winding	Active coils	Coil sides	Bars	Slots	Y_b slots	Y_c bars	Y_f slots	Dummy coils
Simplex lap_____	60	120	60	60	10	1	9/11	0
Duplex lap_____	60	120	60	60	10	2	8/12	0
Triplex lap_____	60	120	60	60	10	3	7/13	0
Simplex wave____	59	118	59	60	10	20	10	1
Duplex wave_____	59	118	59	60	10	19	9	1
Triplex wave_____	60	120	60	60	10	19/21	9/11	0

Where there are to be more than two coil sides in each slot, it is necessary, when dealing with front and back pitches in terms of slots, to resort to some expedient for equalizing the difference in number between bars and slots. This may readily be done by expressing Y_b and Y_f in Eqs. (26) and (28) in half-slots when there are to be four coil sides per slot, in third-slots when there are to be six coil sides per slot, etc. The back pitch must always represent a whole number of slots, however, in order that all coils may be manufactured to the same shape and dimensions; but the front pitch need not follow this rigid rule, since the connectors extending from the coil to the commutator bars can be bent during assembly of coils into slots, to accommodate the small differences encountered through having front pitches that do not represent whole slots.

Example 4.—A six-pole generator, with interpoles, has 800 inductors on its armature, wound two turns per coil and placed four coil-sides per slot. Fill out a winding table, similar to that of Example 3, for simplex lap, duplex lap, simplex wave, and duplex wave, with front and back pitches in terms of slots.
Solution:

Winding	Coils	Slots	Bars	Y_b slots	Y_c bars	Y_f slots	Dummy Coils
Simplex lap_____	200	100	200	16	1	15½/16½	0
Duplex lap_____	200	100	200	16	2	15/17	0
Simplex wave_____	200	100	200	16	67	17½	0
Duplex wave_____	200	100	200	16	66	17	0

The preceding directions have been presented in the form of arbitrary rules, but the reasons back of them may be seen by inspection of suitable winding diagrams. In simplex lap windings, the coils must tie in to commutator bar after commutator bar successively, in one direction or the other, in order that voltages induced in the coil sides may add together systematically from brush position to brush position; whereas, in duplex windings, only alternate bars and slots are utilized by the first set of coils, and it is again necessary to traverse the armature in order to fill the alternate slots and connect to the alternate bars.

The wave winding differs because the front pitch proceeds forward instead of lapping back, as in the lap winding. For each pair of poles, the winding travels ahead a distance represented by the sum of the front and back pitches or, in going completely around the armature, a distance represented by $P\,(Y_b + Y_f)\,/2$ coil sides or slots. To this must be added, or subtracted, a number that will cause the winding to traverse the armature again through occupation of slots and bars separated the proper distance from those utilized the first time around. This accounts for the term $2m$ in Eq. (27) and m in Eq. (28).

26. Chorded Windings.—From the standpoint of voltage generation, it is best to have full-pitch windings, but this exact span cannot be obtained unless the number of slots is exactly divisible by the number of poles. Even then the operation of the machine may be improved by making the coil width or span somewhat less than the distance between adjacent pole centers; there is also a saving in copper from the use of narrower coils.

Windings having coils of appreciably less width than needed for the full span from pole center to pole center are known as *chorded* windings. If the full-pitch winding is called 100 per cent, then the winding may be chorded to various values down to a minimum of about 80 per cent, the lower limit being reached when the possibility exists that both sides of the coil may cut flux from the same pole at any time.

The benefits to be derived from short-pitch, or chorded, windings are greatest with machines not equipped with the auxiliary poles known as *commutating poles*, or *interpoles*. Since most machines of recent design are equipped with interpoles, the importance of the chorded winding is less than in the years previous to the general adoption and use of the interpole. With the noninterpole type of machine, it was usual to use values 85 to 90 per cent of full pitch, where this expedient served to assist the designer in attaining sparkless commutation for his machine, as well as to reduce the tendency of the armature currents to weaken the flux from the main field poles when the brushes were shifted to improve commutation, such shifting of brushes usually being necessary with noninterpole motors and generators.

27. Equalizers.—If for any reason the reluctances of the several magnetic paths about a given dynamo differ from each other, the voltages in the various paths of the winding will differ, and circulating currents may result. This condition may come about through wear of the bearings, which brings the armature nearer to the poles on the lower side of the machine, decreasing the air gap there and increasing it correspondingly on the upper side; or it may come about through any other lack of mechanical perfection that results in an unsymmetrical location of the armature with respect to the poles.

These circulating currents are not only wasteful of energy but may appreciably limit the load the machine can carry without becoming overheated and may furthermore result in excess current flow through the brushes, with possible overheating of the brushes and commutator.

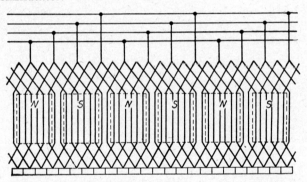

Fig. 41.—Equalizer connections on a lap-wound armature.

The use of equalizing connections between parts of the armature winding that should be at the same potential results not only in keeping the circulating currents from passing through the brushes but also produces, to some extent, a counteracting mmf that tends to equalize the inequality of flux that causes the circulating currents.

Equalizer rings may be secured to the back of the armature, with taps brought out from equipotential points and connected to the rings, there being as many rings as there are groups of points to be equalized. The minimum number is one ring for each pair of poles, with as many taps from the winding to each ring as there are pairs of poles, each tap being at the same point with reference to the poles. On a six-pole machine, there would be at least three rings and nine taps, as illustrated in Fig. 41.

Complete equalization requires that all equipotential segments on the commutator be connected together. Formerly, the equalizing rings were placed at the back of the armature, but recent practice utilizes the *involute* type of equalizer, mounted on the commutator end, with a connection to each coil.

Equalizer connections are required only for lap-wound armatures. Examination of the circuit diagram for a wave-wound armature will disclose that the inductors in each path are distributed

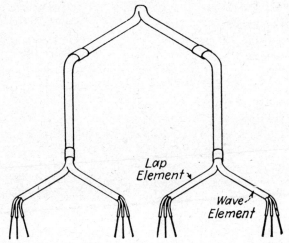

Lap Element

Wave Element

Fig. 42.—Complete frog-leg coil. (*Allis-Chalmers Manufacturing Company.*)

about the armature in such a manner that the voltage produced by each path would be similarly affected by inequalities in flux at different poles. Thus the wave-wound armature is self-equalizing, this being one reason that this type of winding is used on a very large proportion of all d-c armatures manufactured.

28. Frog-leg Windings.—The so-called "frog-leg" winding is a combination of the lap and wave types of armature winding, operating in parallel, occupying the same slots, and connected to the same commutator segments. One lap coil and one wave coil are combined into a single winding unit, which permits a saving in slot space and in the labor of winding.

This type of winding has the distinct advantage of requiring no equalizers, such as would be required for best operating characteristics with the lap winding alone, particularly in the larger armatures; yet all the advantages of the equalized lap winding are retained. Complete equalization is obtained without the use of auxiliary connections, with resulting simplification and economy in the use of conductor material, since each lap element is in series with a succeeding wave element, the beginning end of the former and the finishing end of the latter being connected to commutator segments two pole pitches apart. The two sections have the same number of parallel paths, each has the same cross-sectional area, and the current divides equally between them.

In order to meet the requirements of this composite type of winding, the lap section is usually of the simplex form, and the wave section is usually multiplex to the extent of half the number of poles, thus providing the same number of paths for each section. Since the requirements of the wave winding are usually somewhat more difficult to meet than those of the shunt winding, the wave section of the frog-leg winding is usually the controlling portion of the winding insofar as selection of the various pitches and other winding constants is concerned.[1] This type of winding may be used in any size of machine—motor or generator—but is especially well adapted to the armatures of the larger capacity units.

29. Voltage Calculations.—The voltage generated by a d-c armature winding is the voltage per path. If then the voltage induced in one conductor is multiplied by the number of conductors per path, the result is the generated voltage of the armature. It should be noted, however, that this is not the terminal voltage of the generator when under load, because of the voltage drops in the armature and series field windings, brushes, and brush contacts.

Since the volt is defined as the emf induced when magnetic lines are being cut at the rate of 10^8 per second, we have for the generated voltage of the armature, as indicated in Art. 15,

---

[1] An excellent discussion of the various factors entering into the design of this type of winding, with illustrative examples, may be found in Frog-leg Windings for Direct-current Generators and Motors, by C. S. Siskind, *Research Series* 70, *Bull. Purdue Univ. Eng. Exp. Sta.*, Lafayette, Ind.

$$E = \frac{Z}{\text{paths}} \times \phi \times \text{poles} \times \frac{\text{rpm}}{60} \times 10^{-8} \qquad \text{volts} \qquad (21)$$

where Z = total number of inductors

ϕ = magnetic flux per pole

This is essentially a design formula, since, for a finished generator, the number of inductors, the paths through the winding, and the poles are fixed values. Summing up all constants in Eq. (21), we have for the completed generator only two variables, flux and speed. Thus, in operation, there are only two means of varying the generated voltage; and, since variations in speed are usually limited closely by the prime mover, the means of varying voltage is actually limited, in most cases, to the field, variations in flux being obtained through control of the field current by rheostats.

Example 1.—A four-pole generator has a total of 500 inductors on its armature and is designed to have 2×10^6 lines of magnetic flux per pole crossing its air gap with normal excitation. What voltage will be generated at a speed of 1800 rpm (a) if the armature is simplex wave wound, (b) if the armature is simplex lap wound? (c) If the allowable current is 5 amp per path, what will be the kilowatts generated by the machine in each case?[1]

Solution: Substituting in Eq. (21),

(a)
$$E = \frac{500}{2} \times 2 \times 10^6 \times 4 \times \frac{1800}{60} \times 10^{-8}$$

$$= 600 \text{ volts, for wave-wound machine}$$

(b)
$$E = \frac{500}{4} \times 2 \times 10^6 \times 4 \times \frac{1800}{60} \times 10^{-8}$$

$$= 300 \text{ volts for lap-wound machine}$$

(c)
$$5 \times 2 = 10 \text{ amp}$$

$$\frac{10 \times 600}{1000} = 6 \text{ kw for wave winding}$$

$$5 \times 4 = 20 \text{ amp}$$

$$\frac{20 \times 300}{1000} = 6 \text{ kw for lap winding}$$

[1] Note that the kilowatt values here given would not represent the power that the generator could supply to an external load, since an appreciable part of the power generated would be absorbed in overcoming internal losses in the machine itself.

Example 2.—A six-pole generator is driven at a speed of 1200 rpm. The flux per pole is 5×10^6 maxwells. Calculate the inductors necessary to generate 250 volts when the armature is (a) simplex lap wound and (b) duplex wave wound. (c) If the normal generation capacity is 100 kw, what must be the current capacity per path for each type of winding?

Solution: Substituting in Eq. (21),

$$250 = \frac{Z}{6} \times 5 \times 10^6 \times 6 \times \frac{1200}{60} \times 10^{-8} \quad \text{volts}$$

from which

$$Z = 250 \text{ inductors}$$

For the duplex wave winding, there being four paths, only 167 inductors will be required for the same voltage per path.

Line current $= 100,000 \div 250 = 400$ amp

For lap winding

$$\text{Current capacity per path} = \frac{400}{6} = 66\frac{2}{3} \text{ amp}$$

For wave winding

$$\text{Current capacity per path} = \frac{400}{4} = 100 \text{ amp}$$

Problems

1. (a) Draw a circular-winding diagram for a four-pole simplex lap winding having 46 inductors, with one turn per coil, using a back pitch of 11 and a front pitch of 9. (b) Draw a development diagram for the above winding.

2. Repeat Prob. 1 except that pitches are reversed, giving back pitch of 9 and front pitch of 11.

3. (a) Draw a circular-winding diagram for a four-pole simplex wave winding having 46 inductors, with one turn per coil, using a back pitch of 11 and a front pitch of 13. (b) Draw a development diagram for the above winding.

4. Draw a development diagram for the following windings, indicating positions of poles, brushes, and commutator bars: (a) simplex lap winding, four poles, 30 inductors, back pitch 7, front pitch 5; (b) simplex wave winding, four poles, 30 inductors, back pitch 7, front pitch 7.

5. A four-pole generator, when driven at rated speed and under normal excitation, has an average induced voltage per inductor of 2.4 volts. Current capacity is limited by heating to 10 amp per conductor. The generator output is 60 amp at 120 volts generated emf. What kind of winding does the armature have, and what is the total number of inductors?

6. A 10-pole generator has an average induced voltage per coil of 6 volts. The current per conductor is limited to 10 amp. The machine generates 240 volts and delivers a current of 200 amp. State your conclusions as to the type of winding on the armature, the number of paths, and the total number of coils.

7. A six-pole generator has 540 inductors on its armature, each of which generates an average emf of 2.5 volts and carries a current of 15 amp. What should be the voltage, current, and kilowatt rating of the generator (*a*) if the armature inductors are connected as a simplex lap winding and (*b*) if they are connected as a simplex wave winding?

8. A six-pole dynamo requires 420 inductors on its armature, with three turns per coil and two coil sides per slot. Tabulate the data relating to coils, bars, slots. and pitches as in the table under Art. 25 for simplex, duplex, and triplex lap and wave windings.

9. If the armature of Prob. 8 can be rated 240 volts, 180 amp for the simplex lap winding, list the volt, ampere, and kilowatt ratings for each of the windings tabulated.

10. Assume the armature of Probs. 8 and 9 is to be used on a four-pole dynamo. What factors will be affected by the change? Tabulate and compare, assuming the same speed and flux per pole as before.

11. An armature is to be wound with 800 inductors, for eight poles, with two turns per coil and two coil sides per slot, and can be rated 250 volts, 300 amp when wound with a simplex lap winding. Make out a table as in Art. 25 for simplex lap, duplex lap, simplex wave, and duplex wave winding.

12. The armature of a four-pole generator is to be driven at 1800 rpm and is to be wound with 360 inductors having a diameter of 102 mils and average length of 30 in. per turn. Calculate the flux per pole necessary to generate 125 volts when the armature is (*a*) simplex lap wound and (*b*) simplex wave wound. (*c*) Calculate the resistance of the armature as wound in (*a*) and (*b*). (Use $\rho = 10$ ohms per circular mil-foot.)

13. A six-pole generator has 480 inductors on its armature, each generating an average of 2 volts and carrying a current of 5 amp. Determine the voltage, current, and power rating of the generator if the armature is connected (*a*) simplex lap, (*b*) simplex wave, (*c*) duplex lap, and (*d*) duplex wave.

14. Given an armature with 63 slots, two coil sides per slot, for a four-pole generator designed for 2.1×10^6 maxwells per pole and for operation at 1400 rpm, in order to generate 600 volts. Determine the type of winding best suited to the conditions, and calculate the turns per coil required.

15. A six-pole generator has an armature wound with 108 coils of two turns each. The active length of the armature is 12 in., and its diameter is 10 in. The pole pieces cover 70 per cent of the armature, and flux density in the air gap is 60,000 lines per sq in. Calculate the emf generated at a speed of 1200 rpm if the armature is (*a*) simplex lap wound and (*b*) simplex wave wound.

16. Given a six-pole armature with 300 inductors, wound one turn per coil, the winding being composed of No. 10 Brown and Sharpe gauge conductor and the average length of the winding element being 30 in. Calculate the resistance of the armature at an operating temperature of 75°C if the armature is (*a*) simplex lap wound and (*b*) duplex wave wound.

17. A six-pole generator armature has 396 inductors, wound two turns per coil and placed two coil sides per slot. Determine and tabulate (a) front pitch, (b) back pitch, (c) number of slots, (d) commutator pitch, (e) commutator bars, (f) dummy coils, and (g) paths if wound (1) as simplex lap winding, (2) as duplex wave winding, using the same number of slots as in (1). The above armature has a length of 10 in. and a diameter of 15 in., the pole pieces cover 70 per cent of the armature, and the rated speed is 1200 rpm. What air-gap density will be necessary in order to generate 240 volts with the simplex lap winding?

18. The armature of a 10-pole generator is to generate 300 volts at a speed of 1500 rpm. It is planned to have 100 slots and four coil sides per slot, flux per pole = 1.5×10^6 lines. Determine the type of winding best suited and the number of turns per coil that will be necessary. Choose suitable front and back pitches for the winding. If the current rating is to be 200 amp, what will be the current through the individual conductors?

19. A four-pole d-c generator has a simplex winding on its armature. When driven at normal speed and excitation, it has an average induced voltage per conductor of 1.5 volts. If the current per conductor is limited to 10 amp and the generator delivers 40 amp with an induced voltage of 150 volts, does the armature have a lap or a wave winding? What is the total number of conductors on the armature? What would be the line current and induced voltage if the armature were rewound with the other type of simplex winding, speed, size, and number of conductors being the same?

20. The armature of a six-pole generator is to be rated 240 volts, 60 amp. It is to have 50 slots, with 100 coils of two turns each, wound as a duplex wave winding. If the speed is to be 1500 rpm, what flux per pole will be necessary? If the resistance per coil is 0.032 ohms, what will be the resistance of the armature?

CHAPTER IV

COMMUTATION, ARMATURE REACTION

30. The Commutation Process.—The current in a given armature coil reverses in direction as the sides of the coil—the inductors—pass from one pole to the next of opposite polarity; and the
function of the commutator is to maintain the current unidirectional in the external circuit, while at the same time maintaining a
maximum of voltage between the positive and negative sides of the
line. By reference to an armature winding diagram like Fig. 36,
it may be seen that the inductors between a pair of adjacent
brushes—positive and negative—are cutting magnetic lines under
adjacent, and therefore unlike, poles but that the voltages are additive in a direction to send current through the coils consecutively
from negative brush, or point of entry, to positive brush, or point
of departure from the armature.

It may also be noted that current flowing in through a negative
brush divides, half flowing by each of two paths to adjacent positive brushes, and that the current flowing out through each positive brush is the sum of two equal currents coming into it from
opposite sides. In order to produce a maximum of voltage between terminals, therefore, the brushes should be so located that
the greatest possible number of inductors between brushes are cutting magnetic lines in a direction to add to this voltage. This location is found to be that which places the brushes in contact with
inductors midway between poles, this location usually being referred to as the *no-load neutral* position of the brushes.

The diagrams shown in Fig. 43 indicate the steps by which the
current in each coil is reduced to zero, reversed in direction, and
caused to build up again, during the brief interval that the brush is
in contact with the commutator bars to which the coil ends are
attached. Coil 3–8 is emphasized for convenience in following it
through the various diagrams and in diagram *a* is shown approaching the position in which it will be short-circuited by the brush.
At *b* and *c*, it is in the short-circuit position but because of self-

induction continues to carry current, although there is now a direct
path to the brush from either direction without going through this

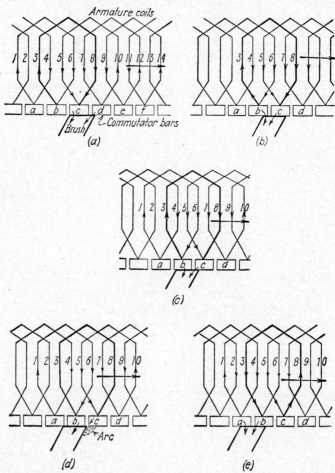

Fig. 43.—The commutation process without the assistance of a reversing field.

coil. At *c*, the current should be building up in the coil in the
opposite direction but instead is just being reduced to zero; and in
d the current has been reduced to zero but not yet completely
reversed so that it is easier for the current from coil 10–5 to follow

the brush tip through an arc than to make its way through coil
8–3, which is now directly in its path. In position *e*, the current in
coil 8–3 is shown completely reversed.

It is also evident that the position of the brushes determines
the point of reversal of coil current and that shifting the brushes to
one side or the other of the neutral point may place some of the
coils in position to generate a voltage counter to the flow of current

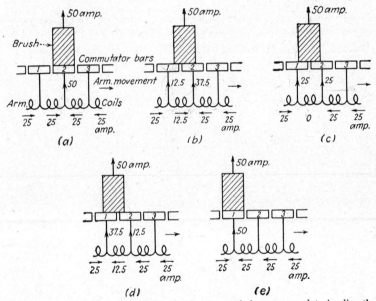

Fig. 44.—Straight-line commutation. The current is here assumed to be directly
proportional to area of brush contact.

through the series of coils, thus resulting in a reduction of voltage
between brushes.

31. Straight-line Commutation.—Straight-line, or linear, commutation requires that the current through the coil undergoing
commutation change at a constant rate from full value at the instant of contact between the brush and bar at start of the commutation period to full value in the opposite direction at the instant
contact is broken, marking the end of the commutation period.
This may be understood by reference to Fig. 44; but it should be

understood that this result is achieved only by assuming that resistance between the brush and the commutator bar varies inversely as the area of contact, that resistance of the armature coil is negligible, that the armature coils have negligible self- or mutual inductance, and that the coil is cutting no flux during the commutation period. Since none of these assumptions is true for the actual armature, the attainment of strictly linear commutation is hardly possible for the practical case.

Referring to Fig. 45, it may be seen, that the total change in current through the coil has been 50 amp during the commutation period. Assuming, for example, that this occurs in a machine whose armature rotates at 1800 rpm, the commutator diameter being 5 in. and the bar and brush 0.5 in. wide, the commutator velocity is 471 in. per sec, making the commutation period approximately 0.001 sec, which gives a rate of change amounting to 50,000 amp per sec. This high rate of change may be reduced to some extent through the use of thicker brushes, which serve to prolong the commutation interval.

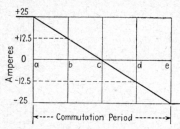

FIG. 45.—Straight-line commutation. A graph of the current change taking place in coil 1-2 of Fig. 44.

Brushes are usually made of sufficient thickness to cover two to four commutator bars. The limit in this direction is quickly reached, however, since the commutation zone is narrowly defined, and the high rate of current change continues as a major factor in the commutation problem.

32. Overcommutation and Undercommutation.—Since armature coils are practically surrounded by a steel path of low reluctance, the currents in them cause large numbers of magnetic flux lines to be set up in the surrounding portions of the armature core as well as in the air immediately adjacent to the armature. During the commutation period, the collapse and reestablishment of these magnetic lines, in the very short interval of time allowed for the dying down and building up of current in the coil undergoing commutation, results in an appreciable emf of self-induction despite the small number of turns involved. The effect of this coil reactance is to hinder the current reversal, since the emf of self-induction, by Lenz's law, first opposes the dying down of current in the coil undergoing commutation and then turns about and opposes the building up of current in the opposite direction. The result of coil reactance, therefore, is to delay the current reversal behind that of linear commutation, as indicated in Fig. 46, making necessary an accelerated rate of change near the end of the commutation period. This results in an arc if the reversal is not completed be-

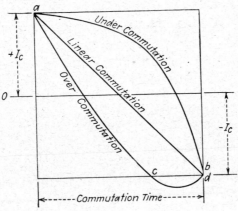

FIG. 46.—Coil-current changes due to undercommutation and to overcommutation.

fore the brush breaks contact with the coil involved, as at point b. This is referred to as *undercommutation*, since the current reversal is delayed as compared with the ideal, or linear, commutation.

In order to hasten reversal of the current, means are employed, as will be discussed in later articles, to cause the setting up of a voltage in the coil undergoing commutation that will hasten the reversal, thereby counteracting the effect of coil reactance. This is not likely to result in strictly linear commutation but, if the induced voltage is of correct value, will result in the current's being completely reversed at—but not before—the end of the commutation period. If the counteracting voltage is too great, the result will be *overcommutation*, as indicated by the lower curve in Fig. 46.

This is less likely to result in visible arcing than is the opposite, or undercommutation, effect but may result in excess heat at the brush contacts as well as in the coil, since the latter has more than normal current flowing through it for a brief interval. Since the energy loss due to brush heating is determined from a summation of instantaneous currents squared times brush-contact resistance, linear commutation would produce the minimum heating effect at the brush contacts. Thus, although a certain amount of under- or overcommutation may not produce visible arcing at the brush contacts, the heating may nevertheless be above that which would be produced by linear commutation.

33. Brush Materials.—The first brushes used on electrical machinery were made of copper, usually in the form of a bundle of thin strips in order to give elasticity to the brush and provide for maintaining the contact under pressure. The copper brush, however, has been superseded by the carbon-graphite or electro-graphite brush for two reasons: first, because the carbon brush, by reason of its higher contact resistance, assists in the process of commutation and, second, because this brush can, through the admixture of a certain amount of graphite, be made self-lubricating, whereas formerly much time and attention had to be devoted to the matter of commutator lubrication.

Carbon has a negative resistance-temperature coefficient, and its resistance therefore decreases as the temperature rises. Also the contact resistance, between the carbon brush and the copper of the commutator, is not constant but has an inverse relation to the current. Resistance of the armature, including the brushes, will therefore be found to vary with the current value, having relatively high values of resistance at low values of current and appreciably lower values of resistance at high values of current. This results in an approximately constant voltage drop across the brush contacts for normal ranges of operating currents. As a brush material, electrographite, produced by more heat-treatment than is given the older forms of carbon graphite, has largely superseded carbon graphite. It has the advantage of larger permissible current densities and also of lower friction losses and reduced abrasive action. It may be used with current densities up to 70 amp per sq in. as contrasted with the usual upper limit of 40 amp per sq in. for carbon-graphite brushes.

For low-voltage heavy-current generators, such as those used in electrochemical industries, brushes are made of metal-graphite mixtures in order to obtain low resistance and low contact drop. Such brushes may be operated at current densities as high as 150 amp per sq. in.

Since operating conditions have much to do with the selection of proper brushes, in addition to design factors entering into the machine in question, the choice of a proper grade of brush for a particular machine calls for expert judgment as a result of wide experience with brushes and commutator problems and should usually be referred to a brush specialist.

With brushes of the proper hardness, adjusted to the correct tension, the commutator soon becomes glazed, with a highly polished surface and deep brown color. With this glaze established and maintained, the wear on commutator and brushes is slow, and long life is assured. The absence of such glaze and polish may usually be considered to indicate an improper selection of brushes, defects in the design of the machine so that good commutation is not attained, improper setting of the brushes, or possibly an improper application of the machine.

Special treatment of brushes is necessary for aircraft applications because of the rapid deterioration of ordinary brushes at high altitudes, due apparently to disappearance of the film, permitting the brush to be ground down through contact with the bare copper. The admixture of iodides with the brush material permits maintenance of the film under the difficult conditions of high-altitude flying, thus reducing brush wear. Similarly treated brushes are found to have much longer life when applied to the more difficult ground-level applications, such as high-speed electric locomotives.

34. Brush Shifting.—A major proportion of modern dynamos, both motors and generators, are provided with interpoles, or commutating poles, that set up a reversing field in the zone of commutation; but older machines, and recent ones that are not provided with interpoles, must depend upon brush shifting for assistance in securing the quick reversal of current that is essential for sparkless commutation.

The aim, in the shifting of brushes away from the geometrical neutral position, is to have commutation occur while the coil in question is under the influence of a weak flux field that will generate a coil voltage in opposition to the coil reactance voltage, thereby providing a coil emf that assists, rather than hinders, current reversal.

To secure the benefit of an emf in the coil that will assist in current reversal, it is necessary, in the case of a generator, to shift the brushes forward, in the direction of rotation, a sufficient distance to provide the field strength necessary for good commutation. The reason for this will be obvious when one considers that the current flow through the inductors in the generator is in the same direction as the induced voltage and that, if commutation is delayed until the coil sides are cutting flux from the succeeding pole, commutation will take place under the influence, or with the assistance, of a current-reversing voltage. To secure this effect with motors, it is necessary to shift the brushes *against* the direction of rotation, since current flow through the inductors of the motor armature is in opposition to the induced voltage.

The amount of reversing voltage required for best commutation will depend upon the value of the current being reversed. The extent to which brushes need to be shifted will therefore vary with the load upon the machine. The ideal solution might appear to be an automatic arrangement for shifting the brushes to the correct position for each load upon the machine, and, in fact, such devices have been tried but found to be impractical. With good design and the use of brushes of proper quality, however, it has been found that a brush position corresponding to average load conditions will be satisfactory for ordinary loading of the machine, although it will not necessarily provide satisfactory commutation for extreme overloads. Correct brush position for average load conditions is usually indicated by the manufacturer in the form of suitable markings upon the brush rigging and end frame of the machine.

35. Sparking at Brushes.—Complete absence of visible sparking at the commutator under all load conditions is hardly to be considered necessary, since slightly visible sparking is likely to result in no undue heating and only negligible damage to the brushes or commutator. As the sparks become larger and more obvious, however, the harmful effects become greater in that the brushes wear away more rapidly than they should and the commutator becomes overheated and blackened or roughened. In the worst cases of poor commutation, the commutator becomes pitted and its surface rough and irregular, with a tendency to wear into grooves. Also the copper may wear away and leave the mica insulation projecting, which prevents proper brush contact and accentuates the tendency toward sparking.

If the brushes are too soft, or if the commutator becomes oily or greasy for other reasons, the commutator will become dirty. This encourages the formation of conducting paths across the mica insulation from bar to bar. The leakage currents thus started usually burn themselves out because the conducting particles are heated to incandescence, producing a visible ring of fire encircling the commutator. This *ring fire* commonly occurs only as a result of neglect and should be considered as warning of further bad effects that may occur unless better maintenance is provided.

36. Flashovers.—The phenomenon known as *flashing over* or *arcing over* is distinct from sparking or arcing at the brushes and from ring fire; but either of these conditions may, if conditions are right, result in an arc that spreads from bar to bar until it covers the entire space between positive and negative brushes and constitutes a virtual short circuit across the machine terminals. Such an occurrence may result in serious damage to commutator and brush holders or may cause the machine to be disconnected from the line through operation of circuit breakers.

One or more of several factors may produce an abnormal bar-to-bar voltage at some point on the commutator, which causes an initial breakdown at this point, followed by successive flashovers between bars until the arc extends from brush holder to brush holder. One of the factors most likely to be involved in such an occurrence is *armature reaction*, resulting from the flux set up by and about the armature conductors. Armature reaction distorts the flux of the field poles, causing larger voltages to be induced in coils that are moving through the denser sections of the flux field. Since armature reaction varies directly with current in the arma-

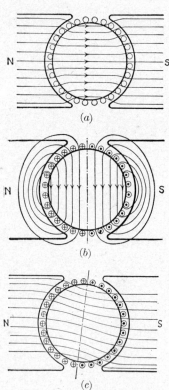

(a)

(b)

(c)

Fig. 47.—Flux distribution due to field and armature-magnetomotive forces, neglecting variations in reluctance of the magnetic path.

ture coils, the distortion effects are greatest under heavy load conditions.

Not infrequently, flashovers occur under transient or very abrupt load changes. In a generator, they are most likely to occur when load is suddenly reduced, as when a circuit breaker opens under overload or short-circuit conditions, because under this condition the transient voltages due to sudden collapse of flux lines about the armature conductors are added to the abnormal voltages due to flux distortion as a result of armature reaction, all tending toward an excessive bar-to-bar voltage. In a motor, on the other hand, the conditions most favorable to flashover occur when heavy loads are suddenly applied to the motor. Railway motors are particularly subject to flashover because of the severity of the service conditions under which they operate.

The likelihood of flashovers may be greatly decreased through the use of commutating poles and compensating windings, the latter being of greatest assistance, since by the use of such windings the distortion of flux and consequent unequal distribution of voltage drops across the commutator bars may be entirely prevented.

37. Armature Reaction.—Since all conductors are surrounded by magnetic flux lines when carrying current, the armature of a motor or generator will, when the machine is in operation, become a source of magnetism. The resulting flux lines will cross the air gap and occupy the lower sections of the field poles in common with the flux set up by the main-pole windings. The field through which the armature conductors move will thus be the resultant field as determined by the relative strengths and directions of the armature and main-pole mmfs.

Armature reaction may be considered as the mmf set up by currents flowing in the armature conductors, or it may be considered as the effect resulting from this electromagnetic action of the armature. Generally it is most naturally considered in terms of its distorting effect upon the flux underneath the main poles, the nature of and reason for which may be seen from a study of the diagrams of Figs. 47 and 48. One effect of this distortion, it will be observed, is the shifting of the neutral plane, or point of zero flux, ahead of the position it occupies when influenced by the main field alone.

The armature-reaction mmf may be calculated by use of the following equation:

$$H_a = \frac{Z \times I_a}{2 \times \text{poles} \times \text{paths}} \qquad \text{amp-turns per pole} \qquad (30)$$

where Z is total inductors on the armature and I_a is total armature current, two inductors being required to make one turn.

Example.—A six-pole generator with a simplex lap winding has a rated armature current of 72 amp. There are 750 inductors on the armature. What will be the armature-reaction mmf at rated load?

Solution:

$$H_a = \frac{750 \times 72}{2 \times 6 \times 6} = 750 \; NI \text{ per pole}$$

38. Distortion Effects.—Referring to Fig. 48, it is seen that the point of maximum mmf of armature reaction lies midway between the field poles but that the maximum flux density falls near the pole tips, the reason being the higher reluctance of the air path in the between-pole region as compared with that of the path underneath the poles. The first figure indicates the relatively uniform

field due to the main poles alone, and the third figure shows the
effect when the armature reaction flux is superimposed upon the
main field flux. This obviously results not only in a shifting of the

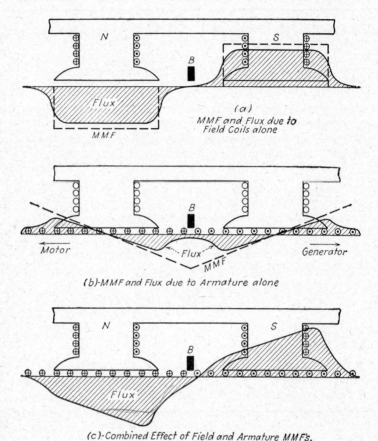

Fig. 48.—Flux distribution due to field and armature magnetomotive forces.

neutral flux plane, as previously mentioned, but also in an undesirable crowding of flux toward one pole tip, with the consequent
tendency toward saturation at one side of each pole.

If there were no change in permeability of the flux paths by reason of the distortion due to armature reaction, the total flux crossing the air gap would be unchanged by the superposition of armature flux upon the main-pole flux, and the average voltage generated would be unaffected, although the uniformity of voltage distribution would be disturbed. The tendency toward saturation at one pole tip, however, does decrease the permeability of the magnetic path at that side of the pole as compared with the opposite side, and an appreciable diminution in total flux crossing the air gap is therefore likely when the generator or motor is operating under load as compared with the total flux at zero load. More load upon the machine, whether it be motor or generator, means more current in the armature conductors; therefore armature-reaction effects may be expected to vary quite widely as loads change.

As stated in Art. 36, the distorting effect of armature reaction is largely responsible for flashovers at the commutators of motors and generators. This is due to the higher bar-to-bar voltage that results from the increased density of flux at one side of each pole. The inductors cutting the pole-tip flux have abnormal voltages induced in them that may result in abnormally high voltages between certain bars of the commutator. If this voltage is high enough to establish an arc between two or more bars, thus in effect short-circuiting these bars, there is a tendency for the region of high flux density to shift farther toward the center of the pole. This may result in a progressive arcing over successive bars until the arc extends from brush holder to brush holder, which means that the machine terminals are short-circuited. This usually results in a shutdown of the machine, with more or less damage to the commutator and brush holders.

Flux distortion and its effects may be prevented by use of *compensating windings* in the pole faces, which set up an opposing flux of equal value.

39. Demagnetization Due to Brush Shifting.—When brushes are shifted for the purpose of producing better commutation, as discussed in Art. 34, the effects of armature reaction are somewhat altered, since brush position determines the direction of the field set up by the armature flux.

As may be seen by reference to Figs. 49 and 50, the effect of shifting brushes for improvement of commutation is to introduce a demagnetizing component of armature reaction. It should be understood, however, that the two components thus indicated are not vector quantities, and no attempt should be made to treat them as such. However, if the direction of the armature mmf is changed by brush shifting, a portion of this mmf will be in direct opposition to the main field mmf, and a reduction in net effective

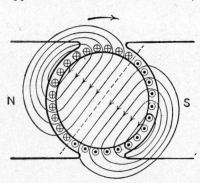

mmf and air-gap flux will be present under load conditions —with appreciable current flowing in the armature conductors—as compared with the no-load condition. This, in addition to the decrease in flux due to saturation of the pole tips, will result in a further drop in generated voltage when the machine is operating under load. Also it is evident that a pronounced brush shift, as shown in Fig. 49, will cause an opposing voltage to be gener-

Fig. 49.—Effects of a pronounced brush shift upon generated voltage and the direction of the armature-reaction flux lines.

ated in some inductors of each armature path, thus causing a further reduction in the effective voltage of the generator.

Referring to Fig. 50, it will be evident that, with brushes in the position shown and the angle α indicating the degrees of brush shift, the pairs of inductors within the top and bottom belts defined by the four angles α may be considered as turns effective in supplying mmf in opposition to that of the main-field poles. The pairs of inductors within the side belts defined by the two angles β may likewise be considered as turns effective in supplying mmf at right angles to that of the main-field poles.

Since two inductors per turn are required and two poles are shown in Fig. 50, the following equation may be utilized in the calculation of the demagnetizing ampere-turns due to armature reaction.

$$dH_a = \frac{4\alpha}{360} \times \frac{Z}{2 \times 2} \times \frac{I_a}{\text{paths}}$$

$$= \frac{\alpha}{360} \times \frac{ZI_a}{\text{paths}} \qquad \text{amp-turns per pole} \qquad (31)$$

where α is the brush shift in mechanical degrees, Z the total number of inductors, and I_a the total armature current.

The cross-magnetizing ampere-turns may be determined by subtracting the demagnetizing ampere-turns, as determined by Eq.

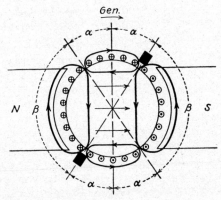

Fig. 50.—Armature reaction magnetomotive forces when the brushes are shifted for improvement of commutation in a generator.

(31), from the total armature-reaction ampere-turns determined by Eq. (30); or an equation similar to Eq. (31) may be set up as follows:

$$cH_a = \frac{2\beta}{360} \times \frac{Z}{2 \times 2} \times \frac{I_a}{\text{paths}}$$

$$= \frac{\beta}{720} \times \frac{ZI_a}{\text{paths}} \qquad \text{amp-turns per pole} \qquad (32)$$

Equations (31) and (32) apply for any number of poles, since additional poles result in proportional additions to both numerator and denominator, yielding the same final result.

Example.—The armature for an eight-pole generator has a simplex wave winding of 428 inductors and 107 commutator bars. The current rating is 100 amp. Calculate

(a) The cross-magnetizing ampere-turns per pole with the brushes on the geometric neutral.

(b) The demagnetizing ampere-turns per pole if the brushes are shifted forward the width of two commutator bars.

(c) The cross-magnetizing ampere-turns with the brushes shifted as in (b).

Solution:

(a) Since, with the brushes on geometric neutral, the entire armature-reaction effect is cross-magnetizing, Eq. (30) applies, and

$$H_a = \frac{428 \times 100}{2 \times 8 \times 2} = 1337.5 \ NI \text{ per pole}$$

(b) It is unnecessary in this case to calculate the value of angle α, since the ratio $\alpha/360$ will be equal to the ratio of bars shift to total bars; hence, by Eq. (31),

$$dH_a = \frac{2}{107} \times \frac{428 \times 100}{2} = 400 \ NI \text{ per pole}$$

(c) The cross-magnetizing NI with brushes shifted may be determined by subtracting the demagnetizing NI determined in (b) from the total armature NI determined in (a), as

$$1337.5 - 400 = 937.5 \ NI \text{ per pole}$$

or this determination may be made through application of Eq. (32). In this case, it is necessary to calculate the value of angle β. With eight poles, there will be 16 angles α and 8 angles β.

$$\alpha = \frac{2}{107} \times 360 = 6.73 \text{ deg}$$

therefore

$$\beta = \frac{360 - 16 \times 6.73}{8} = 31.54 \text{ deg}$$

and, from Eq. (32),

$$cH_a = \frac{31.54}{720} \times \frac{428 \times 100}{2} = 937.5 \ NI \text{ per pole}$$

40. Effects of Armature Reaction.—The details of the effects of armature reaction upon the operating characteristics of motors and generators will be considered in later articles. It may be stated in general, however, that the effects other than upon commutation will be slight if the brushes are allowed to remain in the geometric, neutral position, since under this condition there will be comparatively little decrease in flux because of armature reaction as the machine is loaded. Since it is usually necessary to shift brushes in motors and generators not provided with commutating poles, however, the demagnetizing effect of armature reaction will be brought into play in such machines, and the effects will be the same as those which result from diminution of flux for any other reason. Hence, in generators, the result will be a decrease in generated voltage as load current increases in the armature; and, in motors, the result may be an actual increase in speed, or the speed may be held more nearly constant than would be the case if there were no armature-reaction effects present, since normally motor speeds tend to decrease with load. The net result of armature demagnetization is therefore a wider range of voltages at the generator terminals, with changes in load upon the generator, and a more constant motor speed than would be available without this armature-reaction effect. In general, therefore, the effect of armature reaction might be considered detrimental to satisfactory generator operation and beneficial to motor operation, since it is usually undesirable to have voltages drop under increased loads upon a generator and desirable to have motor speeds remain as nearly constant as possible under load changes. In motors, however, a prominent armature-reaction effect may sometimes result in rises in speed with load and a tendency toward instability, causing the motor speed to rise and fall, or "hunt," the result of which is likely to be blown fuses or circuit breakers in the supply line.

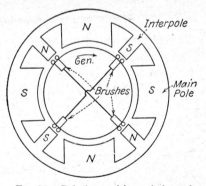

41. Interpoles, or Commutating Poles.—The function of the interpole, or commutating pole, is to establish a commutating or reversing field at the geometric neutral point, midway between the main poles of a generator or motor. Such a pole eliminates the necessity

FIG. 51.—Relative positions of the main poles, commutating poles and short-circuited coils in which current is being reversed.

of shifting brushes, because its use results in the establishment of a field of the proper strength and polarity in the neutral zone. Machines equipped with commutating poles should therefore be subject to none of the bad effects chargeable to armature-reaction demagnetization produced by brush shifting, provided that the brushes are kept accurately placed in the no-load, or geometric neutral, position.

Since the interpoles supply the commutating fields for which the brushes would otherwise be shifted, the polarity of each such pole must be the same as that of the main pole toward which the brush would be shifted for betterment of commutation, which means the same polarity as the next pole in the direction of rotation for a generator and the same polarity as the last preceding pole for a motor.

The strength of the commutating field required will of necessity vary in proportion to the current to be reversed, and the interpole winding is therefore connected in series with the armature circuit. This assures a field of proper strength for all normal loads upon the machine. Under heavy overloads, however, the magnetic circuit of the interpole may become saturated to such an extent that the commutating field may become inadequate.

The mmf of the interpole winding must first be directed toward clearing the commutation zone of the flux due to armature reaction. Then a number of additional turns are added to set up a commutating field of proper strength. Thus Eq. (30) should first be used to determine the armature ampere-turns that must be counteracted; then a sufficient number of ampere-turns should be added to provide the actual reversing field. The factor by which the NI determined from Eq. (30) must be multiplied to achieve satisfactory results is largely a matter of trial and experience. The factor 1.3 is frequently used and has in general yielded satisfactory results, although it is usually desirable to make a final adjustment by trial, using shunts or nonmagnetic shims to reduce the magnetic effect of the interpole if it is found to be stronger than it should be for best results.

The required commutating fields may be furnished by as many interpoles as main poles; or only half this number of interpoles may be used, the reduction being made by providing double flux to be cut by one side of each coil in lieu of single-flux fields to be cut by both coil sides.

The use of interpoles eliminates the demagnetizing component of armature reaction because the brushes are not shifted when interpoles are used but are set permanently at the no-load, or geometric neutral, point. It should be understood, however, that these poles do not overcome armature reaction except in the immediate region underneath the pole and that the field distortion and saturation effects of armature reaction are still present in the

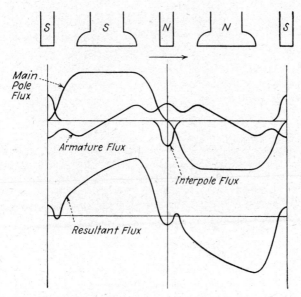

Fig. 52.—Flux distribution in the air gap of an interpole generator when operating under load.

interpole machine. Figure 52 illustrates this, beginning with the effect of the interpole core, which actually increases the armature-reaction flux in the neutral zone because of reduction of reluctance by reason of the added steel core, and ending with the complete flux-distribution picture, which shows clearly that the addition of the interpole field has no effect upon flux distortion under the main poles. This drawing does not show the reduction in flux that may come about as a result of pole-tip saturation, but it does show that distortion results in crowding the flux to one pole tip or the other. This will cause the flux to be confined to a region more highly saturated than before and may result in a diminution in total flux crossing the air gap. In order to eliminate flux distortion, compensating windings must be used.

Fig. 53.—Stator, with end-bells removed to show main poles and interpoles, completely assembled. (*Fairbanks, Morse & Company*.)

42. Compensating Windings.—The flux due to armature mmf is nearly all due to the current-carrying conductors underneath the poles, rather than between poles, because of the high-reluctance air path in the between-pole region. The armature-reaction flux may, therefore, be almost completely removed by the insertion of conductors in the pole faces, in the manner illustrated in Fig. 54, if these conductors carry currents opposite in direction to those in the armature conductors underneath the poles. It is not necessary that there be an equal number of conductors in the compensating and armature windings or that they carry equal currents, provided that the ampere-turns per pole of the compensating winding are equal to the armature ampere-turns underneath the pole. Thus five conductors in the pole-face winding carrying 50 amp will compensate for 10 conductors on the armature carrying 25 amp in the opposite direction, since the ampere-turns will be equal and in opposition across the air gap. This of necessity leaves out of consideration the *NI* due to the armature conductors in the neutral region between poles. The flux resulting from these con-

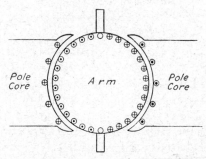

FIG. 54.—A compensating winding for a two-path armature.

ductors, however, is slight because of the high reluctance of their path, and any harmful effect upon commutation due to this flux in the neutral zone may be removed through the use of interpoles.

From the preceding discussion, it may be seen that the interpole and compensating windings supplement each other and that the combination removes all the harmful effects of armature reaction. However, although the use of interpoles is general and extends to quite small sizes of dynamo machines, the use of compensating windings, because of their cost and the limited need for them, is not so general, being limited to relatively large machines or machines that require protection against commutation and flashover troubles resulting from unusually severe operating conditions.

Although the compensating winding has proved the most satisfactory means of neutralizing armature-reaction effects—particularly when used in conjunction with interpoles of the proper strength—these effects may also be reduced appreciably by increasing the reluctance of the air gap in the vicinity of the pole tips. This may be accomplished by stamping the pole-core iron to a radius greater than that of the armature, thus making the air gap longer at the pole tips than at the pole centers, as in Fig. 55a; or it may be done by making the pole-core stampings with only one

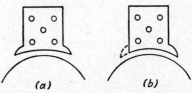

Fig. 55.—Means of reducing the effects of armature reaction (a) by variation in air-gap length (b) by variation in cross-section of pole-tip metal.

tip, as indicated in Fig. 55b, then alternately reversing the core punchings as they are stacked. This appreciably reduces the cross section of metal near the pole tips as compared with that in the body of the pole core, thus causing greater saturation and increased reluctance in the vicinity of the pole tips.

Fig. 56.—Main-pole and coil assembly of a compound-wound generator with compensating windings. (*Allis-Chalmers Manufacturing Company.*)

Since the conductors placed in the pole faces as compensating windings are conveniently connected to carry the full line current of the machine, the product of pole-face conductors and line current must equal the armature inductors per pole face times the current per inductor, or

$$Z_p I_L = Z_a I_a = Z_a \frac{I_L}{\text{paths}} \tag{33}$$

where Z_p represents conductors of the compensating winding, I_L represents total line current, Z_a stands for the armature inductors covered by each pole, and I_a stands for armature current per inductor, which is the same as current per armature path. Therefore, to determine the number of conductors to be placed in the pole face as a compensating winding, we may use the relation, derived from Eq. (33),

$$Z_p = \frac{Z_a}{\text{paths}} \tag{34}$$

For example, if a six-pole armature with a simplex lap winding has a total of 480 inductors, with a 75 per cent pole span and a current rating of 240 amp, the determination of conductors required for a compensating winding would proceed as follows:

$Z_a = \dfrac{480}{6} \times 0.75 = 60$ armature inductors covered by each pole

$I_a = \dfrac{240}{6} = 40$ amp per path

$Z_p = \dfrac{60 \times 40}{240} = \dfrac{60}{6} = 10$ number of conductors required for the compensating winding

Problems

1. The armature of a six-pole generator has 145 slots, one coil per slot, and two turns per coil, with a simplex wave winding. If this armature has a current rating of 100 amp, calculate: (a) the number of cross-magnetizing ampere-turns per pole, with brushes on the geometric neutral; (b) the number of demagnetizing ampere-turns per pole if the brushes are shifted forward one commutator bar; and (c) the number of turns per pole for an interpole winding.

2. A four-pole dynamo with a simplex wave-wound armature of 720 inductors has its brushes shifted 5 deg in the direction of rotation.

(a) Compute the demagnetizing ampere-turns per pole when the generator delivers 80 amp.

(b) Compute the number of inductors per pole face for a compensating winding if the pole-face width is 0.65 of the pole pitch.

3. A six-pole d-c generator has a simplex lap winding upon its armature. When driven at normal speed and excitation, it has an average induced voltage per inductor of 2 volts. If the generator output is 72 amp with a generated voltage of 250 volts, (a) what will be the total number of inductors upon the armature and the current per inductor? If the generator has no interpoles and the brushes are operated on the no-load neutral, what will be the value of the cross-magnetizing ampere-turns per pole? (b) In which direction should the brushes be shifted in order to improve commutation, and why? (c) Determine the approximate value of ampere-turns required for producing a suitable interpole field.

4. The armature for a six-pole simplex wave-wound motor has 55 slots with four conductors per slot, and 109 commutator bars. The brushes are shifted 4 mechanical degrees against rotation. Determine the demagnetizing and cross-magnetizing ampere-turns per pole for a load of 300 amp.

5. A six-pole motor has a triplex wave-wound armature, with a total of 300 inductors, wound two turns per coil. Rated current for the armature is 250 amp. If the brushes are shifted against the direction of rotation through an angle equivalent to two commutator segments, what will be the cross-magnetizing and the demagnetizing ampere-turns when the motor is operating under rated load conditions?

CHAPTER V

OPERATION OF GENERATORS

43. Magnetization Curves.—If a generator has its field current supplied from an outside source—separately excited[1]—while its armature is rotated at normal speed, generated voltages[2] corresponding to a number of field-current values may be read and plotted, the resulting curve being called the *magnetization,* or *no-load saturation,* curve of the generator. Since the generated voltage is, with constant speed, directly proportional to field flux, and the turns of wire in the field spools are constant, the curve really expresses the relation between flux density and mmf and therefore corresponds to the saturation curves of magnetic materials. The magnetic circuit of a generator, however, includes the air gaps, whose reluctance is independent of flux density, in addition to the steel portions, whose reluctance tends to increase with flux density. It will be noticed that this curve, being the result of the composite path reluctance, does not bend over so quickly nor show such a well-defined "knee" as the typical saturation curve for a single magnetic material.

It will be noted from Fig. 57 that a different curve is obtained for descending than for ascending values of exciting current. This is due to hysteresis in the metal portions of the circuit, resulting in a lag of magnetic flux behind the exciting mmf. In obtaining data for these curves, care must accordingly be exercised to approach from below all points intended for use in determining the lower curve and from above all points for determining the upper curve. The lower curve is usually of greater interest insofar as operation of the generator is concerned.

Since the generated voltage varies directly with speed, a different magnetization curve may be obtained with different speeds; or

[1] See Excitation, Art. 12.

[2] Since no current is flowing through the armature windings, the armature resistance drop is zero, and the generated voltage becomes also the terminal voltage.

points for curves at other speeds may be calculated by proportion after one curve has been determined experimentally.

It will be noted that the lower section of the curve, starting from a small residual voltage due to magnetism remaining in the iron from previous use of the machine, is practically a straight line, most of the reluctance here being in the air gap, but that, after the iron portions begin to show the effects of saturation, the curve bends and again approaches a straight line as full saturation of the magnetic circuit is approached.

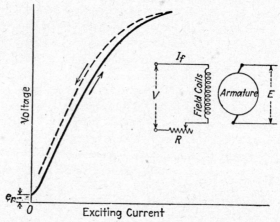

Fig. 57.—Magnetization or no-load saturation curve.

An equation may be set up to represent the magnetization curve to a fair degree of approximation. One such equation, known as *Froelich's equation*, has the form

$$E = \frac{aI}{b + I} \qquad (35)$$

where E represents the generated emf and I the field current, a and b being constants whose value can be determined for a given curve by substituting the values of emf and field current for two points on the curve and solving as simultaneous equations.

The shape of the magnetization curve may be closely predicted by the designer, previous to actual construction of the machine, after the physical dimensions of the proposed magnetic circuit are known and the ratings, number of turns in the field coils, etc., have been decided. The shape of the curve can be controlled through selection of materials and dimensions of the component parts of the magnetic circuit.

44. The Building-up Process.—The term "building up" is frequently used in connection with generator operation and refers to the gradual rise in voltage at the armature terminals when the machine is connected for self-excitation and operated at normal

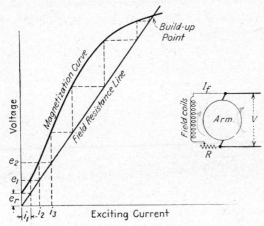

FIG. 58.—The "building-up" process in a shunt generator.

speed. This rise in voltage has its beginning at the value given by the residual magnetism of the field and should terminate somewhat above the rated value for the generator in order to allow for adjustment, the voltage having a tendency to decrease as the generator is loaded.

A study of the building-up process involves reference to the field-resistance line, which shows how the field current varies as the voltage applied to the field terminals is varied and, at constant temperature, is a straight line passing through the origin, determined by plotting field amperes against volts applied to the field terminals. The data for this line may be secured in connection with determination of the magnetization curve by reading one or more values of field amperes I_f and field-terminal voltages E_f. Obviously the slope of the field-resistance line is the resistance of the field circuit. In Fig. 59 are shown field-resistance lines for three values of field-circuit resistance; and it may be seen that added resistance—as in the field rheostat R—gives the field-resistance line a steeper slope and causes it to cut the magnetization curve at a lower point. When connected for self-excitation, the generated voltage of the armature being applied to the field, the building up of voltage proceeds as follows: Referring to Fig. 58, the residual voltage e_r when applied to the field terminals causes i_1 amp to flow in the field circuit. But i_1 amp in the field circuit causes, referring to the magnetization curve, e_1 volts to be generated. e_1 volts, referred to the field-resistance line, causes i_2 amp to flow in the field circuit. But i_2 field amp results in generation of e_2 volts, which causes i_3 amp to flow, etc. This process continues until the bending over of the magnetization curve results in an intersection with the field-resistance line. Below this intersection, an unstable voltage condition exists because any given field current causes the generation of more voltage than is necessary to sustain the current. Above the intersection, conditions are likewise unstable, but because a given field current causes the generation of insufficient voltage to sustain it. The generator will therefore build up to this point of intersection between the lower magnetization curve and the field-resistance line and no farther. The build-up point may be shifted by the addition of resistance to the field circuit, as shown in Fig. 59. However, the addition of sufficient resistance to throw the field-resistance line tangent to the magnetization curve, as shown by line Oa, will result in failure of the generator to build up its voltage. In order to initiate the building-up process, therefore, the field-circuit resistance must be less than this critical resistance value.

45. Critical Resistance and Speed.—Since generated voltage is directly proportional to speed, any rise or fall in speed will shift the entire saturation curve, each point on the curve being raised or lowered in direct proportion to the change in speed. A critical value of field resistance at or beyond which build-up will not occur will therefore exist for each speed at which a generator may be operated, this value being that which produces a field-resistance line tangent to the magnetization curve, as line 0*b* in Fig. 59 for speed S_1 or line 0*a* for speed S_2. It follows also that the higher the speed at which the generator is being operated the higher will be the value of field-circuit resistance that will prevent voltage build-up.

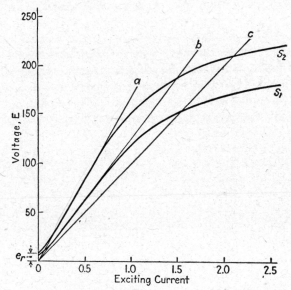

FIG. 59.— Self-excitation and the field-resistance line at different speeds.

Since there is a critical resistance for each speed, it is logical to consider that a critical speed exists for each value of field-circuit resistance, below which the voltage will not build up. The condition most favorable to voltage build-up, therefore, exists when the speed is high and the field resistance low. It is usually sufficient to operate the generator at its rated speed, with the field-control rheostat in its all-out position to initiate the building up of voltage, the resistance being then increased in value as the voltage rises, to prevent overshooting the desired build-up value. The design of the machine should be such that, without load, appreciable resistance will be required in the field-control rheostat to hold the voltage down to rated value. This permits adjustments to be made as may be required, either to compensate for the tendency of the voltage to drop as load is applied to the generator or to compensate for speed changes.

If a generator refuses to build up its voltage when operated at rated speed with all resistance out of the field rheostat, the building-up process may sometimes be started by overspeeding for a short time and returning to normal speed after the voltage has risen to, or near, its rated value.

46. Other Factors Affecting Voltage Build-up.—Assuming that the field and armature circuits are complete, the voltage of a generator may fail to build up for one or more of several reasons. Chief among these are

   a. Field-circuit connections to armature reversed.

   b. Too high resistance in field circuit.

   c. Commutator dirty or greasy.

   d. Brushes too far off neutral.

   e. Speed too low.

   f. Insufficient residual field.

The connection between armature and field must be such as to cause current to flow through the field coils in a direction to help out the residual magnetism and begin the cumulative building-up process. Usually it is necessary to determine the correct connections by trial. If the first trial connection proves wrong, the error may be remedied by reversing connections at the field terminals or by reversing direction of rotation if this is permissible. The latter procedure, however, reverses polarity of the generator, causing the current to flow in the opposite direction through the external circuit.

Too high resistance in the field circuit may be caused by failure to reduce resistance of the field rheostat, by poor connection at some point in the circuit, or by poor contact between brushes and commutator. It may cause complete failure to build up or may limit the voltage to a point below rated value.

If the brushes are too far off the neutral position, a partial neutralization of voltages results in each armature path because some inductors cut magnetic lines under poles of opposite polarity. The terminal voltage is therefore reduced, causing failure to build up or limiting the value to which the voltage rises.

Since the voltage that initiates the building-up process depends upon speed as well as upon residual flux, a reduction in either of these may cause failure to build up or, in case of subnormal speed, may limit the built-up voltage to a point below rated value. Sometimes it may be necessary to overspeed the generator in order to start it building up, after which it may be brought down to rated value, this action compensating for a reduced residual field.

Usually, in practice, a certain fixed polarity must be maintained at the generator in order to keep the external current always in the same direction. If then, as sometimes happens, the polarity of the generator is accidentally reversed, it is necessary to change it back to the original condition. This may be effected by reversing both the field connection and the direction of rotation. If, however, the direction of rotation is determined by the prime mover and is not subject to reversal, the only way lies in a reversal of residual magnetism. To accomplish this, it is necessary to send current momentarily through the field coils, from an external source, in a direction that will set up a field opposite to that of the residual magnetism previously in the field poles.

Unless unusual conditions require it, the switch connecting a generator to its load should be in the open position until the voltage has been built up and adjusted to its rated value. This is necessary not only to protect the load circuit, safeguarding it from the effects of abnormal voltages, but also because the building-up process is hindered by the presence of load current in the armature during the build-up period. Since current flow through the armature coils causes a voltage drop due to resistance of the coils and may also cause a reduction in magnetic flux lines due to armature reaction, which in turn has an adverse effect upon the generated voltage, the terminal voltage at any point during the build-up will be reduced by the presence of the load current in the armature coils during the building-up process, resulting in a reduction in the voltage applied to the field-coil terminals. The voltage build-up is, therefore, hampered by having the generator terminals connected to a load circuit; and, in general, it is not desirable to attempt to place a load upon the generator until the voltage build-up is complete. The load circuit may then be closed and any necessary adjustments of voltage made through manipulation of the field rheostat.

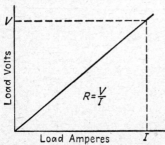

Fig. 60.—Characteristic for a single-resistance load.

47. Loading of Generators.—

Loads supplied by generators may be divided into two general classes, first, those in which current flow is limited only by resistance and, second, those in which current flow is limited by a combination of resistance and counter-acting emf. With the first type of load, the relation between impressed volts and load amperes will be a straight line through the origin, as shown in Fig. 60, the slope of the line being equal to the resistance of the load circuit. If two or more loads, connected in parallel, are supplied by the generators, the total current will be the sum of the two individual load currents, as I_T, equal to $I_1 + I_2$ in Fig. 61, and a line drawn from point c to the origin will represent the load characteristic of the combination.

A storage battery under charge is an example of the second type of load, since the circuit contains both resistance and counteracting emf. Figure 62 illustrates this type of load characteristic for a given state

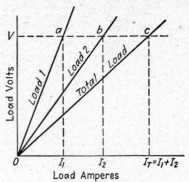

Fig. 61.—Characteristics for two resistance loads in parallel.

of charge, E_b representing the counter voltage of the battery and the sloping line representing the IR drop due to resistance, referred to an origin E_b volts above the true origin of the figure. The voltage that must be applied to secure a given current flow may then be determined by locating the point on the load characteristic that corresponds to the required current and reading the current on the vertical scale.

Most industrial and commercial types of load are connected in parallel, requiring that the voltage be maintained at a reasonably constant value. Thus each incoming load adds its quota of current to that already being supplied by the generator and feeder circuits. This produces added voltage drops in armature windings and supply lines and complicates the problem of holding the load voltage constant.

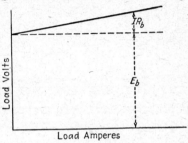

Fig. 62.—Characteristic of a storage-battery load.

48. Parallel Operation of Shunt Generators.—When the power required exceeds the capacity of one generator, it becomes necessary to operate two or more generators in parallel, each assuming its proper share of the total load.

When a single generator is to be connected to its load, the only necessity is that of bringing the generator to approximate speed and voltage before closing the line switch; but, when one generator is to be paralleled with another, it is necessary (a) that the terminal polarities of the incoming generator and of the operating generator be opposed across the switch that is to place them in parallel, (b) that the voltage of the incoming generator be equal, or nearly equal, to that of the operating generator, and (c) that, after the switch is closed, the load be properly adjusted between the two generators by manipulation of their field rheostats.

The voltage characteristics [1] of generators operating in parallel chiefly determine the manner in which the load will be shared by them and the stability of their operation; but the speed-load characteristic of the driving motor, engine, or turbine will also have considerable effect. In general, shunt generators operate satisfactorily in parallel because an increased load upon one unit causes its generated voltage to decrease, thus tending to "unload" upon the other generators with which it is paralleled. After the initial

[1] Curves plotted between output volts and amperes, as in Figs. 71 and 72.

adjustment of load between the generators is made, they should therefore continue to maintain this division, although this may not result in all cases without analysis and adjustment, or compensation of one sort or another, to give the two or more generating units as nearly identical load-voltage characteristics as possible. Generators that are to be operated in parallel should first be tested individually, and records should be made of voltage changes be-

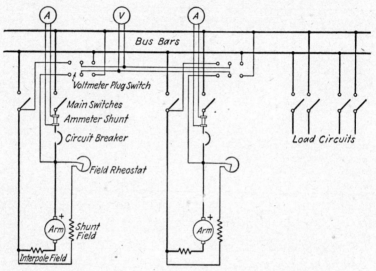

FIG. 63.—Connections for parallel operation of shunt generators.

tween no load and rated load, starting with the same no-load voltage upon each machine. The changes in speed that take place between no load and rated load should also be noted, since the speed drop as load increases will mean additional voltage drop over that inherent in the generator itself. From a comparison of these data, a decision may be reached as to what adjustments, if any, should be made in order that the generators may operate satisfactorily in parallel and share all load changes equally. In general, satisfactory operation throughout the load range requires that the decrease in voltage between no load and rated load be the same for each machine regardless of its capacity. If this is true and the

generators are adjusted to share a particular load equally if of the
same rating, or in proportion to their ratings if of different ratings,
they should share all other loads automatically in about the same
proportion.

Manual adjustment of load between the generators is accomplished by changes in field strength, through manipulation of field
rheostats. With constant speed, the generated voltage varies
directly with field strength; and the greater the generated voltage
above the terminal, or bus-bar, voltage the greater the resulting
current flow. Conversely, lowering the generated voltage, by
decreasing the field current, will result in shifting more of the
load to the other generator, or generators; and, when generated
voltage is equal to terminal voltage, no current will be flowing.
This should be the condition when the generator is connected to,
or disconnected from, the bus bars. If the reduction in field current
is carried to such a point that generated voltage is less than
terminal, or bus-bar, voltage, the direction of current flow reverses,
and the machine begins to develop torque as a motor. This condition is not ordinarily brought about except by accident.

49. Parallel Operation of Compound Generators.—Compound
generators are usually designed to have rising voltage characteristics, the voltage increasing as load current increases, this
effect being brought about through action of the series-field winding, which adds flux lines to the magnetic field initially set up by
the shunt field, causing the terminal voltage to rise with increase in
load current. This characteristic has distinct advantages in some
respects but adds to the difficulty of maintaining stable operation
when compound generators are connected in parallel to a common
load, because a momentary increase in load current of one generator produces more voltage, which in turn causes a greater current to
flow, thus upsetting the balance of load between the two machines.
The cumulative loading of one generator—usually the one of
greater capacity—not only may result in loading it beyond its
safe carrying capacity but may reverse the direction of current
flow through the smaller generators, causing them to act as motors.
Usually the circuits will be opened through operation of circuit
breakers or blowing of fuses before serious damage is done, the

net result being that the generators refuse to stabilize and maintain suitable distribution of load between them.

This tendency to load unbalance may be prevented by the use of a low-resistance *equalizer* connection between the junction points of armature and series field, as illustrated in Fig. 64. The equalizer, connected in this manner, connects the series fields in parallel. Any increase in load current thus divides between the

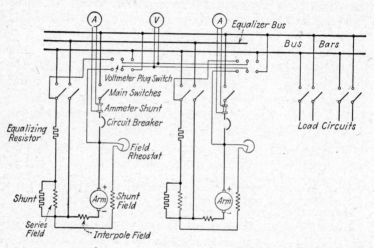

Fig. 64.—Connections for parallel operation of compound generators.

series fields in inverse proportion to their resistances and allows the increased load to be shared by all the generators operating in parallel. A momentary increase in loading of one will cause more current to flow through the series fields of all the generators, thus stabilizing the operation, though it may sometimes be further necessary to adjust the division by means of resistors in the series-field circuits. Thus, as indicated in Fig. 65, if machine A tends to become too heavily loaded, this tendency may be reduced by increasing the amount of resistance R_s in series with its series field. In general, the series-field circuits should have resistances inversely proportional to the ratings of the machines. It should be noted that, for generators operating in parallel, the adjustment for load division is made by inserting resistance in series with one field winding and that, for adjusting the degree of compounding in single generators, the resistance is placed in parallel with the series field. With compound generators, it is even more important than with shunt generators to make previous tests and adjustments before attempting to operate them in parallel. The series-field shunts should be adjusted to give identical voltage characteristics, if possible, or at least the same degree of compounding between no load and rated load. The voltage drops across the series fields at rated load should be checked and suitable adjustments made by means of the series-equalizing resistor so that the voltage drops

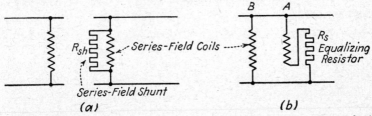

Fig. 65.—Methods of altering degree of compounding in generators and of securing proper division of load between generators operating in parallel.

across the series-field circuits are equal if the generators are of equal rating or if not of equal rating that the voltage drops are inversely proportional to the respective ratings. It is particularly important that the equalizer bus and all connections between it and the generator be low in resistance value. In general, the equalizer should be of equal cross section with the main-load leads and bus bars.

In making connections for the first time, care should be taken that the series fields of both machines are on either the positive or the negative side of the line; for, if one series field is on the positive side and one on the negative side of their respective armatures, the closing of the equalizer connection will short-circuit each armature through the series field of the other machine. Ammeters should be in the armature rather than the series-field lead coming from the machine, in order that true currents may be indicated, as may be observed from Fig. 64.

50. Operating Procedures.—Assuming that one shunt generator is in operation and that it is desired to place another in parallel with it and divide the load between them, the procedure is as follows:

(*a*) Bring generator 2 up to speed, and build up its voltage.

(*b*) Check the relative polarities of the two generators with a voltmeter, across the open paralleling switch, making sure that there will be voltage opposition when the switch is closed.

(*c*) Adjust the voltage of the incoming generator to equal that of the generator already in operation, and close the paralleling switch. Since the voltages are equal and opposite, there should be no current flow and therefore no change in existing conditions when the switch is closed.

(*d*) Adjust the load between the two generators by reducing the shunt-field current of No. 1 and increasing the shunt-field current of No. 2, by means of the field rheostats, with as little change in line voltage as possible. This procedure reduces the generated voltage of generator 1, causing its current output to be decreased, and increases the generated voltage of generator 2, causing its current output to be increased. If necessary, the entire load may be shifted from generator 1 to generator 2 in this manner. When, by observation of the ammeters, it is seen that No. 2 is supplying no current to the load, it may be disconnected and shut down. Care should be observed in making the field adjustments not to run the generated voltage of either machine, at any time, below the line voltage in value, because this would cause the current to reverse and would result in the machine's developing torque as a motor, thus adding this machine as a motor to the load already being carried by the other machine as a generator.

The procedure for placing compound generators in parallel is similar to that for shunt generators except for the handling of the equalizer connection. This connection either should be made simultaneously with that of the main-line connections, as when a triple-pole switch is utilized, or should be closed first if a separate single-pole switch is used for the equalizer circuit, in order to forestall the possibility of instability in operation for the period elapsing before the equalizer connection was made. In some cases, no harm would result; but, in other cases, the transient currents resulting from even a few seconds without the equalizer would be objectionable.

51. Division of Load between Generators in Parallel.—The division of load between shunt generators operating in parallel may be analyzed by reference to Fig. 66, which shows two assumed

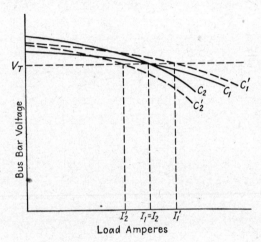

Fig. 66.—Characteristics of two shunt generators operating in parallel and sharing a load equal to $I_1 + I_2$.

voltage-characteristic curves. Since the terminal voltage of any number of generators operating in parallel must be equal, the currents supplied by each may be found by drawing a horizontal line through the known terminal voltage and noting the current corresponding to each intersection. For terminal voltage V_T, for example, the current furnished by generator 1 will be I_1, and that furnished by generator 2 will be I_2, shown as equal in this figure, the total load current being $I_1 + I_2$. If it should be desired to have generator G_1 assume a larger proportion of the load, the bus-bar voltage remaining unchanged, it would be necessary to increase the excitation of G_1 and decrease the excitation of G_2, thus raising the characteristic C_1 and lowering the characteristic C_2, until the desired division was effected, as in the figure, where the field currents of the two generators are readjusted to increase the loading of G_1 to I_1' and decrease the loading of G_2 to I_2', the bus-bar voltage and total load current remaining unchanged.

Since the terminal voltage must remain the same for all generators operating in parallel, a change in terminal voltage will accompany a change in load unless field-rheostat adjustments are made to keep the voltage at its original value. Also, unless the characteristics are identical and superimposed for a common no-load

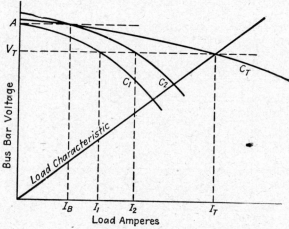

Fig. 67.—Graphical determination of load division between two generators operating in parallel.

voltage, a change in total load will cause the distribution between the generators to be more or less altered. If the characteristics do not intersect at zero load, a continued decrease in total load will cause the terminal voltage to rise until one generator, as represented by C_1 in Fig. 67, is carrying zero load, at point A on the curve, and the second generator is carrying the total load, represented by I_B. Further decrease in load will result in current reversal through the armature of the first generator, causing it to "motor"; and, with no external load at all, there will be a circulating current between the two machines, the value of which may be determined by dividing the difference between the two no-load (generated) voltages by the sum of the two armature-circuit resistances.   These statements may be verified by a study of the accompanying figures, considering the effects of changes in the load demands upon the combined generators.   It should be realized in connection with such a study that, in a practical installation, the changes in load demands are due to factors not controlled or controllable by the operator of the generating equipment, whose responsibility is to see that the supply voltage is held reasonably near a constant standard, or rated, value and that sufficient generating equipment is kept in operation to supply the load demands.

Example.-—Two separately excited generators are connected in parallel, with all load switches open.   Generator 1 has an armature-circuit resistance of 0.1 ohm, and generator 2 has an armature-circuit resistance of 0.15 ohm. If generator 1 has a generated voltage of 120 volts while generator 2 has a generated voltage of 110 volts, what will be the value of the circulating current through the two armatures, and what will be its relative direction?

Solution:

$$I = \frac{120-110}{0.1+0.15} = \frac{10}{0.25} = 40 \text{ amp}$$

This current will be supplied by No. 1 as generator to No. 2 as motor.

52. Voltage Control.—Commercial loads are connected in parallel and operate to best advantage when the voltage is maintained constant *at the load*.   Since the terminal voltage of a shunt generator tends to fall with increased load, either the speed or the excitation must be raised as output increases in order to keep the voltage constant.   Even this does not insure constant voltage at the load, however, since the drop in voltage over the connecting circuits, between generator and load, also increases directly with the current flow.   Therefore, with loads at some distance from the generator, it may be necessary to raise the voltage at the generator terminals above its normal no-load value as the current demands increase.

Compound generators are designed to prevent the voltage drop inherent in the shunt generator or to raise the terminal voltage at a predetermined rate as load current increases, this being brought about automatically by the action of the series-field coils in raising the excitation as load current increases.

Usually it is not considered expedient to depend upon speed

changes to control the terminal voltage. The medium for control, therefore, is usually the field flux, which may be adjusted by hand control in small machines, by motor-operated control in large machines, by various automatic voltage regulators, or by a combination of some one of these with the inherent characteristics of the compound generator with its series-field flux control.

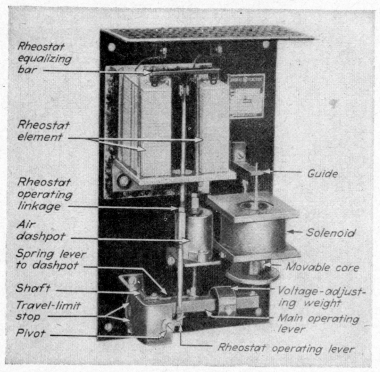

Fig. 68.—Automatic voltage adjuster. (*General Electric Company.*)

A number of voltage regulators are available for automatic control of the terminal voltage of a generator. Some of these depend for their action upon direct and continuous changes in the field-circuit resistance, others depend upon graduated step changes, and still others depend upon a change in the effective resistance brought about by vibrating contacts that alternately open and close a short circuit across a field rheostat. The last type, under the name *Tirrill regulator*, has been used extensively for many years and has provided satisfactory voltage control for industrial applications. Other types more recently devised involve the use of thermionic tubes, these having the advantages of high sensitivity

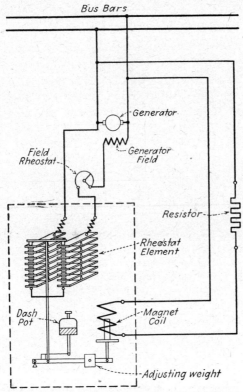

Fig. 69.—Circuit diagram of voltage adjuster. (*General Electric Company.*)

with no mechanical parts to introduce inertia, friction, and electrical contacts, with their resulting wear and need for adjustment.

One type of mechanical voltage adjuster is illustrated in Figs. 68 and 69. It consists of a voltage-sensitive element of the movable-core solenoid type, which operates, through a system of levers, a quick-acting rheostat that is connected in the generator-field circuit. The rheostat element consists of two vertical stacks of special-resistance material, whose resistance varies with position, this being under the control of the solenoid. Any change in generator voltage causes the movable core of the solenoid to move with or against the pull of gravity, thereby operating the rheostat element in the proper direction to restore the voltage to its original value. The regulator is normally at rest, operating only when a change in field current is required.

Problems

1. At 1000 rpm, the saturation curve for a generator having 1000 shunt-field turns per pole is given by

Volts	2	20	41	62	80	100	110	120	140	150
NI	0	500	1000	1500	2000	2600	3100	3700	5450	6800

(a) When the shunt-field resistance is 32 ohms, to what value would it "build up"?

(b) For this resistance, what is the critical speed?

(c) For 1000 rpm, what would be critical field-circuit resistance?

2. If the speed of the generator referred to in Prob. 1 is raised to 1200 rpm, to what value must the field rheostat be adjusted in order to maintain the voltage at the value determined in (a) of Prob. 1, the resistance of the shunt-field coils being 25 ohms? If, at this speed, the field rheostat is cut entirely out, what will the voltage become?

3. A storage battery having internal resistance of 0.2 ohm has an open-circuit voltage of 12 volts. What voltage will it be necessary to apply in order to cause a charging current of 10 amp to flow? If, after charging for some time, the battery emf rises to 13 volts, what will be the value of the charging current, the total circuit voltage remaining unchanged?

4. Two shunt generators operating in parallel are so adjusted that each delivers 50 amp at 120 volts to the common load.

(a) If the voltage characteristics may be considered straight lines, the first generator having a no-load voltage of 125 and the second generator having a no-load voltage of 130 volts, what will be the current supplied by each generator and the total current when the load resistance is altered in such a manner that the line voltage rises to 122 volts?

(b) What will be the operating conditions when the load resistance is adjusted to the point at which the line voltage becomes 125 volts?

(c) If the load circuit is opened, reducing the load current to zero but leaving the two generators operating in parallel, what will be the terminal voltage and the current circulating between the two generators?

5. Given two generators, with separately excited fields, operating in parallel. The first has a rating of 30 kw at 150 volts, with a no-load voltage of 155; and the second is rated 15 kw at 150 volts, with a no-load voltage of 160 volts. If, with a bus-bar voltage of 150, each machine is carrying its rated load, what will be the total load and its division between the two machines when the bus-bar voltage is (a) 152 volts and (b) 155 volts, assuming straight-line voltage characteristics? (c) What will be the current and voltage conditions when the external load is zero?

6. Two shunt generators operating in parallel are rated 200 and 300 kw, respectively. Their voltage characteristics, plotted between terminal volts and kilowatts output, are approximately straight lines. The first generator has a drop of 12 volts between no load and rated load, and the second generator has a drop of 8.5 volts between no load and rated load. If these machines have their excitations so adjusted that at no load each has a terminal voltage of 250, what will be the bus-bar voltage and the division of load when they are supplying a total load of 250 kw? of 500 kw?

CHAPTER VI

GENERATOR CHARACTERISTICS

53. Generator Voltage Equation.—Referring to the expression for generated voltage (Art. 15), it is evident that, after a generator has been designed and constructed, all factors in the voltage equation are constant except two, these being flux and speed. For this condition, therefore, the voltage equation has been expressed in the form

$$E = K_1 \phi S \tag{22}$$

where ϕ = flux per pole

S = speed

It should be noted, however, that Eqs. (21) and (22) refer to generated voltage, a part of which is used to overcome the IR drops in the circuit between negative and positive terminals due to the resistance of armature, series-field, and interpole windings, brushes, and brush contacts, commonly referred to as the *armature resistance drop*. Therefore, for a dynamo being driven as a generator and supplying power to an external circuit,

$$V = E - I_a R_a = K_1 \phi S - I_a R_a \tag{36}$$

where V = terminal voltage

E = generated voltage

I_a = armature current

R_a = armature-circuit resistance

Thus, for a given dynamo to function as a generator, the total voltage generated by the inductors of each path will be higher than the voltage at the terminals of the armature circuit. When the machine is operating as an isolated generating unit, the terminal voltage may vary as generated voltage or armature currents vary, but when the machine is operating in parallel with other units, it is necessary for the operator to adjust the excitation to a point at which the generated voltage will be sufficiently above the common terminal, or bus-bar, voltage to enable the generator to supply its proportionate share of the load. If its generated voltage should fall to a point just equaling the terminal, or bus-bar, voltage, as determined by the other generating units operating in parallel with it, the current would drop to zero.

54. External Characteristics.—The curve showing the relation between generated voltage and amperes output of a generator is called the *total characteristic*, and that between terminal voltage and amperes output is called the *external characteristic*. The latter is also frequently referred to as the *voltage-regulation curve*. These

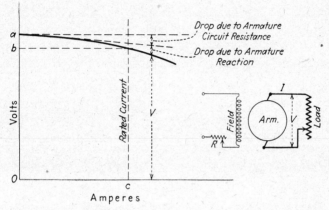

FIG. 70.—External characteristic for a separately-excited generator.

curves may be plotted from data obtained from operation of the generator under load and observation of terminal volts at various values of load current; or they may be determined graphically if the magnetization curve and the armature and field resistances are known, as well as the demagnetizing effect of the armature reaction if such effect exists.

Separate Excitation.—If a given generator is driven at constant speed, with a constant value of field current coming from a source other than the generator itself, then the external characteristic will have the shape shown in Fig. 70.

Referring to the voltage equation [Eq. (36)] for a generator, it will be seen that, with constant speed and flux, the generated voltage will be constant but that the terminal voltage will diminish with increase in current output because of the IR drop in the armature circuit. Especially with noninterpole generators, having the brushes shifted to improve commutation, the field flux will be reduced as the armature current increases, because of the demagnetizing component of armature reaction, and an additional factor tending to cause a decrease in terminal voltage will be introduced. With interpole generators, this factor will not enter to so great an extent, since the brushes will remain at the neutral setting; but there is likely to be some reduction in flux even with brushes

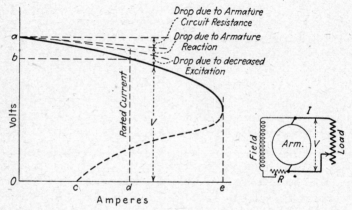

Fig. 71.—External characteristic for a self-excited shunt generator.

properly located on the no-load, or geometric, neutral, as previously noted. The effect of these factors in reducing the terminal voltage as load current increases is shown graphically in Fig. 70. Obviously, with these factors operating to reduce voltage as load current increases, it will not be possible to maintain an exact voltage at the generator terminals without compensation of some sort, such as making adjustments in the field-circuit resistance by means of the field rheostat as the load current changes in value.

Shunt Excitation.—With shunt excitation, the external characteristic shows a more decided drop than for separate excitation because of the decreased excitation that comes about as a result of the decrease in terminal voltage due to the causes previously enumerated. Assuming then as the general case a generator in which armature reaction has an appreciable effect upon the total flux, we have the following factors operating to reduce terminal voltage with increase in current output:

a. Armature drop, $I_a R_a$.

b. Field demagnetization due to armature reaction.

c. Decreased excitation due to lowering of field voltage by factors *a* and *b*.

It will be noted that, beyond a certain critical value, as indicated by the scalar distance *Oe* in Fig. 71, the external characteristic for the shunt generator shows a reversal in trend of current values with decreasing voltages. This point of maximum current output is called the *breakdown point*, and it is evident that in this region the factors working toward reduction in terminal voltage bring about a demagnetization of the field such that continued decrease in external circuit resistance fails to increase the current output but results in diminution of both voltage and current. The limiting condition is one of short circuit across the armature terminals, the current flow under this condition being that due to the voltage of residual magnetism alone. This tendency of the shunt generator to lose its excitation under overload conditions renders it self-protecting to a considerable degree against heavy overloads, although sudden application of a short circuit may result in heavy transient current flow, since the flux requires an appreciable time for reduction to its minimum value.

Compound Excitation.— The use of a double field winding, one in parallel and the other in series with the armature or external circuit, gives operating characteristics much better adapted to the usual applications than either

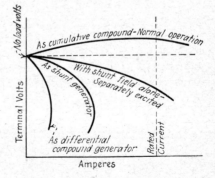

FIG. 72.—Typical characteristic curves obtained from a generator designed for operation with cumulative-compound excitation.

of these windings alone. The tendency of the shunt generator toward a drop in terminal voltage is thus compensated for by the addition of a sufficient number of series turns to offset the effect of IR drop in the armature circuit and field demagnetization, resulting in a flat-compound generator, whose voltage remains practically constant with changes in load. Or, by further addition of series turns, the voltage may be caused to rise with increase in load current, resulting in the over-compound generator.

Most commercial and industrial loads have their various units connected in parallel, requiring that the voltage between lines be maintained at a reasonably constant value. This applies with particular force to lighting loads, since a small change in voltage results in a marked change in light intensity. The flat-compound type of generator is adapted to loads sufficiently near it that the line drop is not appreciable in its effect. The over-compound generator is adapted to more remote loads, since its rising characteristic will compensate for line drop, which increases with the load. The exact degree of compounding for a given requirement may be secured by adjustment of a variable shunt placed in parallel with the series-field coils, as shown in Fig. 73, assuming that the series winding consists of a greater number of turns than are required for the voltage rise desired for the particular application.

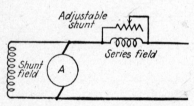

Fig. 73.—Circuit diagram for a short-shunt compound generator with series-field shunt, or diverter, for adjusting the degree of compounding.

55. Voltage Regulation.—The term voltage regulation refers to the change in terminal voltage with change in load current—the generator being driven at constant speed unless its driving motor, engine, or turbine is subject to speed changes with load, in which case it may be desirable to determine regulation of the complete unit rather than limiting it to the generator alone. A generator is said to have good regulation if the change in voltage between rated load and no load is small and poor regulation if this change is considerable. The external characteristic, or regulation, curve usually supplies the information needed for calculating the regulation of a given generator. For accurate determinations, such tests should be made at operating temperature of the generator, after the generator has been operating under load for a sufficient length of time to bring all parts up to full working temperature.

Expressed in equation form,

$$\text{Voltage regulation} = \frac{\text{no-load voltage} - \text{rated-load voltage}}{\text{rated-load voltage}} \quad (37)$$

Since the regulation is based upon the rated-load voltage, the result, as a percentage, will evidently be the percentage rise in voltage as rated load is removed from the machine. Thus, if a

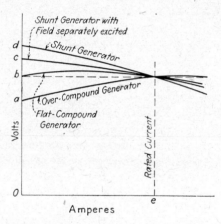

FIG. 74.—External characteristics for three types of generator, with identical full-load ratings.

certain generator has a rated-load voltage of 115 volts and a no-load voltage of 125 volts, the percentage regulation is equal to the difference between no-load and rated-load values expressed as a percentage of rated-load value, as

$$\text{Percentage regulation} = \frac{125 - 115}{115} \times 100 = 8.7\%$$

In Figs. 70 and 71, the percentage regulation would evidently be the distance or voltage represented by ba in relation to the distance or voltage represented by Ob.

Since, in a compound generator, the full-load voltage may be equal to or higher than the no-load voltage, the regulation may be expressed as

$$\text{Voltage regulation} = \frac{\text{rated-load voltage} - \text{no-load voltage}}{\text{rated-load voltage}} \quad (38)$$

unless otherwise specified.[1]

A somewhat different definition was formerly applied to compound generators, based on the extent of departure of the voltage curve from the ideal straight line connecting the no-load voltage point to the rated-load voltage point. This necessitates plotting the regulation curve and determining by measurement the maximum departure of the curve from a straight line, which may then be expressed as a percentage of the voltage that would obtain at the point if the regulation curve had been straight instead of curved.

56. Determination of External Characteristics.—After a generator is designed and built, its external characteristic can readily be obtained by connecting a suitable load, such as a rheostat or bank of lamps, to the generator terminals, and observing amperes and corresponding volts for a sufficient number and range of values that will outline the external-characteristic, or voltage-regulation, curve. During this test the generator should be driven at a constant speed, preferably rated speed, with its field rheostat adjusted to a point that yields rated voltage at rated current output.

Before the generator is an actuality, however, a prediction curve must usually be made in order to check the design and insure correct performance later. This may be done with reasonable accuracy when the magnetization curve at a given speed, the demagnetizing component of armature reaction at a given value of armature current, and the armature resistance are known. Since most modern machines are equipped with interpoles, requiring that the brushes be set accurately at the no-load neutral point, and since materials are used in the magnetic circuit that do not saturate readily, the effect of armature reaction may usually be neglected without serious error. Its effect can easily be included, however, if sufficient data are available.

---

[1] A.I.E.E. Test Code for Direct-current Machines, No. 501, July, 1941.

With any system of field excitation, therefore, there will be a loss in voltage by reason of the IR drop in the winding, brushes, and brush contact. This results in the tendency for terminal voltage to drop as load increases. In the separately excited generator, the field current, being supplied from an independent source, should remain constant regardless of load, although the flux being cut by the armature inductors may be decreased under load because of armature-reaction effects. With the shunt field excited from the machine terminals, *i.e.*, self-excited, however, any decrease in terminal voltage will immediately be reflected in a decreased field current that causes a further drop in terminal voltage.

The addition of a series field, as in the compound generator, results in the production of a greater flux under load conditions than at no load; therefore the compound generator may be designed with a series field of sufficient strength to offset entirely the effects of armature-voltage drop and armature reaction or to add sufficient flux to produce a rising characteristic under load.

The decreased excitation of the shunt-excited generator will not be a factor in the flat-compound generator, since the terminal voltage is practically constant; whereas, in the over-compound generator, the shunt-field current will increase somewhat under load conditions, because of the rise in terminal voltage.

57. Graphic Method—Separately Excited Generator.—Points may be determined for plotting a predicted external-characteristic, or voltage-regulation, curve for a separately excited generator as follows: Referring to Fig. 75, assume the saturation curve to represent that determined by calculation for the generator in question and OA to represent the ampere-turns of field excitation required, at rated speed, to give the desired no-load voltage, represented as OC. Then assume that, for a chosen load upon the generator, AN represents the loss in field excitation due to demagnetizing armature reaction for the armature current corresponding to the assumed load, leaving a net excitation ON. This net excitation yields a generated voltage ND, since the saturation curve is plotted between net, or effective, excitation and generated volts. Subtraction of the armature-voltage drop for the armature current corresponding to the assumed load then yields the desired terminal-voltage value, which may be plotted as a second point upon the external characteristic, the first being the voltage *OC* corresponding to no-load, or zero, armature current. Other points may be determined in similar fashion until the desired characteristic is fully determined. Usually it will be found to be practically a straight line; so that it is necessary to determine only the no-load and rated-load voltages in order to have a reasonably accurate regulation curve. The first choice of no-load voltage may not yield the correct rated-load voltage; but this is easily remedied by raising or lowering the curve, parallel to itself, until it passes through the

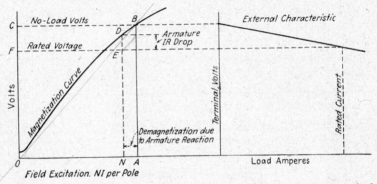

Fig. 75.—Determination of external characteristic for a separately-excited generator by the graphic method.

correct voltage point corresponding to rated current. The corrected no-load excitation may then be obtained by reference of the corrected no-load voltage to the saturation curve. If necessary, a revised characteristic may then be determined.

It should be noted that the armature demagnetization referred to in the previous paragraph is that determined by brush shifting and that, if the brushes are kept precisely at the no-load neutral position, as they are assumed to be in machines with interpoles, the determination of points for the characteristic curve is correspondingly simplified. Since the excitation is not affected by the armature current, it is only necessary, for each load point, to measure down from point *B*, the no-load voltage, by an amount equal to the IR drop in the armature circuit for this load, in order to find the terminal voltage for the load under consideration. Since the armature-circuit resistance, including brushes, is not constant for different values of current, either a curve of resistance values should be plotted and the proper resistance read from it, or the resistance of armature windings alone should be used in calculating the IR drop, and the standard allowance for brush drop deducted separately. For standard values of allowable brush-drop voltage, see Art. 93.

58. Graphic Method—Shunt-excited Generator.—With the shunt-excited generator, the problem of determining points for the external characteristic is complicated by the fact that a third factor—decreased excitation current—is introduced. The presence of this third factor follows from the fact that the field coils are connected across the armature terminals, thus causing the field current to vary with the terminal voltage of the generator and making it necessary to provide some means of determining the basic excitation corresponding to each load current for which a point on the external characteristic is to be determined.

If we reason that a calculable loss in excitation occurs as a result of armature reaction for a particular load current, and that the armature-voltage drop may also be calculated, the one being subtractive along the X axis and the other being subtractive along the Y axis, it may be seen that the problem involved is that of fitting a right-angle triangle into the space between the field-resistance line and the magnetization curve. The base of the triangle is equal to the armature reaction on the horizontal scale of the magnetization curve, and the altitude of the triangle represents the armature IR drop along the vertical scale of the magnetization curve.

One way of locating the position to be occupied by the load triangle is illustrated in Fig. 76, where OD, the calculated value of armature reaction NI for any load, say, rated load for convenience, is laid off to the scale of field excitation NI, and DE, the calculated value of armature IR drop for the same load amperes, is laid off to the vertical scale of volts. Since, in its true position, the point E must lie in the magnetization curve while the point O lies on the field-resistance line, a line drawn from E parallel to the field-resistance line will locate the point E'. From E', a line parallel to line EO will locate point O'. Vertical and horizontal lines from points E' and O', as indicated, will give the gross excitation OF for the load in question, the net excitation OG, the generated voltage OH, and the terminal voltage OK. Inspection of the diagram will indicate that this value of terminal voltage satisfies the requirement that the total excitation determined by application of terminal volts to field terminals, less armature reaction for the load

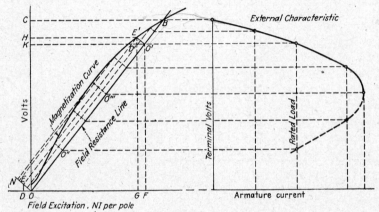

Fig. 76.—Determination of external characteristic for a self-excited shunt generator by the graphic method.

in question, yields a value of net excitation that gives a value of generated voltage greater than the terminal voltage by the armature IR drop for this load.

It should be noted that another value of terminal volts, corresponding to point O'', likewise meets this condition but that this point is on the unstable part of the characteristic, not used in normal operation. Also, the maximum ampere load the generator will supply will be the load that will cause the parallel line EE' to be tangent to the magnetization curve, the terminal voltage for this load being that corresponding to point O'''. The value of this maximum load current may be determined by extending the tangent back to intersection N on the original load triangle and measuring it in terms of the scale to which this triangle was drawn. The hypotenuse ON may also be subdivided and used as a load line for determining other points on the voltage characteristic by a somewhat shortened process, the details of which may be readily worked out by the student.

It should be noted that the construction here given yields the relation between armature current and terminal volts, whereas it is usually desired to know the relation between load current and terminal volts. However, since the shunt-field current is small, the discrepancy involved in substituting armature current for load current is usually negligible; but correction may be made if desired by subtracting the field current, graphically or by calculation, from the determined value of armature current for each load point, before plotting the points for the voltage characteristic.

59. Graphic Method — Compound-excited Generator. — The method to be employed in determining points on the external characteristic for the compound generator is similar to that for the shunt generator, the essential difference being that the field excitation is being increased instead of decreased as the machine becomes loaded and the current and power output increases. Thus, in Fig. 77, OA represents the increased excitation due to the series field for a chosen load. From this must be subtracted the armature-reaction ampere-turns represented by AD, giving a net increase in excitation for this load represented by the distance OD on the scale of excitation ampere-turns. DE represents the resistance drop in armature and series field at the given load, giving the triangle ODE. As before, this triangle may be relocated, with the point E lying in the magnetization curve, as at E'; and it will serve to indicate the generated voltage OH, equal to GE', and terminal voltage OK, equal to MO'. Other points may be determined for various loads in the same manner, or the hypotenuse OE may be used as a load line and subdivided to shorten the process of locating the other points, since the slope of this hypotenuse will be the same for all loads.

It should be noted that the shunt-field current increases with the rise in terminal voltage. At no load, the voltage applied to the shunt field is OC, equal to LB. For the load considered, the terminal voltage has risen to OK, equal to MO', the rise in shunt-field voltage being equal to CK, resulting in an increased shunt-field excitation denoted by LM.

The degree of compounding attained by a given generator will depend upon saturation of the magnetic circuit as well as upon the ratio of series-field to shunt-field ampere-turns. If these factors are such as to cause a rise in voltage between no load and rated load, the rise will become less rapid if the machine is loaded beyond its rated value; and the voltage will utimately reach a maxi-

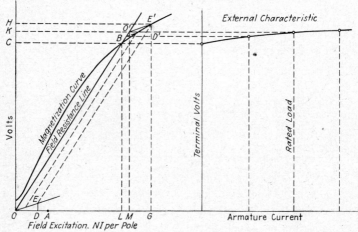

FIG. 77.—Determination of external characteristic for a compound generator by the graphic method.

mum and begin to decrease, because of saturation of the magnetic circuit. For a lesser number of turns on the series field, the generator may have the same voltage at rated load and no load, giving a flat-compound characteristic; but, in this case, the voltage will reach somewhat higher values between no load and rated load.

The compounding of a generator may be increased by increasing its speed, with the no-load voltage kept to its normal value by added resistance in the shunt-field circuit. This has the twofold effect of increasing the ratio of series-field to shunt-field ampere-turns and of causing the generator to operate on a lower, and therefore steeper, portion of the magnetization curve.

Reduction in degree of compounding of a generator already designed and built may readily be brought about by application of a
diverter to the terminals of the series field—this being a low-resistance shunt that divides the current in inverse proportion to the
resistances of diverter and series field, reducing the series-field NI
for a given load current. The resistance of the diverter must be

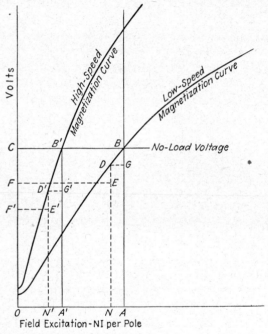

Fig. 78.—Effect of speed upon voltage regulation of a separately-excited generator.

adjusted, of course, to the value that yields the desired degree of
compounding.

60. Effect of Speed on External Characteristics.—For the
separately excited generator, the effect of changes in speed upon
the external characteristic may be studied by reference to Fig. 78,
which includes determinations similar to those given previously
under Art. 57 for two speeds. Since generated voltage for a given
excitation varies directly with speed, each point on the lower

magnetization curve will be raised in direct proportion to the rise in speed, which is about 50 per cent in the case here given.

Assuming that resistance is added to the field circuit as the speed increases, in order to hold the no-load voltage at the same value OC, equal to AB, at both speeds, the terminal voltage for the new speed is derived as in Fig. 78. AN and $A'N'$ represent the equal losses in excitation due to armature reaction, and DE and $D'E'$ represent the equal IR drops, giving as a result OF', equal to

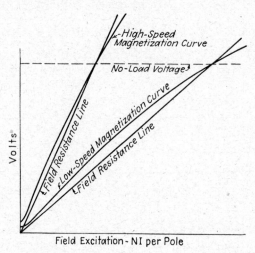

Fig. 79.—Effect of speed upon voltage regulation of a self-excited shunt generator.

$N'E'$, as the terminal voltage under the assumed load at the higher speed as compared with OF, equal to NE, the terminal voltage for the same load at the lower speed.

Armature reaction and armature IR drop will be identical in both cases, since the same armature current is assumed, both being directly dependent upon armature current and independent of speed; but comparison of the values EG and $B'G'$, representing the portion of the voltage loss chargeable to armature reaction shows clearly that this loss is much greater at the higher speed. The drop in terminal voltage from the common no-load value OC to OF' in the case of the higher speed, as compared with OF in the case of the lower speed operation, indicates that the voltage regulation is decidedly worse at the higher speed. Thus better regulation may be obtained with the separately excited generator by operation at reduced speed, this giving a more highly saturated field circuit, against which the armature reaction will have less effect. If the generator has interpoles, with the brushes correctly set on the no-load neutral line, there should be no demagnetizing component of armature reaction, and the regulation is better, the effect of changes in speed upon voltage regulation being less pronounced in the interpole generator than in the noninterpole generator.

A similar conclusion for the self-excited shunt generator may be reached from a study of Fig. 79, which assumes a common no-load voltage for each of the two speeds, the adjustment being made by manipulation of the shunt-field rheostat. Higher speed obviously causes the generator to operate on a steeper part of the magnetization curve, makes the voltage regulation poorer, and also has the effect of reducing the maximum current that may be obtained from the generator.

61. Load Characteristics.— A constant resistance forms the simplest type of load. The current supplied such a load is directly proportional to the voltage impressed upon it, as indicated by Fig. 80. The slope of this load characteristic, obtained by dividing any value of impressed voltage E, by the corresponding value of load current I, is the resistance of the load circuit. For two resistance loads in parallel, the

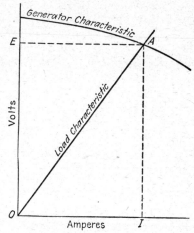

FIG. 80.—Combination of generator and load characteristics.

total load current will be the sum of the individual load currents, as illustrated in Fig. 61, page 94. By adding the currents corresponding to any assumed voltage, such as E, and extending a straight line back to the origin from the point C, representing the total current at voltage E, the total load characteristic may be obtained. The slope of this total load characteristic will be the equivalent load resistance for the circuit equal to $R_1R_2/R_1 + R_2$, according to the rule for addition of parallel resistances.

A storage battery under charge represents a combination of emf and resistance, and its characteristic may be represented as in Fig. 62, for a particular value of battery voltage and internal resist-

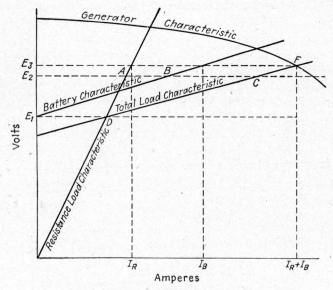

FIG. 81.—Division between different types of parallel loads.

ance, both of which vary with the state of charge. Here one component of the applied voltage must overcome the battery emf which opposes it, and another component must supply the IR drop due to internal resistance of the battery. Thus the applied voltage must always be greater than the battery emf by the amount of the IR drop.

The terminal voltage and current supplied by a given generator to a particular type of load may readily be predicted by a combination of the generator and load characteristics, as indicated by Fig. 80. The intersection of the two characteristics determines the voltage OE and the current OI that will result. With two loads of different types, such as a resistance load and a battery, connected in parallel, as in Fig. 81, it is necessary first to plot the two load characteristics separately and then to derive a characteristic for the combined load. This is done by selecting a voltage, E_2, for example, determining the intersection with each load characteristic, as point A for the resistance load and point B for the battery load, and adding them to obtain one point on the total characteristic. For the example cited, this gives point C as one point on the total load characteristic. The same procedure is followed for another voltage, such as E_1, where the battery current is zero, giving point D as a second point. A straight line through points C and D gives the total load characteristic, whose intersection with the generator characteristic, at point F, determines the voltage and current requirements of the combined loads. Since this will be the voltage applied to each of the loads, the individual load currents may be determined by noting the currents corresponding to the intersection of this voltage line with the individual load characteristics, as I_R for the resistance load and I_B for the battery load, E_3 being the common load voltage.

62. Armature Characteristics.—Decrease in voltage with load increase in the shunt- or separately excited generator may be prevented by increasing the field current sufficiently to offset the drop in voltage. The curve that shows the field current necessary to maintain the terminal voltage constant throughout the operating range of the generator, plotted between field current and armature current, is called the *armature characteristic*. A typical curve is shown in Fig. 82. It is usually

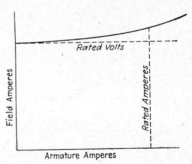

FIG. 82.—An armature characteristic.

determined experimentally by separately exciting the field coils and obtaining the necessary values, but it may also be determined by graphical means. From this curve, or the data from which it is constructed, the number of series-field ampere-turns for flat-compounding a generator may be calculated, since the additional ampere-turns required for rated-load operation at constant terminal voltage may be supplied by a series field as well as by the shunt field.

Example.—A six-pole generator requires 4.5 amp shunt-field excitation to give rated voltage at no load, and 7.0 amp to give the same voltage at rated load of 200 amp. There are 750 shunt-field turns per pole. (*a*) How many series turns must be added to give flat-compound operation, using the short-shunt connection? (*b*) If 12 turns per pole are added, having a resistance of 0.005 ohm per pole, what should be the resistance of a shunt across the series-field terminals to give the desired flat-compound effect?

Solution: [1]

$$(7.0 - 4.5)\ 750\ =\ 1875\ NI \text{ per pole required}$$

(*a*)
$$\frac{1875}{200} = 9.4 \text{ turns per pole}$$

(*b*)
$$\frac{1875}{12} = 156.25 \text{ amp required for excitation}$$
$$200 - 156.25 = 43.75 \text{ amp through diverter}$$

Since for parallel circuits the voltage drops are equal across the parallel paths,

$$I_F R_F = I_D R_D$$

or

$$156.25\ (0.005 \times 6) = 43.75 \times R_D$$

and

$$R_D = \frac{156.25\ (0.005 \times 6)}{43.75} = 0.107 \text{ ohm}$$

63. Rising Voltage Characteristics.—A method similar to that described in Art. 62 may be utilized for over-compounding a generator, the data being determined by actual test where the series field is to be added to an existing shunt generator, or by graphic determination, using the saturation curve to determine the added ampere-turns that must be in effect at rated load in order to provide the *generated* voltage required at this load to furnish the desired *terminal* voltage.

[1] It should be noted that this procedure fails to take account of the series-field IR drop and may need correction to cover this deficiency, although the error is likely to be small.

Example 1.—It is desired to place a series winding upon a generator that will raise the terminal voltage from 230 to 250 between no load and full load. Using the shunt field alone for excitation, it is found that at no load 5 amp and at full load 11 amp are required to give the desired voltages. There are 1000 turns per pole on the shunt field. Rated-load current is 500 amp. How many series turns per pole will be required? (Assume use of the long-shunt connection, and neglect the added IR drop due to the series field.)

Solution:

$$(11 - 5)\ 1000\ =\ 6000\ NI \text{ per pole required}$$

$$I_F\ =\ 5 \text{ amp at 230 volts}$$

$$=\ 5 \times \frac{250}{230} \text{ or } 5.43 \text{ amp at 250 volts}$$

$(5.43 - 5.0)\ 1000\ =\ 430\ NI$ per pole added by the increased shunt-field current

$6000 - 430\ =\ 5570\ NI$ per pole required of the series field

$$\frac{5570}{505.43}\ =\ 11 \text{ turns per pole of series-field winding}$$

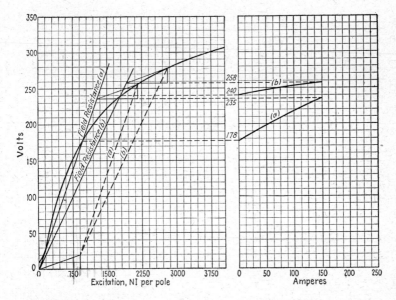

Example 2.—Consider the accompanying saturation curve to apply to a six-pole generator with interpoles, having the brushes properly set and oper-

ated at rated speed. The shunt field has 1500 turns per pole, the series field six turns per pole. Shunt-field resistance, including the rheostat, is 275 ohms. Combined series-field and armature resistance is 0.1333 ohm. Rated current output is 150 amp. The speed is to be considered constant at its rated value.

(a) Determine the percentage compounding of this generator, indicating all steps upon the figure.

(b) If the shunt-field rheostat resistance of 75 ohms is entirely removed, what effect will this have upon the compounding? Determine the new value, the speed being held constant at the same value as before.

Solution: For a field-circuit resistance of 275 ohms, the field-resistance line may be laid off by drawing a straight line through the origin and a point corresponding to 275 volts and 1 amp field current (1500 NI per pole). This crosses the magnetization curve at 178 volts upon the vertical scale, which is the no-load voltage for this field-circuit resistance and the speed for which the magnetization curve was made to apply.

Next the ampere-turns supplied by the series field at rated current, equal to 900 NI per pole, are laid off from the origin on the horizontal scale. Vertically from this the IR drop in the armature-series-field circuit is laid off, this being equal to approximately 20 volts, neglecting the slight effect that addition of the shunt-field current to the output current would have upon this voltage drop. From the vertex of the triangle thus formed, line a is drawn to an intersection with the magnetization curve, from which point of intersection, representing the generated voltage at rated load, a vertical drop equal to the armature-series-field voltage loss yields the value 235 volts, which is the terminal voltage at rated-load output. Percentage compounding under condition (a) is then found by dividing the rise in volts from no load to full load by the no-load volts.

$$\frac{235-178}{178} \times 100 = 32\% \text{ compounding}$$

Following a similar procedure for the field-circuit resistance condition of (b), it is found that the no-load voltage is 240 and the rated-load voltage is 258 volts. The percentage compounding is again calculated, as

$$\frac{258-240}{240} \times 100 = 7.5\% \text{ compounding}$$

This serves to exemplify use of the graphical method for determining the voltages from which the degree of compounding is calculated and also emphasizes the greater effect of a given number of series-field turns when used in conjunction with a light shunt-field excitation.

64. Series Generators.—Generators depending for excitation solely upon a series winding have little practical application, since the voltage regulation is inherently very poor. In order to build up voltage on such a generator, the external circuit must be closed and its resistance reduced to a comparatively low value; but, as the voltage and current rise, the circuit resistance may be increased to its normal value. For moderate values of load current, the excitation varies directly with load amperes; but, for high current values, the magnetic circuit approaches saturation, and the excitation increases at a lesser rate than the current.

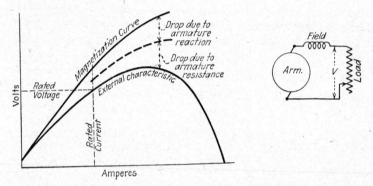

FIG. 83.—Typical curves for a series generator.

If the machine is operated with the brushes on neutral, and if there is no field demagnetization, the total characteristic, or generated-voltage, curve will coincide with the magnetization curve; otherwise the characteristic will rise to a maximum value and beyond this show a decrease. The external characteristic will be less than the total characteristic by the IR drops in the armature and field circuits. Figure 83 illustrates the general trend of these curves.

By designing the series generator to operate with a high value of armature reaction, the external characteristic can be made to approach zero quickly, after having attained its maximum value, giving a wide range of voltage values for a short range of current values. This design was once used for supplying series systems, such as street-lighting circuits, with constant current, but it has been superseded by other methods. It has also been used as a voltage booster, connected as shown in Fig. 154.

Problems

1. A 7.5-kw 120-volt generator is found to have an armature-circuit resistance, including brushes, of 0.125 ohm, a series-field resistance of 0.05 ohm, and a shunt-field-circuit resistance of 60 ohms. What will be the voltage generated by the armature conductors under normal full-load operating conditions?

2. A 50-kw generator, when operated with separately excited field, at normal speed and with full-load current output of 400 amp, is found to have a terminal voltage of 125; but, when the load is removed by opening the line switch, the voltage rises to 135. The armature-circuit resistance is 0.015 ohm. (*a*) What is the cause of the rise in voltage? (*b*) What is the percentage regulation of the generator?

3. If armature reaction causes a 2.5 per cent change in flux crossing the air gap of a separately excited generator, whose voltage at no load is found to be 250, what will be its terminal voltage when full-load current of 100 amp is being supplied by the generator, the resistance of the armature circuit being 0.1 ohm?

4. Given a 25-kw 125-volt 1200-rpm generator having an armature-circuit resistance of 0.04 ohm, with field separately excited. Assuming the generator to be operating initially under rated load, what will be the effect upon voltage and current output of a drop in speed of 200 rpm? (Neglect effect of armature reaction, and assume constant resistance in armature and load circuit.)

5. A shunt generator is tested and the following data secured for plotting a saturation curve at rated speed:

Generated volts....	10	30	70	104	130	152	170	200	222	240	270	290
Field amp.........	0	0.1	0.2	0.3	0.4	0.5	0.6	0.8	1.0	1.2	1.7	2.2

The resistance of the armature circuit of the above generator is 0.30 ohm and of the shunt-field circuit is 200 ohms. The generator has interpoles, and the brushes are properly located at the geometric neutral point. The field winding is composed of 1000 turns per pole.

Plot the saturation curve, and determine by graphical methods (*a*) the no-load terminal voltage of the generator, (*b*) the terminal voltage at rated-current load of 50 amp and, (*c*) the maximum current the generator can supply at this speed and excitation.

6. How many series turns per pole would be required to make the generator of Prob. 5 operate flat-compound? Mark all pertinent steps and points upon the graph sheet.

7. How many series turns per pole would be required to make the generator of Prob. 5 operate over-compounded to an extent that would raise the rated-load voltage 20 volts above the no-load voltage? Mark all pertinent steps and points upon the graph sheet.

8. Given a generator with a saturation curve as listed in Prob. 5, which it is desired to convert into a compound generator with a terminal voltage of 220 at no load and 250 at rated load of 150 amp. There are 1000 shunt-field turns per pole. The machine is to be operated with a forward brush shift such that at rated output the armature demagnetizing effect equals 200 amp. turns per pole. The armature and series-field resistance totals 0.1333 ohm. By calculation and construction, determine the number of series-field turns required—all work to be shown upon the curve sheet. Assume use of the long-shunt connection.

9. Again making use of the saturation curve of Prob. 5, assume that this curve applies to a shunt generator being operated at rated speed of 1500 rpm, that there are 1000 turns per pole of shunt-field winding, and that the armature-circuit resistance is 0.15 ohm.

(*a*) If the shunt-field resistance is 180 ohms, to what voltage will the generator build up at no load?

(*b*) If the speed is increased to 1600 rpm, what will the build-up voltage become?

(*c*) What is the "critical" field-circuit resistance for the rated speed?

(*d*) If a series winding of six turns per pole, with a total resistance of 0.10 ohm, is added, what will be the terminal voltage with 80 amp in the armature—the armature reaction being estimated at 1 amp-turn per amp of armature current?

(*e*) If (*d*) determines the generator to be under-compounded, calculate the voltage regulation; if over-compounded, calculate the percentage of over-compounding.

10. A shunt generator with a saturation curve having the shape and co-ordinate values given in the upper curve of Fig. 59 has an armature-circuit resistance of 0.1 ohm and a shunt-field resistance of 100 ohms. There are 1000 turns of field winding per pole, and, with the brushes in normal operating position, the demagnetizing component of armature reaction equals 200 NI per pole. By reference to the saturation curve, determine the no-load voltage and estimate the terminal voltage when the armature carries a normal current of 100 amp.

11. If the field of the generator of Prob. 10 is excited from a separate source, with current held constant at the no-load value for shunt excitation, determine by reference to Fig. 59 the rated-load value of the terminal voltage, and compare with that of Prob. 10.

12. Determine from Fig. 59 the number of series turns that, superimposed upon the shunt-field excitation, would result in flat-compound operation of the generator of Prob. 10.

13. A six-pole generator requires 4.0 amp shunt-field excitation to give rated voltage at no load, and 7.0 amp to give the same voltage at rated load of 400 amp. There are 800 shunt-field turns per pole.

(*a*) How many series turns must be added to give flat-compound operation, using the short-shunt connection?

(b) If 10 turns per pole are added, having a resistance of 0.005 ohm per pole, what should be the resistance of a shunt, or diverter, across the series-field terminals to give the desired flat-compound effect?

14. It is desired to place a series winding upon a generator that will raise the terminal voltage from 220 to 240 between no load and rated load. Using the shunt field alone for excitation, it is found that at no load 2 amp and at rated load 5 amp are required to give the desired voltages. There are 1000 turns per pole on the shunt field. Rated-load current is 300 amp. How many series turns per pole will be required? (Assume that the long-shunt connection is used.)

15. A separately excited generator has a no-load voltage of 240 and a rated-load voltage of 220, the speed and field current being held constant. What is the percentage regulation?

16. If the speed of the generator of Prob. 15 is increased 50 per cent but the no-load voltage is held at 240 by adjustment of the field rheostat, will the rated-load voltage be greater or less than 220? Explain by reference to assumed saturation curves for the two speeds. What is the effect upon the percentage regulation?

17. Given three generators operating in parallel, with armature-circuit resistances as follows: $R_{a-1} = 0.20$ ohm, $R_{a-2} = 0.25$ ohm, $R_{a-3} = 0.30$ ohm, and line voltage = 250. (a) Find the generated voltage for each machine when machine 1 is furnishing 75 amp, machine 2 is furnishing 50 amp, and machine 3 is furnishing 40 amp to the common load. (b) Find the generated voltage if the exciting currents are so adjusted that each generator furnishes 55 amp of the load current.

18. Two generators operating in parallel have armature-circuit resistances $R_{a-1} = 0.15$ ohm and $R_{a-2} = 0.25$ ohm. The line voltage is 240 volts, and the load is equivalent to 2.0 ohms resistance. Normally the load is shared equally by the two generators. (a) Find the current furnished by each generator and the voltage generated by each for the normal condition of operation. (b) In error, the speed of generator 1 is allowed to decrease until its generated voltage is only 235 volts. Assuming constant terminal voltage, what is the effect upon the operation of the two machines? Find the currents and voltages.

19. Two generators, operating in parallel, have characteristics as indicated by the following data. The curves are to be plotted and determinations made graphically of the terminal voltage, the current supplied by each generator, and the total current when a resistance load of 1.8 ohms is connected to the common bus bars.

Generator 1

Volts..........	220	217.5	215	211	206.5	206.5	191	184	172
Amp..........	0	20	40	60	80	100	120	140	160

Generator 2

Volts.........	228	220	211	200.5	189.5	176.5	162	142	116
Amp.........	0	20	40	60	80	100	120	140	160

20. Assuming the field currents of the two generators in Prob. 19 to be adjusted (raising or lowering the curves) so that the load is divided equally between them, the total load current and the terminal voltage being unchanged, determine the new values of no-load voltage for the two generators.

21. An additional resistance of 5 ohms is connected in parallel with the existing load to the generators of Prob. 19. Determine the current supplied by each generator to the new total load, the terminal voltage, and the current supplied to each load. Why has the current supplied to the 1.8-ohm load changed in value?

CHAPTER VII

DIRECT-CURRENT MOTORS

65. Comparison of Generator and Motor Action.—The fundamental basis for motor action lies in the fact that, when a conductor carrying current is placed in a magnetic field, a force action is set up that tends to drive the conductor through or out of the field, in a definite direction. However, it will be seen that, in moving through the field, the conductor cuts magnetic lines, an action that is in itself the basis of voltage generation. Hence, in the rotation of a motor armature, we have a generation of voltage, in accordance with Eq. (22), Art. 15. This voltage is in a direction opposite to the applied voltage, since armature current is opposite in direction for motor action as compared with generator action, direction of rotation and of magnetic field being unchanged. It is accordingly referred to as the back, or counter, emf.

For motor action, therefore, the voltage equation is

$$V = E + I_a R_a = K_1 \phi S + I_a R_a \tag{39}$$

where V = terminal voltage
E = counter emf
I_a = armature current
R_a = armature-circuit resistance

Comparing the two equations (36) and (39) for generator and for motor action, it will be seen that, in the former, the initial and higher voltage is the generated voltage and that it is utilized in sending current through the armature and the external circuit; whereas, in the latter, the initial and higher voltage is the applied voltage, which is utilized in sending current through the armature and in neutralizing the effect of the counter emf. Furthermore, it will be evident that the action of a given machine as motor or generator is determined by the relative values of generated voltage and terminal voltage. As long as the generated voltage is less than the terminal voltage, the machine is operating as a motor and taking power from the electrical side; but, when the generated voltage

134

becomes greater than the terminal voltage, the machine becomes a generator, supplies electrical energy, and requires an intake of mechanical energy in order to continue operation. As shown in Fig. 84, a given machine may pass from generator action to motor action without change in direction of rotation or of field flux, the direction of current alone being affected.

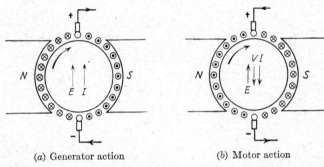

(a) Generator action   (b) Motor action

Fig. 84.—Comparison of generator and motor action.

Example.—Given a shunt generator rated 20 kw 250 volts 1500 rpm, having an armature-circuit resistance of 0.12 ohm, and field-circuit resistance of 100 ohms. (a) When supplying rated output, what will be the generated voltage? (b) If used as a motor with rated current input, at a line voltage of 250, what will be the generated voltage, or counter emf?

Solution:

$$20 \text{ kw} = 20,000 \text{ watts}$$

$$\frac{20,000}{250} = 80 \text{ amp rated current output}$$

$$\frac{250}{100} = 2.5 \text{ amp field current}$$

(a) As generator
$$I_a = 80 + 2.5 = 82.5 \text{ amp armature current}$$
$$E = V + I_a R_a = 250 + (82.5 \times 0.12) = 250 + 9.9 = 259.9 \text{ volts}$$

(b) As motor
$$I_a = 80 - 2.5 = 77.5 \text{ amp}$$
$$E = V - I_a R_a = 250 - (77.5 \times 0.12) = 250 - 9.3 = 240.7 \text{ volts}$$

A demonstration of counter emf may be observed from the readings of a voltmeter applied to the armature terminals of a motor,

connected for operation as shown in Fig. 85, before and after opening the switch. Prior to opening of the switch, the voltmeter reads
the applied voltage E_t; but, after the switch is opened, the voltage
indicated is the generated voltage, or counter emf, which is less
than the applied voltage and results from cutting of the lines of
force by the armature conductors. The energy required for turning the armature comes from the weight and inertia of the moving
parts and is necessarily limited in amount.

66. Theory of Motor Operation.—The counter emf of a d-c
motor acts in a very effective manner as a governor for controlling
the current input to the motor armature, opening the way for an
increased current when the mechanical load on the motor is increased and limiting its value when the load is decreased.

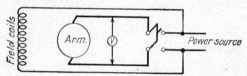

Fig. 85.—Method of demonstrating the existence of counter emf in a motor.

As load is applied to the moving parts of a motor, through the
agency of a belt, gear, or other mechanical connection, the first
effect is a reduction in speed. But, from Eq. (39),

$$I_a = \frac{V - K_1 \phi S}{R_a} \tag{40}$$

it may be seen that reduction in speed brings about a reduction in
counter emf, which makes available an increased voltage for
causing current flow through the armature, the current increases
in value and the developed torque is increased. The slowing-down
process therefore extends only far enough to cause sufficient
increase in developed torque to meet the new load demand. In
some types of motor, a very slight decrease in speed is sufficient to
accomplish this result; in others, a more decided drop is necessary.

When the mechanical load is decreased, the motor speed rises
because more torque is being developed than is required to meet the
new load condition, and the excess is applied to accelerating the

armature. But increased speed develops a greater counter emf, which reduces the voltage available for sending current through the armature. Consequently, the developed torque diminishes, and the speed rises only to the point of balance between torque developed and torque required for the new load condition. Thus the motor, through the agency of the counter emf, adjusts itself quickly and readily to each load condition; and the input power is regulated to the amount required for supplying the motor losses and driving the connected mechanical load.

Example 1.—A certain 230-volt motor has an armature-circuit resistance of 0.3 ohm and runs at a speed of 1200 rpm, with normal excitation and 50-amp armature current. (a) If the load is increased until the armature current has risen to 60 amp, what will be the new value of speed? (b) If the load is reduced until the armature current has dropped to 25 amp, what will the speed become?

Solution:

Normal $E = V - I_a R_a = 230 - (50 \times 0.3) = 215$ volts
With $I_a = 60$ amp, $I_a R_a = 18$ volts, and $E = 230 - 18 = 212$ volts
Since $E = K_1 \phi S$ and ϕ is assumed constant, speed will vary directly,

(a) $$\frac{1200}{S_2} = \frac{215}{212} \text{ from which } S_2 = 1183 \text{ rpm}$$

With $I_a = 25$ amp, $I_a R_a = 7.5$ volts and $E = 230 - 7.5 = 222.5$ volts

(b) $$\frac{1200}{S_3} = \frac{215}{222.5} \text{ from which } S_3 = 1242 \text{ rpm}$$

NOTE.—The effects of armature reaction and changes in armature-circuit resistance with current are neglected in this solution.

When the armature is at standstill, the counter emf is zero, and consequently the total applied voltage is available for sending current through the armature. Since the armature resistance is low, this would result in an enormous current flow if line voltage were applied to the armature under this condition. It is therefore necessary, in starting a motor, to insert resistance in series with the armature winding in order to limit the current to a safe value until the speed of the armature has risen to a value at which the counter emf is sufficiently developed to take over the governing function and afford protection to the circuit.

Example 2.—If an attempt is made to start the motor of Example 1 without auxiliary resistance, what will be the value of the current at the instant of closing the switch? What series resistance should be inserted in order that the armature current at the moment of starting may be limited to 1.5 times the normal value of 50 amp?

Solution:

(a) $$I_a = \frac{V}{R_a} = \frac{230}{0.3} = 766\tfrac{2}{3} \text{ amp}$$

which is 15.3 times normal value.

(b)   1.5 × 50 = 75 amp permissible starting current

$$75 = \frac{230}{0.3 + R_s}$$

from which

$$R_s = 2.77 \text{ ohms}$$

67. Torque and Horsepower.—From Eq. (23), Art. 16, we see that the force applied to move a conductor in a magnetic field is proportional to the density of the field, the length of the conductor in the field, and the value of current flowing through the conductor. After multiplying by the number of armature conductors under the poles at a given instant, and the lever arm, or distance of each conductor from the center of the shaft, and allowing for changing from the cgs to the English system of units, we have as a final expression for torque

$$T = K_2 \phi I_a \tag{41}$$

where ϕ is the flux per pole, I_a is the armature current, and K_2* includes all other factors that are involved in a complete expression for torque but are constant for a given machine.

A study of the factors entering into the formula for developed torque, as indicated by Eq. (41), may be obtained by proceeding as follows:

Let B = flux density, in gausses

L = length of pole face, in centimeters, parallel to the armature conductors, also the length of active conductors, in centimeters

r = distance of conductors from center of shaft, in feet

---

* It should be noted that this constant is not identical or interchangeable with the K_1 factor in Eqs. (22), (39), and (40).

p = paths through the armature
I_a = total current in the armature
Z = total number of inductors on the armature
P = number of poles
C_1 = $10 \times 445{,}000$ dynes per lb
C_2 = percentage of armature covered by the poles

The force on one conductor is, from Eq. (23),

$$F = \frac{BLI_a}{p \times 10 \times 445{,}000} = \frac{BLI_a}{C_1 p} \quad \text{lb} \tag{42}$$

and the torque due to one conductor is

$$t = Fr = \frac{BLI_a r}{C_1 p} \quad \text{lb-ft} \tag{43}$$

the torque due to all conductors is

$$T = ZC_2 t = ZC_2 \times \frac{BLI_a r}{C_1 p} \quad \text{lb-ft}$$

$$= 11.73 \times \frac{Z\phi P I_a}{p} \times 10^{-10} \quad \text{lb-ft} \tag{44}$$

Since flux per pole

$$\phi = \frac{2\pi \times 12r \times L \times B \times 6.45 \times C_2}{P \times 2.54}$$

from which

$$BLr = 5.22 \frac{\phi P}{C_2} \times 10^{-3}$$

and since, for a motor designed and built, the poles, paths, and armature conductors are constant, the torque may be expressed as

$$T = K_2 \phi I_a \tag{41}$$

The value of torque given by Eq. (41) is the total torque developed by the armature and differs from the torque applied to the load by the torque required to turn the armature itself against the friction of the bearings and brushes, the windage or counterforce due to the fan action of the armature, and other counterforces due to movement of the armature. In general, these counterforces may be considered independent of load, thus offering a ready means for their determination from input readings taken with the motor running idle. They are not, however, independent of speed. The difference in numerical value between developed and applied torque is usually small.

The applied, or output, torque of a motor may be determined for any current input within its range by means of a prony brake and balances, the torque, in pound-feet, being the length of brake arm in feet multiplied by the net force indicated by the balance reading. The value thus obtained is the equivalent force exerted at 1 ft radius.

The horsepower output of a motor is dependent upon speed and torque and is expressed by the equation

$$\text{Hp} = \frac{2\pi ST}{33,000} \tag{45}$$

where S = speed in rpm and T = output torque in pound-feet.

In determining efficiency of a motor by means of a brake test, the input voltage and current values are determined by electrical instruments, and the output by prony brake and balances, the speed being determined at the same time by a speed counter or tachometer. The output and input values of power may then be reduced to a common system of units by the factor

746 watts = 1 hp

and the efficiency may be determined by dividing output by input.

68. Field Excitation.—D-c motors, like generators, are divided into three principal types according to the method by which excitation is provided. The *shunt* motor, as the name indicates, obtains its excitation through a field winding connected in parallel with the armature, which means that line voltage is applied to the field-circuit terminals. In order that the field current may be kept at a relatively low value, ordinarily less than 5 per cent of the normal current input to the motor, and at the same time provide sufficient mmf, the field is wound with a large number of turns of small wire, divided equally between the poles. And, although usually a rheostat is placed in series with the field winding in order to provide means for varying the field strength, the design is such that line voltage may be impressed upon the field without risk of damage.

The *series* motor, in contrast to the shunt motor, has its excitation provided by a field winding that is intended for connection in

series with the armature.   It is therefore essential that the winding
be of low resistance in order that no undue hindrance exist in the
path of the current.   And, since the exciting current is large in
comparison with that of the shunt motor, a smaller number of
turns, of much larger cross section, is required.

Fig. 86.—An 800-hp, 600-volt, 150/450 rpm, shunt-wound steel mill motor.
(*Allis-Chalmers Manufacturing Company.*)

The *compound* motor has upon its field poles both series and
shunt windings.   These are entirely separate coils, however, operating to set up flux lines through a common magnetic circuit.   Usually the shunt-field winding is placed first upon the pole core,
and the series winding is superimposed upon it.   Both sets of coils
may or may not be enclosed in a final layer of insulation, according
to the design of the machine.   It is usual practice, however, to place
field coils, before mounting upon the core, in an impregnating tank
and force insulating compound into the pores and recesses, this
being followed by baking in an oven until the entire coil is impervi-
ous to moisture or other deteriorating influences.

The three types of motor mentioned may be further subdivided upon the basis of mechanical construction or of operating characteristics, depending upon the type of service for which they are intended, but the classification given forms the primary basis for choice of motor for a given application, since the operating characteristics are largely determined by the type of excitation used. Other classifications will be given in a later chapter.

69. Torque Characteristics.—The total torque developed in the motor armature at starting is applied to "breaking out" the load and starting rotation. The current input permitted under this condition is usually 1.5 to 2 times full-load current, and, in the shunt motor, the torque developed and applied will vary proportionally. It should be borne in mind, however, that, at the instant of starting, the horsepower output is zero and that, in general, horsepower has little significance until the motor has attained a stable speed.

It is usually necessary, during the starting period, that the motor develop and apply more than full-load torque, this necessity being due to stiffness of bearings, belts, and other moving parts, and to the application of torque to acceleration of moving parts. Frequent starting of heavy loads therefore imposes a hardship upon a driving motor and should be taken into account when the rating of motor required for a given application is considered.

Example 1.—What current will be required in order that a 25-hp 230-volt shunt motor, having an efficiency of 88 per cent, may exert a starting torque 50 per cent in excess of full-load torque?

Solution:

$$\frac{25 \times 746}{230 \times 0.88} = 92.15 \text{ amp} = \text{rated-load current}$$

Assuming field current to be 3 per cent of rated-load current

$$I_a = 92.15 - 2.75 = 89.4 \text{ amp}$$

Torque $= K_2 \phi I_a$, and, assuming that the effect of armature reaction is negligible, torque will vary directly as I_a

Therefore, 1.5 times full-load torque will require 1.5 times full-load I_a or $1.5 \times 89.4 = 134.1$ amp, and current input to motor $= 134.1 + 2.75 = 136.85$ amp.

In comparison with other types of motor, the shunt motor is said to have a light starting torque. This should not be taken as meaning that the shunt motor is incapable of starting a heavy load. Rather it should be considered that the series and compound types of motor are capable of starting heavy loads with less excess of current over normal values than is the shunt motor. It is usually an advantage to limit starting currents as much as possible in order to prevent excessive line drop, which may interfere with operation of other equipment.

For a given setting of the field rheostat, assuming negligible loss of flux due to armature reaction and constant terminal voltage, the field flux remains practically constant, and the developed torque will vary with the armature current alone in the shunt motor, making it a straight-line variation. The output torque will be less than the developed torque by the torque required to drive the motor armature against friction, windage, etc. This torque loss will be practically constant throughout the range of loads ordinarily applied to the motor.

The shape of the torque-current curve for the series motor is affected by the variation in field flux with current input. For light-load conditions, the flux may be considered to vary directly with the current and the torque to vary as the square of the armature current, or

$$T = K_3 I_a^2 \qquad \text{approximately} \quad (46)$$

Beyond rated load, however, with the magnetic circuit becoming saturated, the effect of current changes upon field flux will be diminished, and the curve will more nearly resemble that of the shunt motor. The resulting curve will therefore be parabolic at its lower end and approach a straight line at its upper end. The net result is the production, under heavy-current conditions, of a considerably greater torque for a given line current than is obtainable with the shunt motor.

Since the field is in series with the armature and the field strength is therefore variable, depending upon the armature current, the starting torque developed by the series motor will be greater for a given above-rated current input than the starting torque developed by a shunt motor of similar rating at the same armature current (see Fig. 87). This gives the series motor a decided advantage over the shunt motor for applications involving frequent starting of heavy loads. In many cases, however, the shunt motor will have advantages that outweigh the starting-torque feature of the series motor, resulting in the use of shunt motors of higher rating than necessary for steady-load conditions or the use of compound motors of suitable design to take advantage of the desirable features of both types of motor.

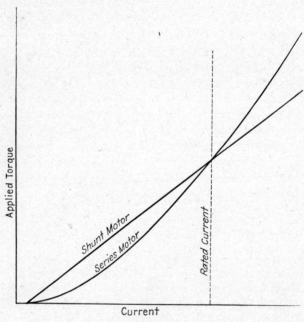

Fig. 87.—Comparison of torque curves for shunt and series motors of same current rating.

Example 2.—Given a 10-hp 230-volt 1000-rpm series motor, having rated-load efficiency of 85.5 per cent, armature resistance, including brushes, of 0.28 ohm, and field resistance of 0.15 ohm. (*a*) Assuming that the field flux varies directly with armature current, what value of resistance should be placed in series with this motor, when starting, in order that the starting current may be limited to a value that will exert a starting torque equal to 1.5 times rated-load torque? Compare the results with those obtained with a constant-flux condition, such as exists in the shunt motor. (*b*) If the starting resistance of (a) is allowed to remain in the circuit, what will be the resulting speed with rated-load torque being developed? What resistance is required for a speed of 600 rpm?

Solution:

(a)
$$\frac{10 \times 746}{230 \times 0.855} = 38 \text{ amp rated current}$$

$$\frac{T_1}{T_2} = \frac{1}{1.5} = \frac{38^2}{I_2{}^2}$$

from which

$$I_2 = 46.5 \text{ amp}$$

$$R = \frac{E}{I} = \frac{230}{46.5} = 4.95 \text{ ohms}$$

$$4.95 - (0.28 + 0.15) = 4.52 \text{ ohms to be added}$$

If the field flux is assumed to remain constant, at rated-load value, the current required to produce 1.5 times normal torque will be equal to 1.5 times rated-load current or $1.5 \times 38 = 57$ amp. The resistance required then equals $230/57 = 4.03$ ohms.

$$4.03 - (0.28 + 0.15) = 3.6 \text{ ohms to be added}$$

(b) Normal counter emf $= 230 - 38 (0.28 + 0.15) = 213.7$ volts. New value of counter emf $= 230 - 38 (0.28 + 0.15 + 4.52) = 41.9$ volts

Then

$$\frac{213.7}{41.9} = \frac{1000}{S_2}$$

from which

$$S_2 = \frac{1000 \times 41.9}{213.7} = 196 \text{ rpm}$$

For a speed of 600 rpm, since the developed torque is assumed to remain the same, the values of I_a and ϕ will be unchanged, and the counter emf will become $600/1000 \times 213.7 = 128.2$ volts.

$$38 (0.28 + 0.15 + R_s) = 230 - 128.2 = 101.8 \text{ volts}$$

from which

$$R_s = \frac{101.8 - 16.34}{38} = 2.25 \text{ ohms}$$

70. Speed Characteristics.—The drop in speed between no load and full load is relatively slight in the shunt motor, and this motor is therefore frequently referred to as a *constant-speed motor*. The speed for any load condition within the operating range of the motor may usually be obtained by varying the field current by means of a field rheostat. The effect of decreasing the field current is to shift the speed curve upward and of increasing the field current to shift this curve downward, the curve in both cases, however, remaining practically parallel to its original position.

For speeds below the base speed at which the motor operates with rated voltage applied to field and armature terminals, the

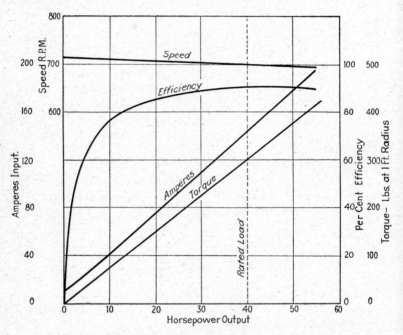

Fig. 88.—Performance curves for 40-hp, 230-volt, shunt motor.

armature voltage may be reduced by the addition of resistance to the armature circuit, resulting in decreased speed at the expense of the constant-speed feature, since, with added armature-circuit resistance, the speed may vary to a considerable degree with load changes. By addition of proper values of resistance to armature and field circuits, however, the motor speed may be adjusted to any desired value between zero and the upper limit at which the motor may safely be operated.

The drop in speed with increased load is characteristically much

more pronounced in the series motor than in the shunt motor. This
motor is therefore not adapted to applications requiring a constant
speed. The reason for the greater drop in speed is to be found in
the fact that the field flux rises with increased current, thus tend-

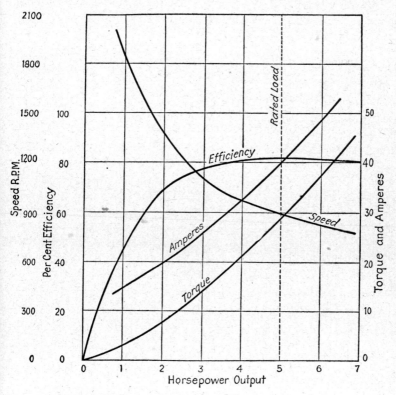

Fig. 89.—Performance curves for 5-hp, 115-volt, series motor.

ing to prevent the reduction in counter emf that is being effected
by the reduction in speed. In the shunt motor, on the other hand,
the field flux is not affected to any considerable extent by changes
in line or armature current. The speed change necessary to produce a given effect on current and torque is therefore less in the
shunt motor than in the series motor. The shape of the curve is

determined by the degree of saturation at which the magnetic circuit is worked. Under heavy-load conditions, with a high degree of saturation, the series-motor speed curve approaches the straight-line trend of the shunt-motor speed curve. The no-load speed of the series motor is likely to be too high for safety, and this type of motor should therefore not be operated without sufficient load to hold the speed within safe limits.

Compound motors, having both series and shunt excitation, will naturally have speed characteristics that lie somewhere between those of the shunt and the series type of motor. Some compound motors are so designed that their excitation is produced chiefly by a shunt field, causing them to resemble the shunt motor in their operating characteristics. Others are so designed that their excitation comes chiefly from the series field, causing them to have operating characteristics resembling those of the series motor. The average motor of the compound type will lie between these extremes, its speed varying with load but not so much as in the series motor, and its no-load speed will be within the limits of safety.

71. Speed Regulation.—The term speed regulation has reference to change in speed with change in applied load torque, other conditions remaining constant. Such changes in speed as occur under these conditions are necessarily due to inherent properties of the motor itself and should not be confused with speed changes effected through manipulation of rheostats or other speed-control devices.

The speed regulation of a motor is generally understood to mean the change in speed with changes in load. It may be expressed as a percentage.

Percentage speed regulation[1]

$$= \frac{\text{no-load speed } - \text{ full-load speed}}{\text{full-load speed}} \times 100 \quad (47)$$

As previously noted, the change in speed of the shunt motor with load torque is relatively small. This motor is said, therefore, to have good speed regulation. It is possible, however, to alter the regulation of a shunt motor by inserting resistance in the armature

---

[1] See standardization rules of the A.I.E.E.

circuit, added resistance giving poorer regulation. This change in speed characteristic necessarily accompanies the use of armature resistance as a method of controlling the speed of a shunt motor (see Fig. 90).

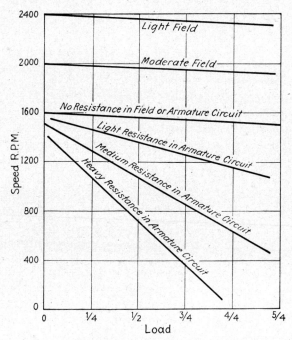

Fig. 90.—Comparison of shunt-motor speed curves, using two speed-control methods.

Example.—A certain motor has, when operated under normal conditions, a no-load speed of 1200 rpm and a full-load speed of 1150 rpm.

When the motor is operated with armature resistance sufficient to reduce the full-load speed to 750, the no-load speed is found to be 1160 rpm. Calculate the percentage speed regulation for each condition of operation.

Solution:

(a) $$\frac{1200 - 1150}{1150} \times 100 = 4.35\% \text{ regulation}$$

(b) $$\frac{1160 - 750}{750} \times 100 = 54.6\% \text{ regulation}$$

Since there is wide variation in speed with changes in load torque on the series motor, its speed regulation is said to be poor. For many applications, such as line-shaft drives and machine tools, this characteristic is seriously objectionable. For others, such as cranes, hoists, and streetcars, it is an advantage, or at least not objectionable, since it results in more deliberate movement of the heavier loads. In these applications also, it is usual practice to have an operator in constant attendance, and the speed for a given load is more a matter of controller adjustment than of inherent characteristics. The slowing down of the series motor under load tends to equalize power demands, since the drop in speed allows a larger torque to be developed with only a moderate increase in power requirement. This is particularly advantageous in the case of railway motors and allows a smaller motor to be used for this type of service than would be necessary if shunt motors, with their constant-speed characteristic, were used.

A compound motor, as normally connected for additive or cumulative excitation, may have a speed regulation approaching that of either the series or the shunt motor, depending upon the percentage of the total excitation furnished by one or the other of the two sets of field coils. If the motor is connected for differential action of the fields, the resultant field will become weaker as load is increased, and the speed will tend to rise. The result may be a dangerous instability, with a tendency toward surging up and down in speed, which may result in opening of the circuit through blowing of fuses or circuit breakers, or the motor may race at dangerous speed. Differential connection of the fields may sometimes be brought about by accident but may also, for special purposes, be used as a means of securing especially good speed regulation. In this case, the series winding should be relatively very light, and provision should be made for short-circuiting the series winding during starting of the motor. Also operation of the motor under more than its normal loading should be scrupulously avoided, and an automatic overspeed circuit-interrupting device should be added to the protective equipment normally associated with the motor.

72. Summary of Characteristics.—Reference to Fig. 91 will give a ready comparison of the speed and torque characteristics of the

shunt, series, and compound motors. Similar curves may be plotted
to current input, the curves then intercepting the horizontal axis
to the right of the origin by a distance representing the no-load
current value. It may be seen from these curves that the series
and compound types of motor have poorer speed regulation but

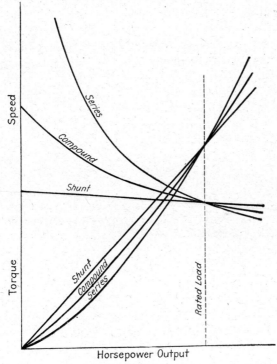

Fig. 91.—Comparison of shunt-, series-, and compound-motor performance.

produce greater torque per horsepower, or per ampere, for values
beyond rated load, thus enabling overloads, or heavy starting loads,
to be handled more effectively. The no-load speed of the series
motor is likely to be excessive, but that of the compound motor is
usually within safe limits. The curves in this figure represent
three motors having identical rated-load values of speed and
torque in order to make comparisons more obvious.

The compound motor may, as previously pointed out, have a weak series field, or it may have a strong series field, relative to its shunt field. It will approach the shunt motor in its characteristics if it has a weak series field or will approach the series motor in its characteristics if it has a relatively strong series field. Shunt motors intended for operation over a wide range of speeds may be "stabilized" by the addition of a very few turns of series winding, this light additional winding enabling operation of the motor at high speeds—with weak shunt field—to be carried out safely without danger of the motor "hunting" or otherwise becoming unstable in its operation.

73. Armature-reaction Effects.—Since modern motors are, for the most part, equipped with interpoles, the correct position for

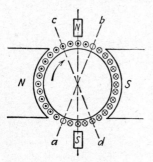

the brushes is on the geometric neutral line, and the major effect of armature reaction is to distort the field, the direction of distortion being opposite to that of the generator, since, with the same direction of rotation and the same polarity, the armature current is in the opposite direction. With brushes shifted, by chance or otherwise, the effects are greatly accentuated over those produced

Fig. 92.—Effect of shifting brushes on a motor with commutating poles.

by similar shifts in the noninterpole motor. A forward shift, as to line *ab* in Fig. 92, results in a pronounced compounding effect, resulting in a greater reduction of motor speed with increase of load than with the brushes in the normal position. This is due not only to the magnetizing component of armature reaction that is brought into play but also to the fact that, under this condition, the interpole field is added to the main field as a voltage-generating field instead of acting only as a reversing field. A backward shift, as to the line *cd*, results in a more constant speed than with the brushes in the normal position, because the effects of the armature reaction and the interpole field are such as to weaken the main field with increase in load. A shift in either direction largely defeats the essential purpose of the interpoles and results in poor commutation, *i.e.*, sparking or arcing at the brushes.

Individual motors vary considerably as to relative values of armature and field mmf. In a machine having relatively large armature mmf, the field distortion will be more pronounced; and, when the brushes are shifted against the direction of rotation, the result is frequently to produce an unstable operating condition, *i.e.*, the motor "hunts" under load, first speeding up and then slowing down, with consequent surges of current that may open the circuit through operation of the circuit breakers or blowing of the fuses. This tendency is more pronounced in the case of interpole motors, and special care must therefore be taken to see that the brushes are kept properly set on the neutral line. One method of "stiffening" the field is to lengthen the air gap, which in turn necessitates more ampere-turns on the field poles but gives the motor greater stability. Another method consists in placing an auxiliary compensating winding in the pole shoes, to compensate for the armature field and thus do away with the detrimental effects of armature reaction as discussed under Art. 42. This latter method adds considerably to the cost of the machine and is rarely justified in the ordinary industrial sizes of motor and generators but it may be necessary for special applications or for very large machines.

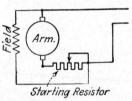

Fig. 93.—The use of starting resistors with shunt motors.

74. Operation of the Shunt Motor.—Shunt motors are usually supplied with starting resistors for insertion in the armature circuit during the starting period (see Fig. 93). Conventional forms of starter are illustrated on pages 170 and 175. These starters include provision for automatic opening of the line circuit if power goes off for an interval, thus guarding the motor against the excess current that would flow when the power came on again, with the motor speed at or near zero. In one form of starter, the circuit of the holding coil for retaining the handle in the operating position is in series with the field; and in others it is made with higher resistance for connection across the line.

Since torque is dependent upon field flux as well as upon armature current, as in Eq. (41), it is desirable that the field current be at its maximum during the starting period. Resistance of the field circuit should therefore be at its lowest value—all resistance out of the field rheostat—with full line voltage impressed upon it. It is for this reason that the field terminal is connected to the line ahead of the starting resistance, as shown in Fig. 93. Reversal of torque, which results in reversal of direction of rotation, may be effected by reversing either the armature current or the shunt-field current, but reversal of line connections does not affect the direction of rotation.

In connecting any motor for operation, even for temporary use or for testing purposes, automatic protection against excess current should be provided in the form of fuses, circuit breakers, or thermal relays.

Speed control of the shunt motor may be effected through the use of rheostats in armature and field circuits. For the higher range of speeds, the field-resistance method of speed control is available; and, for speeds below that obtained with full voltage applied to the field terminals, resort may be had to the armature-resistance method. The reasons for the effects upon speed produced by these resistance variations may be discovered through study of the torque and voltage equations, bearing in mind that, although reduction in field flux tends to reduce the developed torque, the result of such flux reduction is a greatly increased armature current, producing a net increase in torque. There being then more torque developed than is required for the load, the surplus is applied to acceleration of the armature. Increased speed produces greater counter emf, however, and thus the final result is equilibrium at a higher speed. Addition of resistance to the armature circuit decreases the armature current, causing reduction in developed torque. This torque being less than that necessary for carrying the motor load, the speed drops. As speed drops, the counter emf decreases and armature current rises, and thus equilibrium is restored at a lower speed.

Figure 94 illustrates the speed changes that may be obtained by these methods upon a lightly loaded motor. Starting at the base speed, with no resistance in either circuit other than that inherent in it, the speed may be raised as high as permissible by adding resistance to the field circuit, or it may be lowered to zero as a limit by adding resistance to the armature circuit. Thus the two methods may be combined to cover the entire operating range of the motor. Under light-load conditions, the upper speed range will be limited by the risk of damage because of centrifugal forces which may throw the conductors out of the slots; and, under heavy-load conditions, it may be limited by heating, although the ventilation will be better at higher speeds. In general, somewhat greater armature currents can be tolerated at the higher speeds because of the better ventilation.

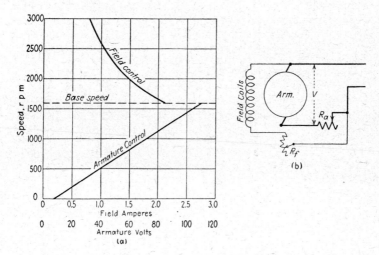

FIG. 94.—Speed control of the shunt motor. (a) Typical no-load speed curves, (b) Circuit for armature- and field-resistance control.

Example 1. — Given a 10-hp 230-volt shunt-wound motor having rated speed of 1000 rpm and full-load efficiency of 86 per cent. Armature-circuit resistance, 0.26 ohm; field-circuit resistance, 225 ohms. If this motor is operating under rated load and the field flux is very quickly reduced to 50 per cent of its normal value, what will be the effect upon counter emf, armature current and torque? What effect will this change have upon the operation of the motor, and what will be its speed when stable operating conditions have been regained?

Solution:

$$\text{Normal torque} = \frac{10 \times 33{,}000}{2\pi \times 1000} = 52.5 \text{ lb at 1 ft radius or } 52.5 \text{ lb-ft}$$

$$\text{Rated-load } I_c = \frac{10 \times 746}{230 \times 0.86} - \frac{230}{225} = 36.7 \text{ amp}$$

Normal counter emf $= 230 - (36.7 \times 0.26) = 220.5$ volts
When flux is reduced, the counter emf is reduced to one-half its former value, or 110.25 volts.

The instantaneous value of $I_a = \dfrac{230 - 110.25}{0.26} = 460$ amp, which is 12.5 times rated value.

The instantaneous value of torque $= 52.5 \times \dfrac{50}{100} \times \dfrac{460}{36.7} = 330$ lb-ft, or 6.25 times normal value.

If fuses do not blow, the motor speed will rise until equilibrium is restored. Assuming the torque requirements to be unchanged, the armature current under the new condition of operation will be double its previous value, or 73.4 amp, since $T = K_2 \phi I_a$, and ϕ has been cut in half. (Note that sudden changes in field current are inadvisable because of the excessive transient armature currents that may result. Slower changes in field current permit speed changes to keep step with excitation, current, and torque changes so that excessive armature currents are avoided.)

The new value of counter emf $= 230 - (73.4 \times 0.26) = 211$ volts

$$\frac{K_1\phi_1 S_1}{K_1\phi_2 S_2} = \frac{1 \times 1000}{0.5 \times S_2} = \frac{220.5}{211}$$

from which

$$S_2 = 1915 \text{ rpm}$$

Example 2.—Referring to Example 1, what value of resistance must be inserted in series with the armature of this motor in order that the speed may be reduced to one-half its normal value, torque and excitation remaining at their normal full-load values? What effect will this change have upon the horsepower output and efficiency of the motor?

Solution: From Example 1, rated $I_a = 36.7$ amp, and normal counter emf $= 220.5$ volts.

If speed is reduced with no change in excitation, the counter emf will be reduced in direct proportion; therefore

The new counter emf $= 220.5 \times \dfrac{500}{1000} = 110.25$ volts

Then

$$I_a(R_a + R_s) = 230 - 110.25 = 119.75 \text{ volts}$$

Substituting

$$36.7 \,(0.26 + R_s) = 9.5 + 36.7 \, R_s = 119.75 \text{ volts}$$

from which

$$R_s = \frac{119.75 - 9.5}{36.7} = 3 \text{ ohms to be added.}$$

Since speed has been cut in half and torque is unchanged, the horsepower output will be one-half its former value, or 5 hp.

Also, since torque and excitation are unchanged, the armature current has the same value as before, making watts input the same, and the efficiency will therefore be one-half its former value, or 43 per cent.

75. Operation of the Series Motor.—Starters for series motors usually take the form of series resistor units, which serve the double purpose of providing means for getting the motor up to speed without excessive current demands and for controlling the speed. Two common types of controller, the face-plate and drum types, are illustrated in Figs. 104 and 106. The resistors are usually mounted outside the controller proper.

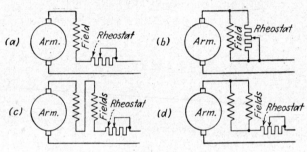

FIG. 95.—Series motor speed control.

Since the field is in series with the armature in this type of motor, a strong field is assured at starting—stronger than normal when the starting current is allowed to exceed full-load value, as is usual practice. Reversal of direction of rotation may be effected through reversal of current in either the armature or the field circuit, as in the shunt motor.

Speed control is usually effected by variation in the series resistance, although other methods, such as those illustrated in Fig. 95, are sometimes used. In the series-parallel method, a controller is used that connects the two sections of the field in series with a rheostat for starting. Forward movement of the controller then cuts out the resistance, step by step. When the resistance has all been removed, the next step throws the two fields in parallel and reinserts the resistance. Further movement again reduces the resistance; and, in the final running position, the two fields are in parallel with no resistance in series. A similar method is used in railway-motor control, where two motors—or two pairs of motors—are connected in series for starting and in parallel for full speed.

The use of series resistance is not an economical method and from this standpoint does not compare favorably with field-control methods. It is cheaper in first cost, however, and, being combined with the starter, provides a very rugged and flexible control system.

Series motors cannot ordinarily be operated with safety under conditions that permit the load to be entirely removed. They should be connected to their loads by gearing rather than by belting and should be used, preferably, for applications that require an operator in constant attendance. In laboratory operation, care should be taken that the load is never lightened to an extent that will permit the motor to run at a dangerous speed.

76. Graphical Study of Motor Performance.—The effects of various factors affecting the speed of motors may be studied by a graphical method similar to that used for generators. Assuming the saturation curve for the motor at its no-load speed to be that given in Fig. 96, let it be assumed that the point V represents the applied voltage on the vertical scale. If a horizontal line is then drawn through V to an intersection with the saturation curve, the excitation required for no-load operation of the motor is determined as OA, equal to VC, provided that the armature-resistance voltage drop is considered negligible at no load or, expressing the same idea in another way, provided that generated voltage at no load is considered equal to the applied voltage. Since the armature current is quite small at no load, this assumption of equal terminal and generated voltages at no load may usually be made with negligible error insofar as its effect upon the final result is concerned.

If, therefore, we consider the no-load speed to occur when the applied and counter emf are essentially equal, the speed at any other load may be determined as follows: First, assuming the excitation to be supplied by a shunt field and that no change in field flux due to armature reaction occurs as the load changes, the armature IR drop corresponding to any load may be measured vertically downward from point C. Assume that, for the load in question, the armature IR drop is equal to CD, in terms of the scale. Then, for this load, the generated voltage will equal AD volts; and, since there has been no change in excitation, the speed is directly proportional to the counter emf voltages. Thus, for the load under consideration, the speed will be AD/AC times the no-load speed.

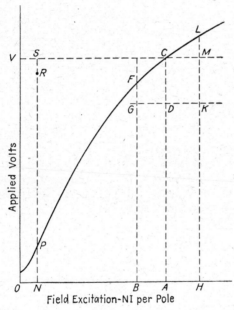

FIG. 96.—Study of motor speeds by the graphic method.

Example.—Assume the no-load speed of a 230-volt shunt motor to be 1500 rpm. If there is no appreciable flux change due to armature reaction and the armature voltage drop is 15 volts at rated load, the rated-load speed may be calculated as

$$S_2 = \frac{230 - 15}{230} \times 1500$$

$$= 1402 \text{ rpm}$$

For the more general case when armature-reaction demagnetizing effect is appreciable, assume that, at the load under consideration, there is an excitation loss represented by AB. With the net excitation OB and no armature IR drop, the generated voltage at the assumed speed would be represented by BF. But, with the IR drop represented by CD, the speed being proportional to generated voltage, the new speed would be BG/BF times the no-load speed.

From this analysis, it may be seen that the effect of the armature IR drop is to reduce the speed and that the effect of armature reaction is to increase it. Thus an increase in armature-circuit resistance results in poorer speed regulation, and the demagnetizing effect of strong armature reaction tends to give the motor better speed regulation and may even produce a rising speed characteristic—a condition not usually considered desirable because of the possibility of instability. This condition is reached when the ratio BG/BF becomes greater than unity, which may occur with a combination of low armature resistance and strong demagnetization due to armature reaction.

With the compound motor, the flux is increased under load conditions because of the series field. Referring again to Fig. 96, assume that, for a given load, the net increase in excitation, after armature-reaction effect has been deducted, is represented by AH on the excitation scale, giving a total excitation OH. With the same armature IR drop as before, the generated voltage will be represented by HK, and the speed for the load under consideration may be calculated as HK/HL times the no-load speed or the speed of the given magnetization curve. This will evidently yield a speed value less than that obtained with the shunt excitation alone, with or without the effect of armature reaction, since any addition of flux, for the same value of armature-resistance drop, will increase the denominator and therefore reduce the value of the ratio by which the no-load speed is multiplied. As the magnetic circuit becomes more highly saturated, however, the speed changes are less pronounced.

Speed changes in the series motor may be analyzed in the same manner by regarding the series motor as a compound motor with very light shunt excitation—approaching that due to residual magnetism. If ON represents a light-load excitation—not necessarily no-load—and the corresponding armature-voltage drop is assumed to be represented by SR, the speed for this load condition will be NR/NP times the speed at which the saturation-curve data were secured. Obviously this will yield very high speeds at light loads and indicates clearly why it is unsafe to operate the series motor without load.

FIG. 97.—A 50-hp, 230-volt, shunt-wound, stabilized d-c motor. (*General Electric Company.*)

77. Motor Instability.—Under certain conditions of operation, motors may become unstable in their operation, with the speed rising and falling at more or less regular intervals; or, in extreme cases, the motor speed may surge upward to a dangerous value without warning. Such manifestations do not occur usually until considerable load has been applied to the motor. They may be due to (*a*) operation of a shunt motor at high speed, with a weak shunt field; (*b*) operation of a compound motor with the series field omitted from the circuit or short-circuited; (*c*) operation of a compound motor with the series field reversed, resulting in a differential instead of an accumulative relation between the two fields; or, finally, (*d*) operation of an interpole motor with the brushes shifted from the neutral position, against the direction of rotation.

In any of these cases, with the possible exception of (c) at starting, the motor is likely to start and operate smoothly without load, or with light loads, but begin surging or speeding up excessively after considerable load has been imposed upon it, because of reduction of flux in the field magnetic circuit by the armature current, which reduces the back emf, resulting in still greater armature current and an increased torque. The excess of torque over load requirements causes the speed to rise, reducing the armature current and causing a flux increase, which reduces the speed. The result, depending upon several factors, such as weight of the moving parts and variation of load with speed, may be only a slight regular rise and fall in speed, or it may be a recurring swing that goes farther with each cycle until circuit breakers open or fuses blow.

The inertia of the load is a considerable factor and, if high, with no appreciable rise in load with speed, may produce a condition in which the torque of the motor is always ahead of the load requirement. Thus a difference between the counter emf required for equilibrium and the actual counter emf will continue to exist while the speed rises to dangerous heights. The remedy in any case of instability is obviously, first, to disconnect the motor from the line if the speed is rising rapidly or to reduce the load if the case is less acute and, second, to remove if possible the cause of the instability.

Motors normally have speed characteristics that drop more or less with load but may be given rising speed characteristics by design, by incorrect setting of brushes, or by accidental reversal of the series field. Such motors may operate stably over a limited portion of their load range but will become unstable if their loading is increased beyond a certain point. The reason for this may be seen from a study of the diagram of Fig. 96, which shows the loading zones in which the ratio by which the no-load speed is multiplied becomes greater than unity.

78. Maximum Output.—Referring to Eq. (39),

$$V = E + I_a R_a = K_1 \phi S + I_a R_a$$

an expression for power input to the motor armature may be obtained by multiplying both sides of the equation by I_a, as

$$VI_a = EI_a + I_a^2 R_a \tag{48}$$

Thus, neglecting brush and brush contact losses, the input to the armature may evidently be broken down into conductor heat loss $I_a^2 R_a$ and the power represented by the product EI_a, which produces rotation of the armature. This *developed* motor power must be greater than the *delivered* power by the amount needed to supply the rotational losses due to friction, windage, eddy currents, and hysteresis in the iron core. From Eq. (39), it is evident that armature current will increase as speed decreases, applied voltage being constant. Thus the developed torque will continue to increase as a motor slows down under load and normally will stabilize at a point where the product of generated voltage and armature current provides the necessary motor power for overcoming the rotational losses as well as driving the connected load.

A limit to continued power development with decreased speed is reached at a point where further decrease in speed produces less power; below this, the decrease in speed has more effect than the increase in torque. This limit will occur when

$$\frac{dP_m}{dI_a} = 0$$

Thus

$$\frac{dP_m}{dI_a} = \frac{d\,(VI_a - I_a^2 R_a)}{dI_a} = V - 2\,I_a R_a = 0$$

or

$$V = 2I_a R_a$$

from which

$$I_a R_a = \frac{V}{2} \tag{49}$$

Thus maximum power will be developed when the armature resistance drop is one-half the terminal voltage. For this condition,

$$E = V - I_a R_a = V - \frac{V}{2} = \frac{1}{2}\,V \tag{50}$$

or maximum power development, with constant impressed voltage, will occur when the counter emf is one-half the terminal voltage.

With constant field flux, the maximum developed power will therefore occur at approximately one-half the no-load speed. Below this speed, there will be further torque development, but the power developed will decrease.

Problems

1. A shunt-wound dynamo has a field resistance of 60 ohms and an armature-circuit resistance of 0.2 ohm. Calculate its armature current and generated voltage if it is (a) operating as a generator and delivering 50 amp at 240 volts, and (b) operating as a motor and taking 50 amp from a 240-volt line.

2. If the dynamo of Prob. 1 is driven at a speed of 1500 rpm when acting as a generator under the load condition specified in (a), what will be its speed when acting as a motor under the condition specified in (b), the air-gap flux being unchanged?

3. What should be the total resistance and the current capacity of a starting resistor suitable for use with a 15-hp 115-volt shunt motor having an armature-circuit resistance of 0.10 ohm, field-circuit resistance of 57.5 ohms, and rated-load efficiency of 86 per cent.

4. A shunt motor under brake test, with rated operating conditions, yields the following results: armature input, 192.8 amp; field input, 2.2 amp; line voltage, 110; rpm, 1800; balance reading, 26 lb 7 oz; weight of brake arm 2 lb 2 oz; length of brake arm, 3 ft. Calculate the horsepower output and efficiency of this motor.

5. (a) If the armature-circuit resistance of the motor of Prob. 4, with rated current flowing, is equal to 0.025 ohm, what will be the counter emf developed under rated-load conditions? (b) If the load is so adjusted that the armature current is one-half rated, neglecting any variation in armature-circuit resistance, what will be the new value of counter emf? (c) Assuming the effect of armature reaction to be negligible, what will be the speed at the half-load condition?

6. What value of resistance should be placed in the armature circuit of the motor of Probs. 4 and 5 in order that the speed with rated current input may be reduced to 1500 rpm? to 1000 rpm?

7. A 50-hp 230-volt shunt motor has, when operating at normal load, a speed of 1200 rpm and a total current input of 180 amp. The armature resistance, including brushes and interpole coils, is 0.04 ohm, and the shunt-field resistance is 100 ohms. Assuming that flux varies directly with field current, how much resistance must be placed in the field circuit to raise the speed to 1500 rpm, with the armature current unchanged? If with this resistance in circuit the load is reduced until the total current input is 85 amp, what will the speed become?

8. If the motor of Prob. 7 is operated as a separately excited generator at a speed of 1200 rpm, what field current will be necessary to give an output of

180 amp at 230 volts? If operated with a field current of 1.9 amp, what speed will be necessary?

9. The ratings for a series-wound motor are as follows: 10 hp, 220 volts, 40 amp, 1500 rpm. The resistance of the armature, exclusive of brushes, is found by test to be 0.25 ohm and of the field winding to be 0.08 ohm. Specify a suitable starting resistor for this motor.

10. (a) What starting resistance should be used with the motor of Prob. 9 if it is required that the starting current be kept to a minimum while a torque equal to rated-load torque is applied to the load? (b) Repeat for a torque requirement 25 per cent in excess of rated-load torque.

11. Assuming the starting resistances of Prob. 10 left in circuit until the motor has reached a stable speed, and the load adjusted for rated current input, (a) what will be the counter emf in each case? (b) What will the speed become for each condition?

12. What value of resistance should be placed in series with the motor of Prob. 9 in order to give a full-load speed of (a) 1200 rpm and (b) 750 rpm? (c) What will be the horsepower output in each case, assuming the output torque constant at rated-load value? (d) What will be the motor efficiency in each case?

13. The armature of a six-pole motor has a total of 450 inductors, connected as a simplex wave winding. The active length of the armature is 8 in., and the inductors are located at an average distance of 6 in. from the center of the shaft. Normal armature current is 50 amp. The pole pieces cover 70 per cent of the armature, and average flux density in the air gap is 50,000 lines per sq. in.

Calculate (a) the force, in pounds, exerted by each conductor while underneath a pole, (b) the total tangential force acting on the armature, and (c) the total torque developed, in pound-feet.

14. If 5 per cent of the developed torque of Prob. 13 is absorbed in turning the armature, while the motor operates at a speed of 1000 rpm, what horsepower is being applied to the load?

15. What will be the new values of torque produced by the armature of Prob. 13, (a) if the armature current is increased to 60 amp, the flux density remaining unchanged, and (b) if the flux density is increased to 60,000 lines per sq in., with an armature current of 60 amp?

16. A series motor is tested by means of a prony brake and balance. From pulley center to point of attachment, the brake-arm length is 24 in. With motor running at 1350 rpm, current reading 76 amp, voltage reading 115 volts, the balance reads 20 lb 15 oz. With power disconnected and brake loose on the pulley, the balance reads 1 lb 8 oz. Calculate the horsepower output and efficiency of the motor.

17. A motor is rated 5 hp, 115 volts, 40 amp, 1500 rpm. Armature resistance, including interpole coils and brushes, is 0.12 ohm, and shunt-field resistance is 57.5 ohms. If, while operating at rated load, the field flux is suddenly reduced to 80 per cent of its normal value, what will be the instantaneous and final values of (*a*) counter emf, (*b*) armature current, (*c*) torque, and (*d*) speed, the load torque remaining unchanged?

18. If the brushes of the motor of Prob. 17 are shifted against the direction of rotation to an extent that results in a 3 per cent reduction in flux at normal torque load, what will be the value of the speed, the developed torque remaining constant?

19. If by accident the brushes of the motor of Prob. 17 are shifted forward instead of backward, to a point that results in a 3 per cent increase in field flux at normal torque load, what will the speed become? How is this shift likely to affect the operation of the motor as regards commutation?

20. The no-load speed of the motor of Prob. 17 is 1550 rpm. What is its speed regulation? What will the regulation become for operation with brushes shifted, as stated in Prob. 18, assuming the no-load speed constant? What for the condition stated in Prob. 19?

21. When operating under normal load conditions, a series motor requires 38.3 amp, with 115 volts applied, and runs at a speed of 1700 rpm, with output torque of 15.5 lb-ft. It has an armature resistance, including brushes, of 0.30 ohm and a field resistance of 0.035 ohm. If the mechanical load is reduced so that the torque is 10 lb-ft, and assuming that the field flux varies directly with current, what will be the new values of current and speed? What will be the output, in horsepower, for each load condition?

22. A brake test on a compound-wound motor, rated 7½ hp, 550 volts, 2100 rpm, resulted in the following data:

Applied voltage	Armature, amp	Field, amp	Speed, rpm	Gross weight
550	13.1	0.5	2085	9 lb 8.0 oz
550	11.5	0.5	2100	8 lb 8.0 oz
550	10.0	0.5	2115	7 lb 8.0 oz
550	8.6	0.5	2135	6 lb 8.8 oz
550	7.2	0.5	2155	5 lb 9.6 oz
550	5.8	0.5	2175	4 lb 10.25 oz
550	3.0	0.5	2245	2 lb 12.0 oz
550	1.0	0.5	2330	0* lb 0 oz

* Brake removed.

Length of brake arm, 2.5 ft.

Weight of brake arm, 1 lb.

Calculate horsepower output and efficiency for each set of readings. Plot efficiency, speed, torque, and current as ordinates, to horsepower output.

23 A series-motor brake test resulted in the following data, the motor being rated at 20 hp, 230 volts, 750 rpm, for continuous duty:

Applied voltage	Current, amp	Speed, rpm	Gross weight
230	120	550	101 lb 7 oz
230	105	615	81 lb 0 oz
230	90	680	64 lb 2 oz
230	75	760	48 lb 13 oz
230	60	875	34 lb 11.5 oz
230	45	1030	22 lb 13 oz
230	30	1400	12 lb 3.5 oz
230	15	2300	5 lb 4 oz

Length of brake arm, 3 ft.
Weight of brake arm, 2 lb 8 oz.
Calculate horsepower output and efficiency for each set of readings. Plot efficiency, speed, and torque as ordinates, with currents as abscissas.

CHAPTER VIII

MOTOR CONTROL

79. Starting Requirements.—Normally the current input to the armature of a motor is controlled by the counter emf developed through rotation of the armature; but, at standstill, when the counter emf is zero, the current input would be very high in proportion to normal full-load current if extra resistance were not added to the armature circuit. From Eq. (39),

$$I_a = \frac{V - K_1\phi S}{R_a} \tag{51}$$

but, since at the moment of starting $S = 0$,

$$I_a = \frac{V}{R_a} \tag{52}$$

Motor armatures are able to stand 150, or even 200, per cent of rated-load current during the starting and acceleration period, but beyond this there is danger of injury to the windings or commutator. In order to keep the current within safe limits but at the same time make additional torque available for starting, it is therefore usual practice to provide starting rheostats for motors above 1 hp in rating. Thus Eq. (51) becomes, during the starting and acceleration period,

$$I_a = \frac{V - K_1\phi S}{R_a + R_s} \tag{53}$$

where R_s represents the added variable resistance necessary for holding the armature current to a safe value during the starting and accelerating period. This resistance should have its maximum value when voltage is applied to the motor at standstill, when the counter emf is zero, and should be gradually reduced in value as the armature accelerates, reaching zero as full speed is attained. From this point, the counter emf will control the armature current and keep it at the correct value for varying load demands.

Motors are frequently required to exert a torque at starting greater than that required for normal operation. Even if the usual load is removed or reduced in amount, the bearings are likely to be poorly lubricated, because the oil has drained away from the bearing surfaces, belts are stiff, etc. Starting conditions are aggravated by low-temperature conditions also, and machines exposed to severe weather conditions may therefore need to be "broken out" by other means as an assistance to the motor in getting under way.

80. Hand Starters.—The form of hand starter generally used for shunt and compound motors of ordinary industrial capacities is the so-called *starting* box, as illustrated in Fig. 98.

It will be noted that, in addition to providing the necessary resistance for the armature circuit, the hand starter also includes low-voltage protection, the operating handle working against the tension of a spring that returns it to the "off" position if the excitation of the small holding magnet is reduced below a certain value. This feature insures that the motor will be disconnected if the power supply is interrupted and must be started again in the usual way.

In order to provide maximum starting torque, the field must be as strong as possible; hence the field circuit must be completed on the line side of the starting resistance, since connection on the motor side of the starting resistance would result in a greatly reduced voltage at the field terminals during the early part of the starting period. In addition, when a field rheostat is provided for speed control, the resistance should be all out of the field rheostat during the starting period in order to give maximum field current.

As ordinarily designed, starters of this type allow 150 per cent of rated current to pass through the armature circuit when the handle is moved from the off position to the full-on position in about 15 sec. Holding the handle on any of the intermediate positions for a longer time is likely to result in overheating the starter coils, while moving the handle more rapidly tends to cause the armature current to reach greater values than the allowable 150 per cent, particularly if a heavy inertia load is being accelerated.

For large motors—100 hp and above—the starters are usually of quite different form, involving a number of separate switches or contactors that are closed successively to short-circuit blocks of resistance as the motor speeds up. Interlocks between the switches are provided so that they can be closed only in the correct order.

(a)

Lines
L2 L1

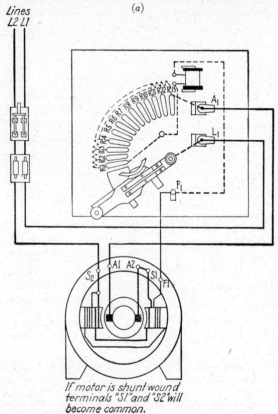

If motor is shunt wound
terminals "S1" and "S2" will
become common.

(b)

Fig. 98.—The three-point starter, for shunt or compound motors. (a) External
view, (b) diagram of connections. (*Cutler-Hammer, Inc.*)

(*a*)

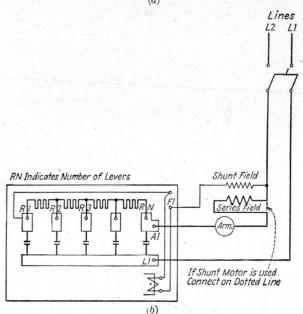

(*b*)

FIG. 99.—A multiple-switch motor starter. (*a*) External appearance; (*b*) wiring diagram. (*Cutler-Hammer, Inc.*)

Also a magnetic hold-in coil is usually provided to insure opening of the circuit when power interruptions occur. Figure 99 shows a typical starter of this type.

81. Determination of Starter Resistances.—The design of motor starters should be such that the armature current is held between an upper and lower limit during the starting period, the first limitation being necessary in order to prevent damage to the motor and the second in order to hold the starting time to a minimum.

Example.—A 230-volt motor requires 100-amp armature current when operating at rated load. It is desired that the starting current be limited to 150 amp when starting under rated-load conditions. The armature-circuit resistance being 0.10 ohm, what will be the total resistance, the number of steps, and the resistance between each pair of contact points on the starting rheostat?

Solution:

Total circuit resistance $= \dfrac{230}{150} = 1.53$ ohms

$1.53 - 0.10 = 1.43$ ohms, total starter resistance

At end of first period, when I_a has decreased to 100 amp, the counter emf $E = 230 - 1.53 \times 100 = 77$ volts, leaving 153 volts applied to the circuit when the starter handle is moved forward to the second point. For the current to rise again to 150 amp,

$$R_b = \frac{153}{150} = 1.02 \text{ ohms}$$

and

$$R_{1\text{-}2} = 1.53 - 1.02 = 0.51 \text{ ohm}$$

At end of second period, when I has again decreased to 100 amp,

$$E = 230 - 1.02 \times 100 = 128 \text{ volts}$$

leaving 102 volts applied to the circuit when the starter handle is moved to the third point.

$$R_c = \frac{102}{150} = 0.68 \text{ ohm}$$

and

$$R_{2\text{-}3} = 1.02 - 0.68 = 0.34 \text{ ohm}$$

Similar procedures result in

$R_{3\text{-}4}$	$= 0.23$	ohm
$R_{4\text{-}5}$	$= 0.15$	ohm
$R_{5\text{-}6}$	$= 0.10$	ohm
$R_{6\text{-}7}$	$= 0.07$	ohm
$R_{7\text{-}8}$	$= 0.03$	ohm

The final calculation yields a total resistance less than the resistance of the armature alone.

The above process may be appreciably shortened as follows:

Let R_x = total resistance remaining in the circuit at any starter point
I_r = running current
I_s = starting current

then

$$R_x = \frac{V - (V - I_r R_{x-1})}{I_s} \tag{54}$$

or

$$R_x = \frac{I_r}{I_s} R_{x-1} \tag{55}$$

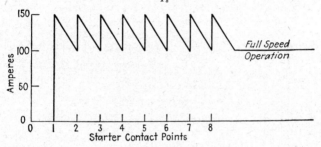

Fig. 100.—Ideal current variation, using an 8-step starter, with constant, rated-torque load upon the motor.

Since in this example $\dfrac{I_r}{I_s} = \dfrac{100}{150} = \frac{2}{3}$, it follows that

$R_b = \frac{2}{3} \times 1.53 = 1.02$ ohms
$R_c = \frac{2}{3} \times 1.02 = 0.68$ ohm
$R_d = \frac{2}{3} \times 0.68 = 0.45$ ohm
$R_e = \frac{2}{3} \times 0.45 = 0.30$ ohm
$R_f = \frac{2}{3} \times 0.30 = 0.20$ ohm
$R_g = \frac{2}{3} \times 0.20 = 0.13$ ohm
$R_h = \frac{2}{3} \times 0.13 = 0.09$ ohm (armature-circuit resistance = 0.10)

The resistance between pairs of these values then yields the resistance to be placed between starter points.

It may readily be deduced from the above that the number of steps required in a starter will be reduced if the current peaks are permitted to exceed the 150 per cent of rated value assumed in the example and if the current is permitted to drop below rated value prior to moving to the next contact point.

When starting under less than rated load, or under no load, the starting-current values cannot be maintained with the regularity assumed above, and the speed will rise more quickly to its final value. Figures 100 and 101 indicate the difference that may be expected for no-load starting as contrasted with starting against maintained rated-load torque.

82. Field and Armature Control Rheostats.—The field rheostat is the most common form of speed-control device for shunt and compound motors. A combination of field-resistance and armature-resistance control provides the widest possible range of control from zero to maximum safe speed, though at the expense of good regulation for the lower speeds, as illustrated in Fig. 90.

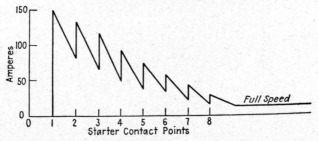

Fig. 101.—Approximation of current variations when starting under light load, using the same starter as in Fig. 100.

Such combinations of control may be effected by separate resistor units, one of relatively high current capacity and low resistance for the armature circuit, and one of relatively low current capacity and high resistance for the shunt-field circuit; or the two resistors may be combined into a single operating unit. In the latter case, an interlock of some form will render it impossible to insert resistance in the armature circuit except on the all-out position of the field rheostat and, conversely, will allow insertion of resistance in the field circuit only when there is no added resistance in the armature circuit.

For convenience, the rheostat for field control of shunt and compound motors is sometimes combined with the starting rheostat, forming the so-called *compound starter*, as illustrated in Fig. 102. Here a double-arm arrangement is used: the first arm *a*, to which the operating handle is attached, carries the second and shorter arm *b* with it while the starting resistance is being cut out. Arm *b* is then held in place by the holding magnet, short-circuiting the

starting resistance and leaving arm a free to be moved to the left
for insertion of resistance into the field circuit for speed control,
the field resistance having been short-circuited during the starting

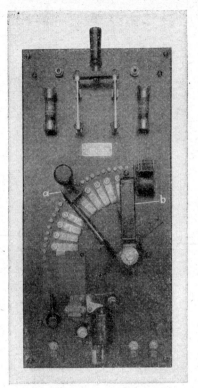

Fig. 102.—A compound starter, with field control and overload release. (*Ward Leonard Electric Company.*)

period. When the power supply is interrupted, the holding magnet
releases arm b, which is returned by spring action to the off position,
carrying arm a with it. The series resistance of the compound
starter is designed for starting duty only; but, by use of heavier
series-resistance material, with suitable means for holding the controller handle on any desired operating point, the range of control
may be extended to cover speeds from zero to base speed by arma-

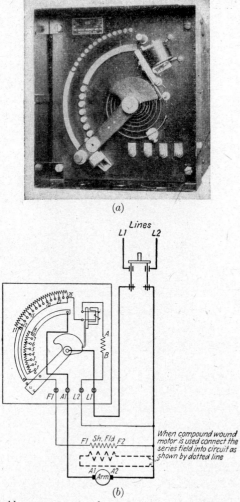

Fig. 103.—A wide-range compound speed regulator. (a) External appearance, (b) circuit diagram. (*Cutler-Hammer, Inc.*)

ture-resistance control, as well as the range of safe operating speeds above base speed by field-resistance control. The series resistance in this type of controller serves both as starting resistance and as speed-control resistance. Figure 103 is illustrative of a wide-range compound controller of the face-plate type, and Fig. 105 shows a compound controller of the drum type, this also including provision for reversal of direction of rotation.

Field control alone, in the standard motor, may be depended upon for a 4:1 ratio of maximum speed to minimum speed, at rated-power output. However, four-pole motors are now available that give twice this speed range—about 8:1—with no change in rated-power output. This is accomplished through the use of separate

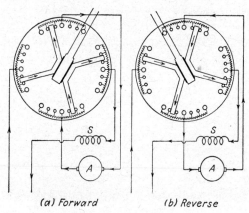

(a) Forward   (b) Reverse

Fig. 104.—Face-plate type controller for crane motors.

control circuits for half the field coils, two adjacent poles being energized in the usual manner to supply practically constant flux, while the remaining two poles, through use of a special resistor device, have their mmf varied from maximum to zero and finally reversed. Thus the resultant field strength can be changed from a value representing the sum of the separate mmfs to a value representing their difference.

For starting and speed-control requirements of the series motor, either a face-plate type (Fig. 104) or a drum type (Fig. 105) of controller may be used. Since an operator is usually in attendance where series motors are used—as in the case of cranes, hoists, street-cars, etc.—no-voltage releases are not included in manually operated controllers for this type of motor. Series-motor controllers of these types usually have the reversing feature included, this feature making it necessary to bring all motor wiring leads to the controller, in order that reversals may be made in the relative directions of current through the armature and field coils.

83. Drum Controllers.—For service requirements necessitating frequent starts, stops, and reversals, or frequent variations in speed, the hand starters and controllers previously described are scarcely adequate. Where the installation does not justify automatic control, the drum type of controller is well adapted, since its sturdier construction will provide trouble-free service.

Fig. 105.—Drum-type, reversing, compound controller. (*Cutler-Hammer, Inc.*)

For adjustable-speed service in connection with the operation of machine tools, the drum type of controller (Fig. 105) is usually preferred. Here the armature-resistance grids are of sufficient cross section to carry full-load operating current continuously and are used for starting the motor and for adjusting its speed to values lower than the base speed obtained with no external resistance in armature or field. As the operating handle is turned, resistance is gradually cut out of the armature circuit, there being zero resist-

ance in the field circuit at this stage.   Then, when zero resistance
in the armature circuit has been obtained, further rotation of the
arm inserts resistance into the field circuit.   Movement of the
handle in the opposite direction starts and speeds up the motor in
the reverse direction.   Insulating barriers are provided for separating the controller fingers; and a magnetic blowout (Art. 89) may be
included by the addition of a coil in series with the armature circuit, so installed that a magnetic field is maintained across the
contacts as they are made and broken.

FIG. 106.—Street-railway type controller. (*Westinghouse Electric Corporation.*)

Series-motor controllers are designed upon the same general
principles as the machine-tool controller but control series-resistance values only.   For traction service, they usually control two
motors, placing the motors in series with each other and with external resistance for starting; cutting out the external resistance as
the car gains in speed; and then placing the two motors in parallel
with each other, with resistance again in series which is cut out as
full speed is attained, as illustrated in Fig. 107, which shows only
the four extreme points of the controller.   Diagram *a* shows the

circuit when the controller is on the first notch—the starting position—diagrams *b* and *c* show the circuits for intermediate and changeover points, and diagram *d* shows the final, or full-speed operational circuit. With the motors in series and all resistance out, as in *b*, half speed is attained; and, with the motors in parallel and all resistance out, as in *d*, full speed is attained. A separate

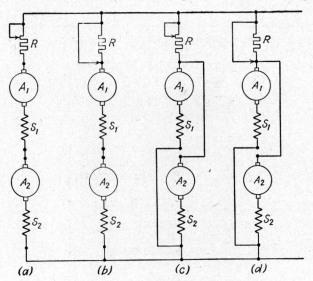

(a)   (b)   (c)   (d)

Fig. 107.—Series-parallel control for traction motors.

and smaller controller is utilized for reversal of the motors, an interlocking arrangement being provided so that reversal can be effected only when the main controller handle is in the off position.

This method provides smooth acceleration and has the advantage of high torque for starting or for handling heavy loads at reduced speed, without abnormal current demands.

84. Automatic Starters.—Any type of starter, manual or automatic, is designed to limit the armature current to a safe value—usually 150 to 175 per cent of rated current—during the starting and acceleration period of the motor. With the motor at standstill, the full amount of resistance is required, since the back emf is zero; but less resistance is required as the speed of rotation increases, until finally full speed is attained, and there is no further need for added resistance in the armature circuit.

When manual starters are used, the rate at which the starter resistance is decreased depends entirely upon the will or whim of the operator and cannot be controlled with any degree of accuracy.

Fig. 108.—Two-pole, 100-ampere magnetic contactor. (*Ward Leonard Electric Company.*)

Automatic starters remove the variables in the operation of starting and accelerating the motor and serve not only to prevent damage due to reducing resistance too rapidly but also to avoid loss of time due to reducing it more slowly than necessary.

The simplest form of automatic starter is the "across-the-line" magnetic contactor for starting small motors, as shown in Fig. 108. The shunt coil, which pulls the contact arms into place and holds them, is actuated by push button (Fig. 109); or may be actuated by float switch in sump pumps, by pressure gauge relay in water pumps, etc. An arc chute (Fig. 125) is usually provided to assist in rupturing the arc when the contacts are opened.

For automatic starters, which are required to control the insertion and withdrawal of resistance from the armature of motors during acceleration, several contactors, each controlled in its action by suitable electromagnets, are designed to operate in accordance with time, voltage-drop, or current limitations, the first closure serving to insert the total resistance in the armature circuit, and the succeeding operations serving to speed up the motor as rapidly as

Fig. 109.—Push-button master switch, for remote control. (*Cutler-Hammer, Inc.*)

may be desirable. There are many kinds of automatic starters, of varying degrees of complexity, but the majority of them may be considered to belong to either the time-limit or the current-limit type. These types have many features in common. In each, there are two distinct sets of wiring and connections, one handling the control electromagnet and push-button circuits, the other handling the main motor circuits; the former being of light wire and carrying small currents, and the latter being of heavier wire to carry the larger currents of the power circuits. In each, a main contactor makes the initial connection to armature and field—through suitable resistors in the case of the armature—when the start button is pressed and opens these circuits when the stop button is pressed.

It is usually not necessary to hold the starter button in the depressed position longer than it takes for the first contactor to move into its closed position, this movement serving, in addition to closing the main contact, to establish a bypass around the starting button so that its release does not interrupt the continuing sequence of contactor movements. This bypass also includes added resistance in the control circuit in order that unnecessary and wasteful heating of the electromagnet coils may be avoided. Opening of the main contactor may require that heavy currents be interrupted, and it is therefore provided with an arc-blowout device (Art. 89) to hasten extinction of the arc and reduce burning of the contacts.

Overload protection is usually included in the form of bimetallic strips in the control circuit, with small heater units connected in the motor circuit so that overload upon the motor will cause heat to be applied to the bimetallic strips in sufficient amount to cause them to spread apart, thus opening the control circuit and shutting down the motor. It is usually necessary to reset the overload device by hand before the motor can be started again, although automatic resetting can be provided where required.

In the time-limit type of starter (Fig. 110), the follow-up steps—after the initial contactor movement, which is controlled by the starter button—take place at a fixed time rate regardless of the load upon the motor and the currents that may be necessary to accelerate the load. An escapement device allows the progressive movement to take place at a predetermined rate, and resistance is thus removed from the armature circuit step by step until full voltage is applied. This type of starter is usually smaller, cheaper, and less complicated than the current-limit types but is adequate for many applications, particularly applications where the motor starts under less than rated-load torque.

The current-limit type of starter is designed to have the succeeding operations, after the closure of the first contactor by the starter button, depend upon armature-current values, or upon voltage or flux magnitudes that are dependent upon the armature-current requirements of the motor during its acceleration period. Also, since the rate at which armature current decreases with a given amount of resistance in the armature circuit is dependent upon acceleration rate, the timing of contactor movement adjusts itself automatically to the load being accelerated, cutting out the armature resistance rapidly with a light load and quick acceleration, and more slowly with a heavy load.

In the "lockout" type of starter, the accelerating contactors are controlled by the differential action of two coils, one tending to close the contactor and the other tending to hold it open. For large values of current—as in the early stages of acceleration—the pull of the lockout coil exceeds the pull of the closing coil, and the contactor remains open. When the current reaches a sufficiently lower value—as in the later stages of acceleration—the pull of the

(a)

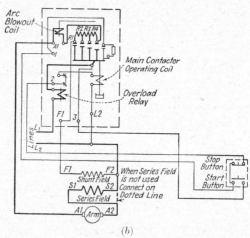

(b)

FIG. 110.—Time-limit automatic starter, with thermal overload relay. (a) External appearance. (b) Circuit diagram. (*Cutler-Hammer, Inc.*)

closing coil predominates and closes the contactor. This action is based upon saturation of the closing-coil magnetic circuit as contrasted with the nonsaturated state of the lockout-coil magnetic circuit, which contains an air gap. Thus, for high current values, the flux produced by the lockout coil—and its magnetic pull—is the greater; but, at some predetermined current value, the two pulls balance; and, for still lower currents, the pull of the closing coil exceeds that of the lockout coil. The proper setting at which the two pulls balance and below which the contactor closes, short-circuiting the next step of resistance, will be, of course, the highest safe value of current that may be allowed to pass through the motor armature in order that the load may be accelerated rapidly but without risk of damage to the motor.

As each contactor closes, the current rises sharply, because of the decreased armature-circuit resistance, and then decreases with the subsequent rise in speed. When the preset value of current is reached, the next contactor closes, cutting out the next step of resistance and causing the current to rise sharply again, this sequence being repeated until all the starter resistance has been short-circuited and the motor is operating at full speed, with full line voltage applied to the armature terminals. The number of steps required depends upon the current limits for which it is designed but usually does not exceed four or five steps from total starter resistance to zero resistance in series with the armature.

Figure 100 illustrates the current variations with successive controller steps, although the number of points in the hand starter here illustrated is larger than is usually considered necessary with automatic starters.

Another type of starter, known as the *series-relay* type, is illustrated in Fig. 111. This cuts out the resistance in three steps, but the same method can be extended to include any number of steps desired. The contactors are given a rolling contact to equalize the wear and prevent sticking. The detailed operation is as follows:

With the line switch closed, control is effected through operation of the switch or push button C, which may be located at any convenient point. Closing the control circuit by means of this switch causes the first control magnet C_1 to operate and close the circuit through the armature and field of the motor, with the starting resistance—shown at top of the diagram—in series with the armature. The starting current causes the relay R_1 to operate and hold open the circuit to control magnet C_2 until the motor armature has attained sufficient speed to cause the current to be reduced to a point—determined by a control spring—that allows the armature of relay R_1 to drop and close the circuit through C_2, thus short-circuiting the first section of starting resistance. The same cycle of operations is repeated with relays R_2 and R_3, causing control magnets C_3 and C_4 to close in succession as the speed of the motor

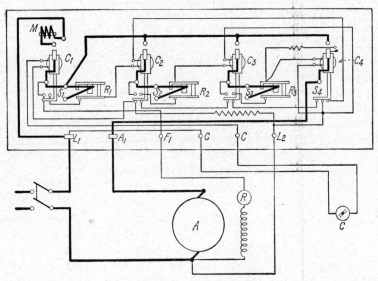

FIG. 111.—The series-relay controller.

armature increases. With the closing of the fourth contactor, however, the control circuits for C_2 and C_3 are broken, and these contactors drop open. The control circuit for C_4 is also broken but is reestablished through a series resistance that reduces the current through the coil at C_4 in order to avoid unnecessary waste of energy. The current through C_1 is also limited by a series resistance during normal operation of the motor. Stoppage of the motor is effected by opening the control switch or push button C, which causes the first contactor to open, which in turn opens the circuit to C_4. Since the opening of the main circuit always takes place at the first contactor, a magnetic blowout coil and arc chute are provided at this point.

The larger the motor the more important it is that automatic control be provided. The bulk of industrial installations are so equipped even in the smaller sizes, which utilize push buttons for closing or opening the line connection from one or more convenient locations.

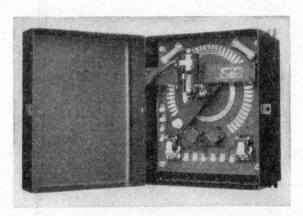

Fig. 112.—A motor-operated field rheostat, with interlocking relays. (*Cutler-Hammer, Inc.*)

Electric railway cars are usually provided with automatic control equipment that takes from the operator all control of motor acceleration, the operator's control being limited to a master controller that provides for starting, stopping, or reversal of the motors, the acceleration being carried out automatically at a rate determined by adjustments on the control apparatus not available to the operator. Trains of two or more cars, as on elevated or subway systems, may thus be operated by a single master controller. The acceleration of elevator motors is also usually controlled by automatic means, the operator's control being limited to start, stop, and reverse. This makes for smoother operation, with less risk of abuse to the electrical equipment. Modern elevator control also usually includes automatic means for bringing the elevator to rest with the floors in close alignment and for rendering the starting equipment inoperative until the car door is properly closed. Automatic starters for industrial motors may include relays for short-circuiting the field rheostat during the starting period and reinsertion of this resistance when base speed has been reached. Quick stoppage of a motor may be brought about by installing additional equipment that applies dynamic braking action automatically as soon as the stop button is pressed and the line contactor opens.

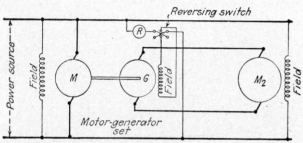

Fig. 113.—The Ward Leonard control system.

85. The Ward Leonard Control System.—For motor systems requiring unusually wide and sensitive ranges of speed control, special generators are sometimes provided for each motor or group of motors. This is especially true of installations involving the use of motors of exceptionally large capacity, as in the case of electrically operated steel mills, where motors of 3000 to 5000 hp may be required.

One such method of obtaining a wide and finely graduated control, with good speed regulation throughout the operating range, is known as the Ward Leonard system, after its inventor, and involves the use of a separate motor-generator set, as indicated in Fig. 113. The fields being separately excited, the voltage of the generator may be varied at will to control the speed of motor M_2, which is connected to the mechanical load, giving a wide range of control and also an efficient control, since the only current variation is that controlled by the generator-field rheostat. For high speeds, resistance may also be added to the motor-field circuit as required. Reversal is readily effected by reversing the excitation of the generator. If, as is frequently the case, the primary source of power is a-c, an auxiliary exciter generator will be necessary for supplying d-c power to the field circuits of the generator and the driven motor. The driven motor may be a single motor or a group of motors driving different sections of a given machine or combination of machines, the speed of which must be varied in unison.

The speed range obtainable by armature-voltage control is usually limited to about 10:1, because the speed regulation tends to become poor at lower speeds, and the motor has a tendency to stall on slight overloads. An additional speed range of 4:1 can be obtained by field control on the motor—with the armature voltage held at its full value—giving a total continuous speed control, at good regulation throughout, of 40:1. Thus, for a base speed of 500 rpm, the motor could be operated between 50 and 500 rpm by armature-voltage control, through variations in generator-field current, and between 500 and 2000 rpm by motor-field control. Special devices may be used to secure speed ranges as high as 100:1.

A modification of the Ward Leonard system adds a flywheel to the motor-generator set with a view to smoothing out its power demands. In order to make the flywheel effective, the motor must have poor speed regulation (Art. 71). The Ilgner-Ward Leonard system, as this modified arrangement is called, finds application in connection with large mine hoists, steel-mill drives, etc., where the power demands of the motor-generator set upon the supply system are likely to be very heavy.

Other modifications of the fundamental Ward Leonard system may be obtained by adding auxiliary field windings to a special exciter for the generator to provide the operating characteristics desired for specific applications. The flexibility and wide range of control obtainable by this method, as well as its high over-all efficiency, have established it as a preferred type of drive for many heavy industrial applications; and the possibility of using a-c power as a primary source has further encouraged its extension to smaller motor drives, some involving motors of 1 hp or less. In the smaller sizes, however, the cost of the exciter and control equipment tends to become a disproportionately large part of the total cost; whereas, on the larger sizes, these items are a relatively small part of the total cost. Consequently, many attempts have been made in the direction of simplification of the control equipment and elimination of the exciter, while retaining the best features of the conventional system.

One rather unique method of simplification of the basic Ward Leonard control, for application to the smaller drives, involves the use of a series generator, as illustrated in Fig. 114. This drive provides the high starting torque characteristic of the series motor but, when brought up to speed from standstill by starting the motor-generator set, provides a "soft" start. Stopping the motor-generator set allows the motor and its drive to drift to a stop. An

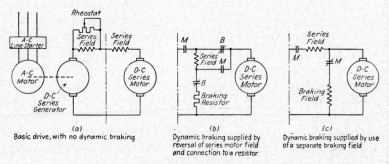

(a)
Basic drive, with no dynamic braking

(b)
Dynamic braking supplied by reversal of series motor field and connection to a resistor

(c)
Dynamic braking supplied by use of a separate braking field

Fig. 114.—The series variable-voltage drive.

example in which these characteristics meet the requirements nicely is that of a large hangar door. Where necessary to provide quick stoppage, dynamic braking (Art. 88) can be provided by the use of special contactors that disconnect the motor from the generator, reverse the series field, and reconnect it across the motor armature in series with a suitable resistor, as in Fig. 114b; or by application of a separate braking field across the armature terminals of the motor, after it has been disconnected from the generator, as in Fig. 114c. The first method is used more generally for the smaller drives, because of lack of space for an extra braking-field winding, and the second method provides a simpler control for the larger drives.

Figure 115 shows the typical series-generator voltage characteristic and the typical series-motor speed characteristic, with the

ideal resultant speed characteristic of the series combination. The
low voltage of the generator at light loads limits the motor speed,
and the high voltage of the generator at heavy loads raises the
motor speed above that normal to the series motor with constant
voltage applied. Figure 116 shows actual speed curves obtained
from such a set. The speed regulation, although not so good

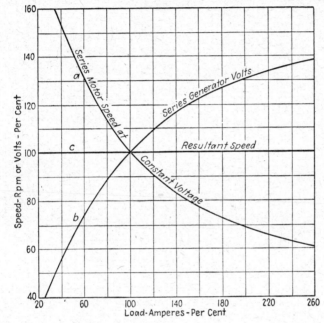

Fig. 115.—Ideal speed characteristic of a series motor in series with a series
generator. (*From G. A. Caldwell, Adjustable-speed D. C. Drives, Westinghouse
Engr., August, 1942.*)

throughout the range of speeds as may be obtained from the conventional type of Ward Leonard control, is satisfactory for many
practical applications. This drive is normally limited to a 10:1
speed range but can be operated as low as one-twentieth maximum
speed and still maintain good speed regulation. Decreased ventilation at the lower speeds, however, limits the time for which such
speeds may be maintained.

86. The Amplidyne and Rototrol Control Systems.—The ampli-dyne and Rototrol generator has proved highly satisfactory as a control device in so-called "closed-cycle" systems, a closed-cycle system being defined as "one in which the controlling agency is actuated in part by some function of the final output in such man-

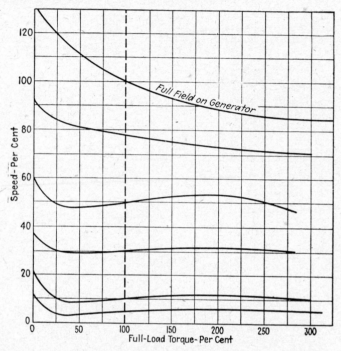

Fig. 116.—Actual speed curves obtained with the series variable-voltage drive. (*From G. A. Caldwell, Adjustable-speed D. C. Drives; Westinghouse Engr., August, 1942.*)

ner as to minimize any deviation of this output from an ideal value." [1] It is essentially a highly sensitive, wide-range power amplifier and consists of a d-c generator with one or more auxiliary

---

[1] SHOULTS, EDWARDS, and CREVER, Industrial Applications of Amplidyne Generators, *Gen. Elec. Rev.*, March, 1940.

fields, in addition to the main field, and an extra set of brushes which are short-circuited, as shown in Fig. 117.

Referring to Fig. 117, current in the controlling circuit sets up a flux ϕ_1. Rotation of the armature conductors in this field generates a voltage that causes current I_2 to flow through the short circuit connecting the brushes B_1 and B_2. This current, flowing through the armature conductors, sets up flux ϕ_2. Rotation of the armature in this field generates a voltage E_3, which results in current I_3 flowing through the external controlled circuit. The cur-

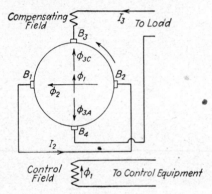

FIG. 117.—Principle of the amplidyne generator.

rent I_3, distributed through the armature conductors, produces a reaction flux ϕ_{3A}. A compensating field winding is inserted in the controlled load circuit to eliminate as far as possible this armature-reaction flux—the flux ϕ_{3C} set up by this winding being of equal value and opposite in direction to the flux ϕ_{3A}.

Elimination of the armature-reaction flux ϕ_{3A} leaves the armature free for the relatively small control flux ϕ_1 and the secondary flux ϕ_2, which directly controls the generated voltage of the load circuit. Additional shunt- and series-field coils, as well as commutating-field poles and coils, may be added for further amplification and smoothness of operation, but the essential features remain as outlined above.[1]

[1] For further discussion of this interesting machine, see Alec Fisher, Design Characteristics of Amplidyne Generators, *Gen. Elec. Rev.*, March, 1940.

An example of the manner in which the amplidyne generator may be applied is shown in Fig. 118, where the output of the amplidyne generator supplies the field circuit of a d-c generator, the output circuit of which is in series with the control winding of the amplidyne generator. One method used to secure the necessary refinement in the control is to superimpose the excitation due to the generator-load current upon an opposed excitation from a constant field provided by current from an auxiliary source. The controlled factor in this case is the line current of the d-c generator,

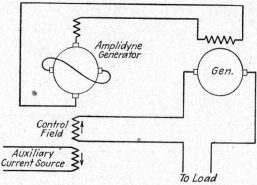

Fig. 118.—An example of amplidyne control.

but it might also be the speed or any other variable of a machine or device so arranged that the control-field current is proportional to the controlled function.

Amplidyne control is being applied to an increasing number of industrial applications, in steel mills to control tension in the reeling of strip metal, in paper mills, to control speed of papermaking machines, to hold the register of a web of paper during rewinding and cutting processes, etc.

A similar control system has been developed by another manufacturer under the name Rototrol control, the heart of the system being a small d-c generator provided with more field windings than are provided for the standard generator. It is in effect a sensitive amplifier, small inputs to its field circuit producing large outputs from its armature. A self-energizing field is supplemented by one or more separately excited fields, the output being under the control of the separately excited fields, which are energized by small currents proportional to motor torque, motor speed, or other control functions that can be expressed in terms of voltage or current.

Assuming that the speed of a d-c motor is to be held constant regardless of load variations, by the Rototrol system, the circuit shown in Fig. 119 will serve to illustrate the general method. This circuit, it will be noted, is similar to the standard Ward Leonard system except that the Rototrol generator is employed to furnish

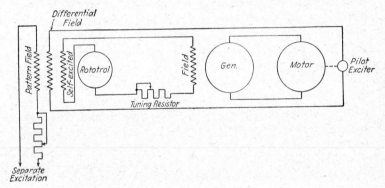

FIG. 119.—The Rototrol method of motor-speed control.

excitation current for the main generator. A standard, or calibration, voltage is impressed upon one separately excited field, called the *pattern field*. A voltage proportional to the speed being controlled is obtained from a small pilot exciter coupled to the driven motor and impressed upon a second separately excited field connected differentially with respect to the first field so that the net excitation is proportional to the difference of mmfs supplied by the pattern field and the differential field. A self-energizing series field supplies the basic power required to effect the control, and the differential action of the other fields serves as the control medium. As load on the motor increases, the speed tends to decrease. This causes a decrease in pilot-exciter voltage, which in turn brings about a reduction in flux from the differential-field winding, increasing the net field strength, which increases the Rototrol voltage, the generator field strength, generator voltage, and motor speed until equilibrium is again attained. The series-generator characteristic of the Rototrol is designed to allow the attainment of equilibrium only when the differential field exactly balances the constant pattern field. Thus, after any change in load upon the motor, the resulting voltage change of the pilot exciter, impressed upon the differential field, brings about a compensating net excitation which persists until the differential-field strength is again equal to the pattern-field strength. This occurs only when the speed of the motor has returned to its original value. If the load upon the motor were decreased, causing a rise in speed, the differential field would of course become stronger than the pattern field, bringing about a reduction in motor torque and causing its speed to be lowered until equilibrium was again restored at the original speed.[1]

87. Other Control Systems.—A multivoltage system is sometimes used for motor control, the field being permanently connected to a constant-voltage source but the armature circuit being arranged for shifting to either of the two or more supply voltages. In its simplest form, such control could be effected through use of a three-wire system, the voltage between the outer wires being double that between the center and outer wires, as, for instance, 115 volts between the center and outer wires and 230 volts between the outer wires—the field-circuit terminals being connected permanently between the outer, or 230-volt, wires. For low speed the armature would then be connected between inner and outer wires, and for high speed it would be connected between the outer wires. This would provide only two speeds, quite widely separated, unless a field rheostat were used for raising the speeds above the base speed for either connection.

The next step in extending such a system would be to provide different voltages between the inner and two outer wires, as, for instance, 90 volts between the center and one outer wire and 140 volts between the center and the second outer wire, this resulting

[1] A more detailed discussion of the operation of the Rototrol control system may be found in W. H. Formhals, Rototrol, A Versatile Electrical Regulator, *Westinghouse Engr.*, May, 1942. Its application to mine-hoist drives is described by J. G. Ivy in *Westinghouse Engr.*, July, 1944.

again in 230 volts between outer wires. A further extension would result from the use of a four-wire system, with a different voltage between each pair, which, by taking advantage of all possible combinations, would provide a total of six different voltages. Such systems need not, of course, be confined to a single motor but can be extended throughout an entire shop or factory building where variable-speed motors are used; and, with field-rheostat control in addition to the several armature voltages, such a system can provide a wide range of motor speeds, with good speed regulation at each speed level.

A somewhat similar system is used for control of series motors on railway cars or locomotives where two or four motors are required. Figure 107, Art. 83, illustrates the application of this system of control to a case involving two motors per traction unit, the motors first being connected in series with each other and a suitable resistor for starting, and the resistance being gradually reduced in value as the car accelerates. When the maximum speed attainable with this connection has been reached, a shift is made to parallel connection of the motors, again with resistance in series. The resistance is then gradually reduced, as higher speeds are reached, until full line voltage is applied to each motor.

Four motors per traction unit may be connected in a manner similar to that described above, but usually a four-motor system would be handled as two *pairs* of motors. A diagram similar to Fig. 107 would thus include, for low-voltage systems, two motors in parallel for each of the single motors there illustrated. For high-voltage systems, 2400 to 3000 volts, it is usual practice to wind each motor for half the line voltage and connect two motors permanently in series. Thus the control system would start with the four motors in series but end with two parallel pairs of motors in series.

The advantages of the series-parallel system of control are (*a*) the provision of two economical running speeds, with no rheostatic losses at either of these speeds, (*b*) the rheostatic losses during acceleration are reduced by 50 to 60 per cent, and (*c*) material savings are possible in the weight of the necessary resistor units.

The use of electron tubes for supplying direct current to standard

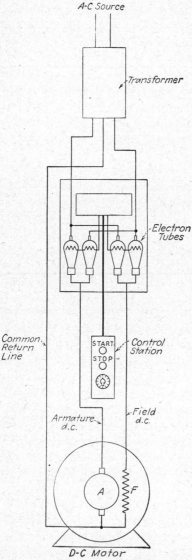

FIG. 120.—Basic circuits for d-c motor drive from an a-c source by electronic rectification and control.

shunt motors from a-c supply lines has progressed well beyond the experimental stage and now, under trade names such as Mototrol[1] and Thymo-trol,[2] offers many control advantages for industrial drives of power ratings in the range of ⅛ to 15 hp, besides utilizing less space than would be required for a separate motor-generator set such as would be required in the Ward Leonard system. As shown in Fig. 120, the essential parts of the system are (a) a suitable transformer for power supply to the tubes; (b) a panel containing the rectifier tubes— one set for supplying the armature voltage and another set for supplying the field voltage—along with the necessary contactors, protective relays, and control devices; and (c) a d-c shunt motor of standard design but having suitable characteristics for the purpose.

Besides the advantages inherent in the d-c driving motor, it is claimed that these systems provide wide ranges of speed control—as high as 100:1 if required—at good

[1] Westinghouse Electric Corporation.
[2] General Electric Company.

speed regulation throughout the operating range. They have a simple, single control dial by which speeds may be preset, in advance of starting; and the motor acceleration current is therefore limited to a safe value, with smooth but rapid acceleration, the motor current not rising above the preset value even when the motor stalls. Dynamic braking is provided automatically when the stop button is pressed, the armature being disconnected from the line and connected across a load resistor. When extremely

fast stopping is required, an electronic regenerative braking method can be supplied. Reversing or "inching" controls can also be supplied. Since all controls are automatic, actuated by dial or push-button operation, the wear and tear on motor, con-

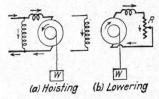

(a) Hoisting   (b) Lowering

Fig. 121.—Dynamic braking, with compound motor.

trols, and driven machine are likely to be materially less than with manual controls. The motor is automatically disconnected in the event of failure of one or more of the rectifier tubes.

88. Dynamic Braking.—Motor controllers may be provided with additional contact points for placing a variable resistance across the motor-armature terminals after the motor has been disconnected from the power source—the field, however, being left connected for excitation from the power source. Strong braking action may thus be produced, since the generated emf of the armature causes current to flow through the resistor—the machine thus acting as a generator and supplying power, which heats the resistor. This type of braking is applicable only where the load tends to overhaul or drive the motor as in elevators, hoists, cranes, railway cars, etc. It is not effective for complete stoppage, since the braking action is dependent upon generation of voltage by the moving armature conductors. Figure 121 illustrates one connection scheme for dynamic braking, using a compound motor.

Regenerative braking also utilizes the ability of the motor to act as a generator; but in this type of braking the power is returned to the circuit, instead of being wasted as heat in a resistor, and serves to relieve to some extent the load on the powerhouse. This principle is used on many main-line electric locomotives. Motors used for assisting the braking operations, using either the resistance or the regenerative system of loading, do not have the same opportunity for cooling as have motors not so used and should therefore be of more liberal rating in order to avoid overheating.

Most railway driving motors are of the series type, which is less applicable to regenerative braking systems than the shunt type of motor. However, it may be adapted to this system of braking through the use of special control connections whereby the series fields are separately excited from a low-voltage motor-generator set. With shunt motors, no special control arrangements would be required, since a slight over-speeding, with full field, would reverse the direction of power flow. A shunt motor would therefore tend to maintain a uniform speed upgrade and downgrade, with the motors taking power from the line on the upgrades and feeding power to the line on the downgrades.

Fig. 122.—Reversing, time-limit automatic starter, with dynamic braking and field accelerating relay. (*Cutler-Hammer, Inc.*)

89. Control and Protective Devices. Magnetic Blowouts.—Present industrial standards allow little use of manual control equipment. In general, motors under the direct control of operators are started, stopped, and otherwise controlled through the agency of push-button stations conveniently located on or immediately adjacent to the driven machine. The actual control equipment is likely to be mounted in a protected location separate from the motor and its driven machine. The use of properly designed and applied control equipment greatly extends the usefulness of motorized equipment and sometimes makes it possible to obtain performance characteristics that could not otherwise be obtained.

The basic functions of any motor controller are to start and stop the motor at the proper time by closing and opening the power circuit, to cause it to operate at the correct speed or to deliver a required torque, and to protect the motor from damage due to improper loading or other abuses.

A large proportion of the control devices sold for use in connection with industrial motors are of standard design, as are the motors, but controllers for special devices are individually designed especially for the particular application and provide all necessary special features of operation or protection.

The closing or opening of power circuits by automatic or remote-control apparatus is performed through the agency of contactors or magnet-operated switches. Usually the magnet operates against the force of gravity or of a spring in such a manner that, when the magnet is deenergized, the contacts fall apart and open the circuit. Small auxiliary contacts attached to some part of the contactors serve to close or open other circuits that control the functioning of other contactors whose action is dependent upon the position of the first contactor. In general, therefore, the controller wiring is separated into two main divisions, the power circuits and the control circuits.

Relays are electromagnetic devices whose functionings are responsive to current, voltage, or other circuit conditions. They serve to initiate the proper sequence of events that cause the motor or other driven device to do the proper thing at the proper time.

A master switch, usually a small drum controller or pushbutton, serves to open and close main control circuits by energizing or deenergizing the operating coils of magnetic contactors. Following closure of the main control circuits, the rate of acceleration, final speed, etc., are usually cared for automatically much more smoothly and accurately than could be done by the operator in direct control.

A push-button station is a simple form of master controller.

Such push buttons should be of sturdy construction, and one or more of them may be mounted in readily accessible positions near the equipment each is designed to control. It is held open— or closed—by a spring and operates to close—or open—a control circuit through the simple operation of pressing the button momentarily. For completely automatic operation, the push button or master controller may be replaced by some such device as a float

switch—for maintaining liquid levels between two limiting points—or a pressure switch— for maintaining pressures between upper and lower limits.

Protective devices are usually incorporated within the control devices. Most commonly, these include protection against overload and undervoltage, since these abnormal conditions are likely to occur at times in the operation of almost any electrical machine. Since, in the electromagnetic type of controller, the contactors are held closed by an energized electromagnet, working against the pressure of a spring, it is only necessary that the

Fig. 123.—Double-pole circuit breaker. (*Westinghouse Electric Corporation.*)

spring pressure be suitably adjusted so that reduction of line voltage to a value unsuitable for continued operation of the machine will allow the spring to open the control circuit. This also assures opening of the control circuit when voltage is completely interrupted, as by the opening of a switch or circuit breaker.

Overload protection may be provided by a thermal relay, consisting of a bimetallic strip mounted near a heating element through which passes the current to the motor or other device under protection. With proper calibration, the excess heating effect, due to

an overload, will cause the bimetallic strip to bend sufficiently to
open the control circuit of which it forms a part. In the older forms
of control equipment, electromagnets of the plunger type were used
in the power-supply lines, the plunger, operating under the influence of excessive currents, serving to interrupt the flow of current
to the holding magnet of the supply-line contactor. These, however, have the disadvantage of inability to distinguish between
peak loads of short duration and sustained overloads, with the

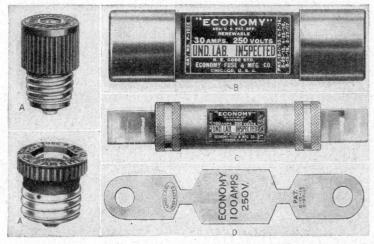

Fig. 124.—Standard fuses. (*Economy Fuse & Manufacturing Company.*)

result that unnecessary interruptions are likely to occur; whereas
the relay of the thermal type operates under the influence of heat,
which is the harmful element in overload operation, and its operation more closely measures the harmful effects of an overload upon
an electrical device, since it takes account of the time element as
well as the magnitude of the overload current.

As back-up protection to motors and control equipment, as well
as to supply circuits, the ordinary fuse is commonly used and provides dependable protection if fuses of proper rating are used. The
fuse operates upon a heat-time basis also and is not likely to open
the circuit by reason of a momentary slight overload but will open

it when a heavy overload occurs momentarily or when a slight overload persists for a considerable time. Fuses, properly applied, provide the most inexpensive form of dependable back-up protection for equipment and lines.

It has been shown (Art. 16) that a conductor carrying current is acted upon when in a magnetic field by a force tending to drive the conductor out of the field, the direction in which the conductor is forced depending upon the relative directions of flux in the field and of current in the conductor. The same action is found to exist in connection with an electric arc as exists in connection with a conductor carrying current, *i.e.*, the arc is forced to one side. This principle is applied to advantage in connection with circuit breakers and control devices of various kinds, particularly in connection with automatic controllers for d-c motors, forming the so-called *magnetic blowout*. The "deion" type of circuit breaker effectively uses this principle in that the arc formed upon separation of the contacts is forced by a magnetic field into a stack of closely spaced metal plates, where it is broken into a series of shorter arcs and quickly extinguished.

Fig. 125.—Magnetic blowout and arc chute. (*Cutler-Hammer, Inc.*)

Figure 125 illustrates the application of the magnetic blowout to a contactor on a motor starter. The contactor *A* opens in the "arc chute" *B* provided by the extended and flattened poles of an electromagnet formed by the coil *C*. Because this coil is in series with the circuit formed by the closure of the contactor, a magnetic field is assured as long as the arc is maintained. Relative polarities are such that the arc is forced upward, which is its natural trend, because of the tendency of the heated air in the chute to rise. Thus it is quickly "snapped out" as the contactor opens.

Reference has been made in Art. 83 to the application of this principle for arc extinction in the drum controller, the magnetic field being so located that all arcs due to breaking of contacts are subject to its influence and are quickly interrupted by reason of being pushed aside and elongated to the point of rupture.

90. The Four-quadrant Speed-torque Chart.—From the application point of view, the control of motor operation is extremely important and must be given careful consideration if the motor is to operate to best advantage. In many cases, it is not only necessary that the motor operate at varying speeds and under varying loads in either direction of rotation but it is also necessary that the rotation be stopped or reversed very quickly. For quick stoppage, dynamic braking is frequently employed while "plugging," or reversing the torque quickly, by reversal of field or armature connections while the armature is rotating, is less frequently employed. Dynamic braking results in slowing down the motor quickly but loses its effect at slow speeds, whereas plugging reverses the direction of rotation very quickly unless the supply circuit is opened at or near the zero-speed point. Plugging a d-c motor is not permissible without the addition of sufficient external resistance to the armature circuit to keep the current within safe limits. To plug a shunt motor, for instance, without added resistance to the armature circuit would be likely to cause the commutator to flash over, resulting in appreciable damage, and should blow the circuit fuses, since the current would exceed all permissible limits.

In studying the operation of a reversible motor, from the standpoint of control, with reference to possible use of dynamic braking, regenerative braking, or plugging, the four-quadrant speed-torque chart should be employed. Its significance is indicated by Fig. 126, with a hoist used as an example of the reversible, overhauling type of load.

From the origin at the center, speeds in the positive direction—upward movement of load—are plotted vertically upward, and the corresponding torques are plotted to the right. Speeds for the negative direction—downward movement of load—are plotted vertically downward, and the corresponding torques are plotted to the left. Thus the first quadrant becomes the hoisting quadrant,

and the third quadrant becomes the lowering quadrant. Reversals
of torque thus make the second quadrant a braking quadrant for
upward-moving loads, and the fourth quadrant becomes the braking quadrant for loads being driven downward. Note that motor
torque is in the direction of load movement in quadrants 1 and 3
but is opposite in quadrants 2 and 4, where the motor torque is
being used to brake the load movement.

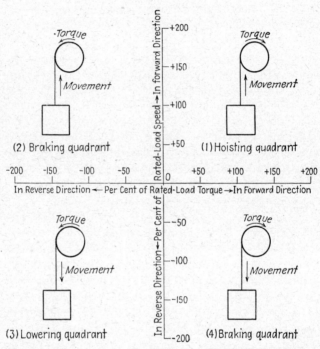

Fig. 126.—The four-quadrant speed-torque chart, as applied to a hoist.

Figure 127 shows speed-torque curves for the shunt motor, using
field control, giving practically straight-line variation, with good
speed regulation for all values of excitation within the operating
range. Regenerative braking may thus readily be used, since,
with no change in connections, a comparatively small increase in
speed past the zero-torque point, because of an overhauling load,

will cause the motor back emf to go sufficiently above the applied voltage to cause the machine to load up to rated current or higher as a generator, the power flow reversing automatically to feed back into the supply circuit. This braking action may be controlled

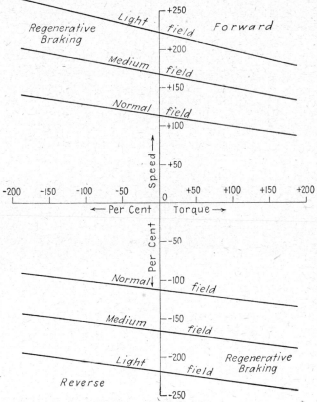

FIG. 127.—Chart of shunt-motor performance, using only field control.

through variations in the shunt-field current by rheostatic control but will lose its effect when the speed decreases to any considerable extent.

Figure 128 shows the effect of adding resistance to the armature circuit upon the speed regulation. The curve marked R_0 represents the base speed curve, with no added resistance; and the curves marked R_1, R_2, R_3, and R_4 represent the effect of adding more and more resistance to the armature circuit. Obviously the speed regula-

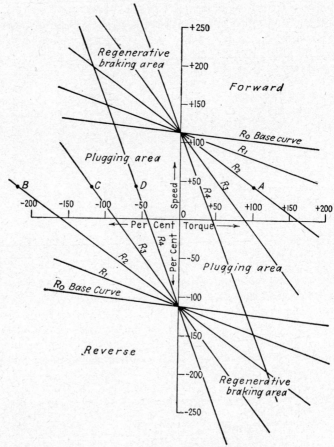

Fig. 128.—Chart of shunt-motor performance, using only armature-resistance control.

tion becomes poorer as resistance is added, and the over-all efficiency also drops appreciably because of the losses in the control rheostat. Regenerative braking may still be utilized in case of overhauling types of load but is more effective where control of the field circuit is available in addition to the armature-resistance control. Also, for quick stoppage or reversal, plugging may be utilized if sufficient resistance is present in the armature circuit to keep the armature current and the reverse torque within safe limits. For instance, when a 100 per cent torque load is being handled, at 40 per cent speed, at point A, in the forward direction, reversal of torque without change in armature-circuit resistance would result in application of over 200 per cent negative torque (point B), entailing a severe shock to the motor, load, and circuit. If, however, as the reversal is made, shift is made to curve R_3, operation is changed to point C, with a resulting reverse torque of about 118 per cent; and shift to curve R_4—point D—causes a reverse torque of only 60 per cent to be applied. Likewise, when operating in the third quadrant, torque reversal will shift the motor operation to one of the speed-torque curves extending from the first quadrant into the fourth quadrant, resulting in a quick stop or reversal if the motor torque is adequate for stopping and accelerating the load in the reverse direction.

Of necessity, regenerative braking may be utilized only as long as there is sufficient speed to make the braking action effective, and plugging is likely to bring about reversal unless provision is made for opening the circuit at or near the zero-speed point. Dynamic braking is likewise dependent upon adequate speed for its effectiveness, and therefore none of the three methods mentioned—regenerative or dynamic braking, or plugging—is wholly to be depended upon. Each must be supplemented by other brakes or braking methods for operation at greatly reduced speeds or for holding loads at zero speed. In connection with the charts, it is interesting to note that plugging and regenerative braking occur in the same quadrant but with different connections to the power source. Portrayal of dynamic braking through the agency of similar curves would call for a set of curves passing through the origin, since torque is dependent upon speed supplied by the overhauling load and there would be no positive torque due to motor action. The curves would therefore appear only in the second and fourth quadrants.

The chart of series-motor performance (Fig. 129) indicates that regenerative braking is not available with series motors without a change in connections. However, special control features may be added to the standard motor by means of which the series field may be shunted across the line, in series with added resistance, in

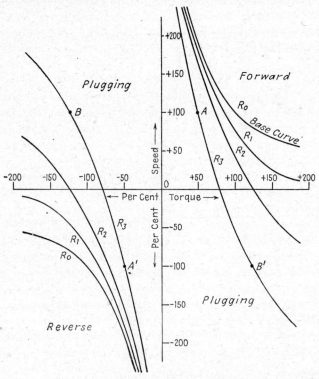

Fig. 129.—Chart of series-motor performance, using series-resistance control.

order to provide regenerative braking control; or dynamic braking may be supplied through use of connections that keep the field energized but connect the armature to a variable resistor. Special series-motor controls may also enable variable-resistance shunts to be inserted across the armature or across the series field for added refinement or more desirable characteristics for special purposes.

Plugging may be utilized with the series motor if sufficient resistance is present in series with the armature or is added as the reversal in connections is made. For instance, when operating in either direction on curve R_3, at 100 per cent speed, 50 per cent torque (points A or A'), torque reversal would shift operation to curve R_3 in the adjoining quadrant (points B or B') with an opposite torque of about 120 per cent. Addition of more resistance as the torque is reversed would, of course, limit further the opposing torque that would be brought to bear upon the motor and load.

Thus it may be seen that complete studies may be made of operational possibilities with overhauling types of load or heavy, reversible motor applications by a proper layout of the speed-torque curves upon a four-quadrant basis. Many variations and refinements are possible beyond the few simple examples shown.[1] No mention has been made of compound motors, but, since their characteristics are intermediate between shunt and series motors it is obvious that the same methods of analysis could readily be applied to compound motors as to shunt and series motors. Any analysis of the sort will naturally require a reasonably accurate set of speed-torque curves for the motor whose performance is to be studied, under the control conditions necessary for the case in hand.

Problems

1. A shunt motor is rated 15 hp, 115 volts, 113 amp. Its armature resistance, exclusive of brushes, is 0.082 ohm, and its field-circuit resistance is 57.5 ohms. Calculate the number of contact points needed for a hand-starting resistor for this motor and the resistance between each pair of contacts, assuming that, as the motor speed rises, the resistance is to be reduced at a rate such that the current varies consistently from 150 per cent of rated value, at the instant of contact with each new step, to rated value, at the instant preceding closure of contact with the next succeeding step.

2. A 120-volt 10-hp motor having an armature resistance of 0.10 ohm has an efficiency of 85 per cent. The shunt-field resistance is 80 ohms. Compute (a) the number of steps and the resistance per step in a starter designed to

---

[1] A more extended discussion of motor application and control problems may be found in Shoults, Rife, and Johnson, "Electric Motors in Industry," John Wiley & Sons, Inc., 1942.

permit the starting current to reach 150 per cent of rated current and (b) the number of steps and the resistance per step if the starting current may be permitted to reach 175 per cent of the rated value.

3. On level track, a streetcar with two series motors in parallel runs at 35 mph and takes 40 amp from the 600-volt trolley. On a hill, where the torque required is five times as much as on the level, the motors are connected in series. If the trolley voltage is now 500 volts and flux is assumed proportional to field current, (a) what current will be required and (b) at what speed will the car operate, the combined resistance of armature and field of each motor being 0.6 ohm?

4. A locomotive with its four motors in parallel operates at 30 mph on level track and takes 100 amp at 550 volts from the trolley. The combined resistance of the armature and series field of each motor is 0.8 ohm. Traveling up a grade where the torque requirement is four times as great, the motors are connected in series-parallel, two pairs of motors in parallel, the two parallel groups in series. Assuming constant trolley voltage and flux proportional to field current, at what speed will the train travel up the grade?

5. A multiple-voltage system provides three voltages, 90, 140, and 230, to which the armature of a motor may be connected. With constant field strength, what rated-load speeds may be obtained from a motor having 0.2 ohm armature-circuit resistance and 50 amp rated armature current if it operates at 1700 rpm when connected to the 230-volt supply lines? If field control may be used to reduce the excitation from 100 per cent, with full voltage applied, to 50 per cent as a lower limit, what will be the complete speed range that can be covered when driving a load such that rated armature current is required at all times?

6. Assume that a four-wire multivoltage system is available for the motor of Prob. 5, the voltages being 60, 75, 115, 135, 190, and 250. What will be the speeds obtainable at rated armature current in the motor (a) with constant field current, of the same value as in Prob. 5, for the 100 per cent setting and (b) with the addition of field control between the same limits as in Prob. 5?

7. If, in a Ward Leonard control system such as that illustrated in Fig. 113, the rated-load efficiency of the motor M is 92 per cent, of the generator is 91 per cent, and of the motor M_2 is 90 per cent, the latter motor being rated 60 hp and the supply-line voltage being 500 volts, what will be the kilowatt rating of the generator and the horsepower rating of the motor M? What current will be required from the supply line when motor M_2 is operated at its rated load? What will be the over-all efficiency of the system and the kilowatts loss in each machine when motor M_2 is being operated at its rated load?

8. A face plate type of controller, as illustrated in Fig. 104, is to be used for speed control of a series motor rated 10 hp, 230 volts, 38 amp, 1700 rpm. Resistance of the armature circuit is 0.12 ohm, of the series-field coils 0.08 ohm. With zero hoist load, the motor input current is 8 amp. Assuming that field flux varies directly with current, what will be the motor speed with no hoist load and full voltage applied? What resistance will be required in the control rheostat in order that the zero-load speed may be held to a maximum of 3500 rpm, with 8 amp current input? If, as a maximum, the load may be such as to cause the motor current to reach 50 amp, what will the speed become with full voltage applied? If it is desired to reduce the maximum-load speed to 600 rpm, what resistance will be necessary in the controller?

Under the conditions outlined, and if in addition it is to serve as a starting resistance capable of holding the starting current to a maximum of 60 amp, what should be the resistance range of the controller?

CHAPTER IX

LOSSES, EFFICIENCIES

91. Losses in Electrical Machinery.—Since certain losses are involved in the passage of electric current through conductors and in the operation of moving parts against the friction of bearings, etc., the output of any electrical machine or apparatus will be less than the input. The energy consumed in this way is transformed into heat, which generally goes to waste, and is referred to as *heat loss.*

Losses may be classified generally as copper losses, mechanical losses, and core losses. Copper losses are due to energy wasted as heat in the passage of current through the various electrical circuits, all of which have more or less resistance. Under mechanical losses are included the energy losses, appearing as heat, due to friction between stationary and moving parts of the machine, and also the windage loss by reason of the fanning action of the moving parts, this being accentuated purposely when fan vanes are installed on the moving parts in order to increase the circulation of air for ventilating purposes. The core losses include the energy, also appearing as heat, required to rotate the iron or steel core of the armature in the magnetic field set up by the north and south poles of the field structure.

In addition to the above losses, there may also be appreciable losses known as *stray-load losses*, although these are usually of importance only in the larger machines. Also, particularly in larger machines, there may be losses external to the machine itself but a necessary part of its operation, such as the energy involved in the operation of field rheostats, separate exciters, and ventilating equipment.

The value of the losses in a given machine must be kept within reasonable limits in proportion to the useful output, and it is the problem of the designer to accomplish this result as well as to provide for disposal of the heat in order to prevent unduly high operating temperatures in the interior parts of the machine.

92. Mechanical Losses.—Under this heading are included bearing friction, brush friction, and air friction, or windage. The losses from these sources may be kept at a relatively low value by proper design, construction, and operation. They are variable to some extent with the speed and cannot be readily calculated but may be determined experimentally by driving the motor or generator idle, without excitation, by means of a calibrated driving motor. The brush friction may be determined by driving the machine with and without the brushes in contact with the commutator, but the bearing and windage losses are not readily separable. For constant-speed generators, or motors having reasonably good speed regulation, the mechanical losses may usually be considered independent of the load upon the machine. This makes it possible to determine these losses with the machine running idle at its rated speed.

Although the fanning action of the armature in its rotation utilizes power that is generally considered as wasted, it should be remembered that the added ventilation, due to the movement, results in a more rapid transfer of heat from all parts of the machine to the surrounding air and enables it to carry greater loads than would be possible without this ventilation. From this standpoint, therefore, the power absorbed in the fanning action of the armature is not entirely wasted but is a necessary adjunct to the operation of the machine. As mentioned previously, the natural fanning action may be increased purposely by the addition of metal vanes around the outer periphery of the armature in order that still greater quantities of air may be moved through and across the parts of the machine most likely to undergo increases in temperature as the machine is loaded.

93. Copper Losses.—The copper losses are determined from the resistance of the circuit and the current flowing under the load condition being considered. They are usually referred to as I^2R losses, since they are conveniently calculated by multiplying the resistance by the square of the current.

The armature-circuit I^2R losses include not only the losses due to current in the armature conductors themselves but also the losses due to current flow through the brushes and across the contact area between brush and commutator. The field-circuit I^2R losses include the losses due to current in shunt-field, series-field, and commutating-field windings, including any shunts which may be used in conjunction with these circuits.

Since the resistance of conductor materials varies with temperature, resistance measurements should be made with the machine and all its parts up to normal operating temperature, or made at room temperature and the resistance calculated for an assumed operating temperature, 75°C being the commonly accepted standard reference temperature. Also, it should be noted that resistance of the brush contacts is not constant but varies with the current. When armature-resistance measurements include the brushes, several determinations of resistance should be made at various current values and the results plotted in the form of a curve of resistance against current. The proper value of resistance for a given load condition may then be determined by reference to the curve. The contact-resistance loss is usually calculated separately, however, by assuming a drop of 2 volts for all loads.[1] Although all machines do not have exactly this contact voltage drop, the error involved is not large, and the effect upon the final result in an efficiency calculation is negligible under all ordinary conditions.

94. Core Losses.—The rotation of the iron core of the armature, in the magnetic flux from the field poles, requires power to overcome two losses in the core, as follows:

a. Hysteresis loss.

b. Eddy-current loss.

Hysteresis Loss.—Since any given section of the iron core passes, in succession, from a pole of one polarity to a pole of opposite polarity, the direction of the field with reference to the core will be continually reversing; and, since an expenditure of energy is required to carry the iron through a cycle of magnetization, a certain power is necessary in order to keep up the reversals.

---

[1] The Test Code for Direct-current Machines of the American Institute of Electrical Engineers (A.I.E.E. No. 501, July, 1941) recommends the use, for carbon and graphite brushes, of 1 volt for all brushes of each polarity when the brushes are provided with shunts, or "pigtails," this to be increased to 1.5 volts where the brushes are not provided with shunts—the drop to be taken the same for all loads at which the losses are to be calculated.

The value of the loss due to hysteresis depends upon flux density, the quality of iron making up the core, and the frequency of flux reversal. In equation form, it may be expressed as

$$P_h = K_h V f B_m^{1.6} \tag{56}$$

where V is the volume of the iron or steel, f is the frequency, and B_m is the maximum flux density. K_h is a constant depending upon the magnetic quality of the iron or steel and the units chosen. The exponent 1.6, known as the *Steinmetz exponent*, may vary somewhat with different grades of core steel.

Eddy-current Loss.—Since the iron of the core is revolving in a magnetic field and cutting across magnetic flux lines, a condition exists for generation of voltage. And, since the iron is a conductor, it may be expected that currents will flow in response to these voltages. If solid iron cores were used, the losses due to eddy currents would be very large. In order to reduce them and limit the loss and consequent heating of the core to a small value, the core is made up of thin laminations, stacked and secured at right angles to the path of the eddy currents. These laminations are insulated from one another by a thin coating of varnish; and, although they do not eliminate the eddy currents entirely, they limit the loss from this source to a comparatively low value. The laminations are at right angles to the shaft and therefore do not interpose additional reluctance in the path of the flux from the poles. The eddy-current loss may be expressed as

$$P_e = K_e V f^2 t^2 B_m^2 \tag{57}$$

where t represents the thickness of the laminations and K_e is a constant depending upon the electrical resistance of the iron or steel and the units chosen.

It should be noted that, for a motor or generator in service, the power losses due to hysteresis and eddy currents vary only with speed and excitation. It may be noted also that any portion of a magnetic path in or about electrical equipment that is subject to rapid reversals of flux should be made of laminated iron or steel in order to limit the heating and power losses.

95. Determination of Losses.—Copper losses can be readily calculated for any assumed load upon a machine when the resistances of the various circuits are known—the principal current-carrying circuits being the armature, the shunt-field winding, the series-field winding, and the commutating-pole field winding.

The core losses depend upon speed and excitation and cannot, by direct test of the assembled machine, be divided into the component hysteresis and eddy-current losses but can be determined jointly with the friction and windage losses either by operating the machine as a motor under certain specified conditions or by driving it with a separate motor, the input and losses to which can be accurately determined. The friction and windage losses may then be separated from the core losses by calculation or by extrapolation of the total loss curves, depending upon the method employed.

Separation of brush friction from bearing friction and windage may be accomplished by the separate-drive method, determining first the power necessary to drive the machine, without excitation, with the brushes in place against the commutator; then the power required with the brushes lifted, the difference between the two input values to the machine being the power required for brush friction. When being tested in this manner, the machine should of course be driven at its rated speed.

The mechanical and the core losses are sometimes conveniently grouped together as rotational or stray power losses. These losses should not be confused, however, with the so-called stray-load losses, which are certain conductor losses present only under load conditions and due to conductor eddy currents and flux distortion effects. The mechanical and core losses depend upon speed and excitation and so do not vary materially with load where changes in load do not result in decided changes in these factors. They are readily determined for a given operating condition.

The rotational losses for a given machine may usually be measured conveniently by operating it as a shunt motor under rated conditions of speed and excitation and measuring the input to the armature. Since the output under this condition is zero and the armature copper loss usually negligible,[1] all power input to the armature goes to supply the mechanical and core losses.

---

[1] This loss may readily be computed and subtracted if desired, although it is generally considered of too small value to affect the final result within the limits of ordinary accuracy.

The circuit diagram for a determination of this kind is shown in Fig. 130. Normal excitation may be secured indirectly by applying a voltage E to the armature equal to the generated voltage—or counter emf in a motor—for the operating condition for which the rotational losses are being determined. The speed may then be adjusted to rated value by variation of field current, and the power

input to the armature may be taken as a measure of the mechanical and core losses. The value of the rotational power loss will vary somewhat with load in a generator or motor, particularly in compound machines; and, for accurate determinations

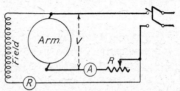

FIG. 130.—Wiring diagram for determination of mechanical and core losses.

of losses and efficiency, the loss should be determined for each operating condition for which results are to be calculated.[1]

In very large machines, the preferable method is to drive the machine at normal speed by means of an auxiliary motor, whose losses are known or can be determined, or which can be operated under conditions that render exact calculation of its losses unnecessary. The output of this motor is then the input to the larger machine; and, since the output of the larger machine is zero, this input is a measure of the loss for the particular condition involved. An advantage of this method is that the core losses and friction losses may be separated. Under some conditions, it may not be necessary to calculate the losses in the driving motor, the losses in the driven machine being taken as the difference between input watts to the driving motor under various test conditions. For more accurate determinations, however, the losses in the driving motor may readily be calculated and its output determined for the various test conditions of the driven machine.

96. Efficiency.—In a motor electrical measurements are made upon the input side, and in a generator these measurements are made upon the output side. Two expressions for efficiency may therefore be stated, one of these being best adapted for use in the

---

[1] A more detailed discussion of this and other types of test is included under Chap. XII.

calculation of motor efficiencies and the other being best adapted for use in the calculation of generator efficiencies.[1]

For motors:

$$\text{Efficiency} = \frac{\text{output}}{\text{input}} = \frac{\text{input} - \text{losses}}{\text{input}} \tag{58}$$

For generators:

$$\text{Efficiency} = \frac{\text{output}}{\text{input}} = \frac{\text{output}}{\text{output} + \text{losses}} \tag{59}$$

A typical curve of efficiency to power output for electric motors and generators shows the efficiency to be a maximum at, or near, full load and to vary only slightly between half load and 25 per cent overload. Below half load, the efficiency drops rapidly, becoming zero when the output becomes zero.

The over-all efficiency as referred to in the above equations may be broken down, for a generator, into the efficiency of conversion and the electrical efficiency, because not all the mechanical power delivered to the generator is converted to electrical power. For a motor, likewise, the over-all efficiency may be divided between the efficiency of conversion and the mechanical efficiency, because not all the electrical power delivered to the motor is converted into mechanical power.

These relations may best be expressed as follows, where, it will be noted, core loss is for convenience classified as a mechanical loss, although it is electrical in origin.

For generators:

Electrical power generated = mechanical power input
$$\qquad\qquad\qquad\qquad - \text{ friction, windage, and core losses}$$

$$\text{Efficiency of conversion} = \frac{\text{electrical power generated}}{\text{mechanical power input}} \tag{60}$$

$$= \frac{\text{electrical power output} + \text{copper losses}}{\text{mechanical power input}} \tag{61}$$

---

[1] Efficiencies determined in this manner from measurement or calculation of losses are termed *conventional efficiencies* to distinguish them from efficiencies determined by direct measurement of output and input, with the machine under load. See A.I.E.E. standards.

$$\text{Electrical efficiency} = \frac{\text{electrical power output}}{\text{electrical power generated}} \quad (62)$$

$$= \frac{\text{output}}{\text{output} + \text{copper losses}} \quad (63)$$

For motors, the corresponding equations are

Mechanical power developed = electrical power input
$$- \text{copper losses}$$

$$\text{Efficiency of conversion} = \frac{\text{mechanical power developed}}{\text{electrical power input}} \quad (64)$$

$$= \frac{\text{mechanical power output} + \text{friction, windage, and core losses}}{\text{electrical power input}}$$
$$(65)$$

$$\text{Mechanical efficiency} = \frac{\text{mechanical power output}}{\text{mechanical power developed}} \quad (66)$$

$$= \frac{\text{output}}{\text{output} + \text{friction, windage, and core loss}}$$
$$(67)$$

It is obvious that, for the generator, the over-all efficiency is the product of the conversion efficiency and the electrical efficiency, and that, for the motor, the over-all efficiency is the product of the conversion efficiency and the mechanical efficiency.

Example.—A long-shunt flat-compound generator, rated 500 kw at 500 volts, has the following losses at rated output:

	Watts
Armature loss	10,000
Series-field loss	2,360
Shunt-field loss	7,500
Friction, windage, and core loss	10,240
Total losses	30,100

To find the over-all efficiency, the efficiency of conversion, and the electrical efficiency.
Solution:

$$\text{Over-all efficiency} = \frac{\text{output}}{\text{input}} = \frac{\text{output}}{\text{output} + \text{losses}}$$

$$= \frac{500}{500 + 30.1} = 0.943 = 94.3\%$$

Since

$$\text{Mechanical power input} = 500 + 30.1 \text{ kw} = 530.1 \text{ kw}$$

$$\text{Efficiency of conversion} = \frac{500 + 19.86}{530.1} = 0.981 = 98.1\%$$

$$\text{Electrical efficiency} = \frac{500}{500 + 19.86} = 0.961 = 96.1\%$$

Check

$$0.981 \times 0.961 = 0.943\%, \text{ the over-all efficiency}$$

97. Maximum Efficiency.—For most electrical machines, certain losses are essentially constant, and other losses are decidedly variable as the load upon the machine varies. Thus, in the shunt generator, driven at constant speed and having good voltage regulation, the shunt-field loss as well as the friction, windage, and core losses will show small variation with load and may be regarded as practically constant, whereas the copper losses in the armature, series-field, and commutating-pole coils vary as the square of the current through them. There are also certain losses, usually low in value, that tend to vary with the first power of the current, such as the brush-contact loss.

If, therefore, we let

$$P = \text{the power output}$$
$$P_c = \text{the constant losses}$$
$$K_1P = \text{the losses varying as first power of the current,}[1]$$
$$K_1 \text{ being a constant}$$
$$K_2P^2 = \text{the losses varying as the square of current,}[1]$$
$$K_2 \text{ being a constant}$$

then the efficiency

$$\eta = \frac{P}{P + P_c + K_1P + K_2P^2} \tag{68}$$

and the condition for maximum efficiency may be found by differentiating this expression with respect to the output and equating to zero.

Thus

$$\frac{d\eta}{dP} = \frac{P + P_c + K_1P + K_2P^2 - P(1 + K_1 + 2K_2P)}{(P + P_c + K_1P + K_2P^2)^2} = 0$$

[1] Neglecting the slight differences between armature-current and load-current values.

Therefore
$$P + P_c + K_1P + K_2P^2 - P - K_1P - 2K_2P^2 = 0$$
or
$$P_c - K_2P^2 = 0$$

Hence, maximum efficiency will occur when the constant losses are equal to the losses that vary as the square of the current, or power output, in our assumed example of constant potential generator. And, since the losses that vary as the first power of the current are small, it is usually considered sufficient for practical purposes to state that maximum efficiency will obtain when constant and variable losses are equal, or

$$\text{Maximum efficiency} = \frac{P}{P + 2P_c} \qquad (69)$$

This provides a general rule that may be applied equally well to both d-c and a-c machines, such as motors, generators, and transformers.

Example.—Referring to the example in Art. 96, if the armature resistance is 0.01 ohm, including brushes, series-field resistance is 0.002 ohm, and shunt-field resistance is $33\frac{1}{3}$ ohms, find the load at which maximum efficiency would occur and the value of the efficiency at this load, assuming that the terminal voltage and speed remain constant, and neglecting any change in core losses by reason of armature-reaction effects.

Solution:

For maximum efficiency,
$$I_a^2 (R_a + R_s) = \text{mechanical losses and shunt-field loss}$$
$$I_a^2 (0.01 + 0.002) = 10{,}240 + 7500$$
$$= 17{,}740 \text{ watts}$$

from which
$$I_a^2 = \frac{17{,}740}{0.012} = 1{,}478{,}333$$

and
$$I_a = \sqrt{1{,}478{,}333} = 1215 \text{ amp}$$

Since
$$\text{Shunt-field current} = \frac{500}{33\frac{1}{3}} = 15 \text{ amp}$$

the output current at maximum efficiency is
$$1215 - 15 = 1200 \text{ amp}$$

and
$$\text{Kilowatt output} = \frac{1200 \times 500}{1000} = 600 \text{ kw}$$

Maximum efficiency is then equal to
$$\frac{500 \times 1200}{500 \times 1200 + 2 \times 17{,}740} = \frac{600}{635.48} = 0.944$$
$$= 94.4\%$$

98. All-day Efficiency.—Since charges for electrical power are based primarily upon energy utilization, it is sometimes of value to determine the all-day efficiency, or ratio of energy output to energy input, for the working day. This may be determined for a given machine by summing up the kilowatt-hour output of the machine for the day and dividing by this summation plus the summation of the kilowatt-hours of losses in the machine for the same period.

Example.—A shunt motor operating at 115 volts, 1150 rpm has a friction, windage, and core loss of 350 watts. The field current is 2.5 amp and the armature current 72.5 amp. Armature resistance is 0.09 ohm, not including brushes. The average day's operation includes 3 hr at normal load, 3 hr at half-normal load, and 2 hr at no load, with the motor running idle. What is the all-day efficiency of the motor?

Solution: Field loss, $115 \times 2.5 = 287$ watts, plus the friction, windage, and core loss of 350 watts gives a constant loss at all loads of 637 watts. At normal load, the armature I^2R is 473 watts, and the brush loss is 145 watts, making a total of 618 watts. At half-normal load, the armature I^2R is 118 watts, and the brush loss is 72 watts, making a total of 190 watts.

Thus, under normal operating conditions, the output is $115 \times 75 - (637 + 618) = 7370$ watts; and, under half-normal load, the output is $115 \times (36.25 + 2.5) - (637 + 190) = 3629$ watts.

$$\text{All-day efficiency} = \frac{\text{energy output}}{\text{energy input}} = \frac{\text{energy output}}{\text{energy output} + \text{energy losses}} \quad (70)$$

$$= \frac{7370 \times 3 + 3629 \times 3}{7370 \times 3 + 3629 \times 3 + 1255 \times 3 + 827 \times 3 + 637 \times 2}$$

$$= \frac{32,997}{32,997 + 7520} = \frac{32,997}{40,518}$$

$$= 0.814 = 81.4\%$$

For some operating conditions, a machine may be operated at rated load for relatively short periods and under varying loads, less than rated load, for much longer periods. The constant losses, in effect at all loads, would therefore tend to lower the all-day efficiency. For such applications, it is possible to have the machine designed for lower constant losses, thus increasing the all-day efficiency, upon which depends the actual cost of operating the machine. Although, under usual operating conditions, it is desirable to have the highest power efficiency near the rated-load point, conditions sometimes are such that, for maximum economy in operation, the high point of power efficiency should be below the rated-load point.

99. Directly Measured Efficiency.—The obvious way of determining the efficiency of a machine lies in the measurement, simultaneously, of input to the machine and output from the machine. This is sometimes done, particularly with small sizes of generators and motors, where suitable loads may be applied and controlled; but, with very large machines, the provision of suitable loads may be inconvenient or even impossible. At best such tests would be expensive, since the energy output of the machine under test would be likely to be wasted. Also, by no means least of the factors to be considered is the accuracy with which the tests may be made. This is probably the determining factor in many cases and leads to the use of indirect methods of making tests, involving the measurement or computation of losses, as described and discussed in the next article. Usually the indirect methods involve the use of less expensive equipment also.

Where direct measurements are to be made, the chief problem lies in accurate determinations of mechanical power, this being the input power to generators and the output power of motors. The electrical power—output of generators, input of motors—is readily determined by the use of ammeters and voltmeters.

The mechanical-power input to a generator under test may be determined by means of a calibrated driving motor whose losses are accurately known. The input to the driving motor, as well as the output of the driven generator, may then be measured with electrical instruments and the known motor losses subtracted from motor input to give motor output, which is the generator input, the motor being direct-connected to the generator if possible in order to avoid differences between motor output and generator input due to belt or gearing losses.

Another, and usually preferable method, involves the use of a driving motor of special design—called an *electromagnetic dynamometer*. This is essentially an electric dynamo of standard type provided with double bearings and a lever arm, as indicated in Fig.

177, page 304, in order that the torque developed may be measured by the force exerted, through the lever arm, upon weighing scales of either the spring or lever types. The double bearings provide for sufficient rotation of the *frame* of the dynamometer to permit measurement of the torque or turning effort, the product of lever arm and net force upon the scales yielding the equivalent pounds at 1 ft radius, which may be reduced to horsepower, the rpm also having been measured, by use of formula (45).

For testing motors, similar means may be used: (a) a calibrated generator, whose losses are accurately known for various load points, may be used for loading the motor under test; or (b) an electromagnetic dynamometer may be used to provide a generator load, the torque input being measured as before by multiplying the lever arm, in feet, by the net weight upon the scales. The same dynamometer may be used for testing motors and generators.

Although the dynamometer method is most widely used for direct measurement tests and is usually the more accurate method, it involves special and rather expensive equipment. For testing motors, a *prony brake* (Fig. 175) may be used to measure the output at less expense. A special pulley is usually necessary in order to provide for a supply of cooling water, but the brake itself may be of wooden construction, the portion bearing upon the pulley being lined with good-quality brake lining. The outer pivot point of the brake arm is then allowed to bear upon a platform scale or work against a spring scale. As before, the product of lever arm and net weight on scales gives the torque, and by the use of this and the measured speed the horsepower or watts may be calculated as before.

100. Calculated or Conventional Efficiency.—The determination of efficiency from measurement and calculation of losses is usually considered preferable to determinations from direct measurement of input and output, for several reasons. It is not always convenient or even possible, except at prohibitive cost, to operate machines under load for test purposes, this being particularly true of the very large motors and generators. It is difficult to secure highly accurate results by the direct method because of the inaccuracies involved in measurements of output and input and because such errors as are made affect the final result directly. Also, the direct method gives no idea of the distribution of losses, a matter usually of no small interest and concern. With the indirect method, readings are made under conditions that are easily controlled; and the power required for the operations is low in comparison with normal ratings of the machine. Certain assumptions are usually made in connection with the use of this method, such as the assumption of constant speed for a shunt motor, which detract to some extent from its accuracy, but the degree of refinement followed in the data taking and calculations may be adapted to the limits of accuracy required for the particular case in hand.

The manner in which the various losses are determined and the efficiency calculated may be seen from the following example.

Example.—A certain $5\frac{1}{2}$-kw 125-volt d-c generator was operated as a shunt motor at no load for determination of core and friction losses. With 135 volts —equal to generated voltage at full load—applied to the armature, and normal speed of 1700 rpm, the current input to the armature was found to be 2.5 amp. Resistance of the armature circuit with full-load current flowing was found to be 0.2 ohm, of the series field 0.025 ohm, and of the shunt-field circuit 100 ohms. Determine the various losses and calculate the full-load efficiency.

Solution:

$135 \times 2.5 = 337$ watts rotational loss (neglecting the small copper loss involved)

$$\frac{5500}{125} = 44 \text{ amp rated-load current}$$

$$\frac{125}{100} = 1.25 \text{ amp shunt-field current}$$

$44 + 1.25 = 45.25$ amp armature and series-field current (assuming a long-shunt connection)

$$\overline{45.25}^2 \times 0.2 \quad = 410 \text{ watts armature copper loss}$$

$$\overline{45.25}^2 \times 0.025 = \quad 51 \text{ watts series-field copper loss}$$

$$1.25 \times 125 \quad = 156 \text{ watts shunt-field copper loss}$$

Total losses $= 337 + 410 + 51 + 156 = 954$ watts
Output at full load $= 5500$ watts
Input $=$ output $+$ losses $= 5500 + 954 = 6454$ watts

Therefore

$$\text{Efficiency} = \frac{\text{output}}{\text{input}} = \frac{5500}{6454} = 0.852 = 85.2\%$$

The core loss in the armature of a motor or generator is dependent upon flux and speed, hence, for any machine having a series-field winding, the core losses will vary as the load upon the machine varies. Therefore, to secure accurate results for a compound or series machine, the rotational losses—core loss, friction, and windage—should be determined for a range of load values and a curve plotted from which these losses for any desired load value may be read. In a compound generator, this would mean determining the rotational losses for a range of generated-voltage values covering the load range for which the efficiencies are to be determined, the speed being held at the rated value.

For a compound motor having fairly good speed regulation, the variations in rotational loss with load may usually be considered negligible in the smaller industrial sizes of machines; but, for large motors or for any size of motor having poor speed regulation, these losses should be determined for a range of load values or for each load for which the efficiency is to be calculated. This involves operating the motor at the correct speed as well as with the correct excitation for each load condition and therefore necessitates a knowledge of the speed curve of the motor or, possibly, operation of the motor under load in order to determine the speed-load curve.

If the efficiencies are desired for particular load-output points upon a motor, it is sometimes necessary to assume an efficiency to start with, determine the current input corresponding to this efficiency, and calculate the losses and efficiency upon the basis of this current input. Since the calculated efficiency is unlikely to agree precisely with the assumed value, a new and more nearly correct value of current may now be calculated by the use of the calculated efficiency, and a corrected set of losses and a still more correct value of efficiency may be determined, this process of successive approximations being carried as far as necessary to secure the desired accuracy.

101. Series-motor Losses.—For determining the rotational loss in shunt motors, a single set of no-load armature-input readings is usually all that is necessary, since the speed varies only slightly with load change, and field flux is constant for a given field current except for the change, usually slight, due to armature reaction.

Changes in field current, as in adjustable-speed motors, will of course change the values of the losses, and it would therefore be necessary to determine the losses and efficiency for a number of excitation values in order to analyze the losses and efficiencies of the adjustable-speed motor. For series motors, however, both the speed and the field flux vary widely with load changes; and it is therefore necessary when testing such motors to make a series of rotational loss determinations at various values of speed and field current.

In making a test of the series motor, therefore, it is necessary to excite the field separately in order to allow for varying the field current independently of the armature circuit. Provision must be made for suitable variations in the field current and also for varying the voltage applied to the armature.[1] Since the speed—ampere input curve of the motor—will usually be known or can be determined readily, it will be possible to operate the motor without load at values of field current and speed corresponding to a number of load conditions, the speed being separately adjustable through control of the armature voltage. Thus the losses, output watts, and efficiencies may be determined for a number of points sufficient to cover the normal operating range of the motor; or a more extended study of losses may be made by application of the method discussed in the next article.

Example.—A railway-type series motor, rated 40 hp, 600 volts, shows upon test the following results: armature resistance, 0.3 ohm; series-field resistance, 0.2 ohm; commutating-field resistance, 0.1 ohm (all resistances corrected to standard reference temperature of 75°C).

Line, amp	Speed, rpm	Stray power, watts
20	975	1800
40	660	1350
60	550	1250
80	500	1200
100	455	1300
120	420	1500

[1] This may be accomplished by connecting the armature in series with the field coils as usual but with an adjustable rheostat connected as a shunt across the armature terminals. A suitable adjustable rheostat should be inserted in the main circuit. The field and armature currents can then be regulated together or separately.

To calculate and tabulate all losses, determine the horsepower output and efficiency for each of the load conditions listed, and plot speed, horsepower output, and efficiency against amperes input. Assume constant brush drop of 2 volts.

Solution:

Amp....................	20	40	60	80	100	120
Speed, rpm	975	660	550	500	455	420
Rotational loss, watts	1,800	1,350	1,250	1,200	1,300	1,500
Armature I^2R, watts......	120	480	1,080	1,920	3,000	4,320
Field I^2R, watts..........	80	320	720	1,280	2,000	2,880
Commutating field I^2R, watts	40	160	360	640	1,000	1,440
Brush $2I$, watts	40	80	120	160	200	240
Total loss, watts	2,080	2,390	3,530	5,200	7,500	10,380
Power input, watts	12,000	24,000	36,000	48,000	60,000	72,000
Power output, watts	9,920	21,610	32,470	42,800	52,500	61,620
Power output, hp	13.3	29.0	43.5	57.4	70.4	82.6
Efficiency, per cent	82.7	90.0	90.2	89.2	87.5	85.6

102. Analysis of Rotational Losses.

—The rotational losses in a motor or generator are due, as previously noted, to hysteresis, eddy currents, and friction. The hysteresis and eddy-current losses are usually grouped together, not being readily separable. They depend upon both speed and flux, whereas the friction loss depends only upon speed. Because of this difference in variation, it is possible, by making tests at different speeds and values of flux, to separate the friction losses from the core losses. Along with this separation, a study may be made of how these losses vary with changes in speed and flux.

To make the above analysis and separation of losses, it is necessary first to operate the machine as a motor without load and to record data for five or six curves of core and friction losses against speed, each curve being for some constant value of field current. One curve should correspond to the lowest value of field current at which the machine can be operated. Figure 131 illustrates a typical set of such curves. From these, it is possible to derive

another set of curves, as shown in Fig. 132, showing the variation
of rotational loss with magnetic flux. The values for each curve
are derived by erecting an ordinate at a chosen speed point and
reading the values of power loss corresponding to each inter-

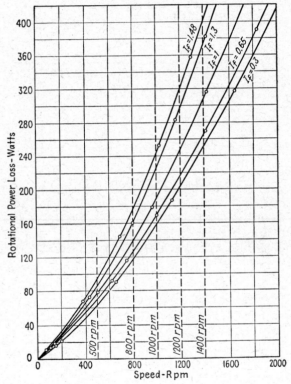

Fig. 131.—Variations in rotational power losses in a small generator.

section between ordinate and curves, these derived values being
shown in Table II.   By extending each of these latter curves until
it intersects the vertical axis, the value of the friction loss at each
of the several speeds may be obtained, since the core losses become
zero when the magnetic flux is zero. The value of the core loss for
any value of speed and flux may then be determined by subtracting

the friction loss at this speed from the total rotational-power loss at that value of speed and flux.

Finally, from the curves plotted by the above procedure, the following additional curves may be derived and plotted:

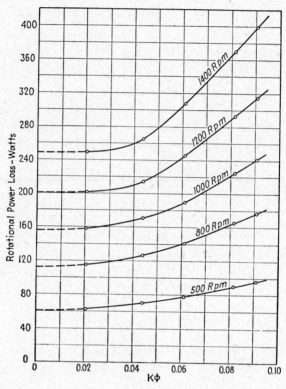

Fig. 132.—Variation of rotational-power losses in a small generator.

a. Friction loss against speed (Fig. 133).

b. Core loss against speed, with constant flux (Fig. 134).

c. Core loss against flux, with constant speed (Fig. 135).

It is possible also to separate hysteresis loss from eddy-current loss by a method similar to that just described, based on the fact

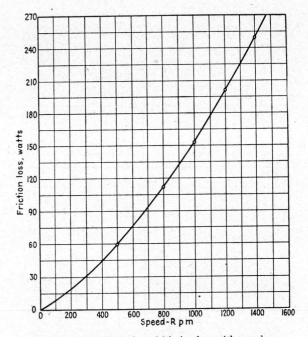

FIG. 133.—Variation of friction loss with speed.

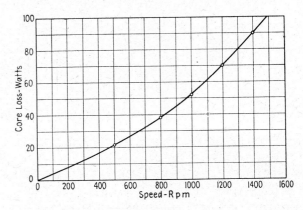

FIG. 134.—Variation of core loss with speed at normal excitation.

that, for a given excitation, hysteresis loss is proportional to the speed, whereas eddy-current loss varies as the square of the speed.[1]

An example of the analysis of rotational losses by the method outlined in the preceding paragraphs follows. The tests were

TABLE I. DATA FOR ANALYSIS OF ROTATIONAL LOSSES

	I_f, amp	I_a, amp	V, volts	Rpm	$I_a R_a$, volts	E, volts	Power loss, watts	$K\phi$	Average $K\phi$
I	1.48	3.2	113	1320	1.4	111.6	352	0.0890	
	1.48	2.8	92	1034	1.5	90.5	253	0.0876	
	1.48	2.4	61	685	1.0	60.0	144	0.0875	0.09125
	1.48	2.0	34.5	378	0.9	33.6	67	0.0888	
	1.48	1.7	7.5	65	0.8	6.7	11	0.1030	
II	1.3	3.4	114	1425	1.5	112.5	382	0.0790	
	1.3	3.2	92	1134	1.5	90.5	283	0.0800	
	1.3	2.7	61	762	1.2	59.8	161	0.0786	0.0812
	1.3	2.2	34	412	0.9	33.1	73	0.0800	
	1.3	2.0	7.5	74	0.9	6.6	13	0.0890	
III	1	4.0	113	1756	1.8	111.2	445	0.0645	
	1	3.5	92	1364	1.6	90.4	316	0.0662	
	1	3.0	61	908	1.3	59.7	178	0.0657	0.0685
	1	2.4	34	502	1.1	32.9	79	0.0655	
	1	2.1	7.5	82	0.95	6.6	14	0.0811	
IV	0.65	5.0	80	1772	2.2	77.8	389	0.0438	
	0.65	4.5	62	1414	2.1	59.9	269	0.0423	
	0.65	4.0	50	984	1.8	48.2	169	0.0490	0.0447
	0.65	3.5	35	740	1.5	33.5	116	0.0452	
	0.65	2.9	7.5	143	1.3	6.2	18	0.0433	
V	0.3	9.4	38	1650	4.2	33.8	317	0.0202	
	0.3	8.0	27	1130	3.6	23.4	187	0.0206	
	0.3	6.8	16.5	648	3.0	13.5	92	0.0207	0.0207
	0.3	5.0	6.5	200	2.2	4.3	21	0.0212	

---

[1] For details of this test, reference is made to Vol. I of Karapetoff's "Experimental Electrical Engineering," John Wiley & Sons, Inc.

made upon a small generator, rated 7 kw, 125 volts. Data were taken for five curves of rotational loss against speed, as shown in Fig. 131, each curve being for a constant value of field current. The losses were calculated as the product of armature current

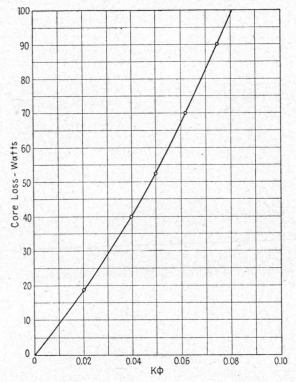

FIG. 135.—Variation of core loss at rated speed.

and generated voltage, generated voltage being determined by subtracting armature IR drop from the applied armature voltage. The values of K ϕ were calculated by dividing the generated voltage by the speed, these values being averaged for each set of readings corresponding to a constant value of field current. From the calculated values, tabulated in Tables I and II, curves were plotted as shown in Figs. 132 to 135.

TABLE II.—DERIVED VALUES OF ROTATIONAL LOSS FROM FIG. 131 WITH THE CORRESPONDING SPEEDS AND $K\phi$ VALUES

	Power loss, watts	Rpm	$K\phi$
1	400	1400	0.09125
	373	1400	0.0812
	308	1400	0.0612
	265	1400	0.0447
	250	1400	0.0207
2	314	1200	0.09125
	296	1200	0.0812
	246	1200	0.0612
	215	1200	0.0447
	202	1200	0.0207
3	240	1000	0.09125
	222	1000	0.0812
	188	1000	0.0612
	170	1000	0.0447
	158	1000	0.0207
4	175	800	0.09125
	160	800	0.0812
	140	800	0.0612
	126	800	0.0447
	116	800	0.0207
5	96	500	0.09125
	86	500	0.0812
	78	500	0.0612
	70	500	0.0447
	62	500	0.0207

Problems

1. A 230-volt 15-hp shunt-wound motor has an armature-circuit resistance, with normal current flowing, of 0.25 ohm. When operating under usual load conditions, the line voltage was observed to be 226, the armature current 40 amp, and the field current 2 amp. When disconnected from the load and operated at the same speed, with 215 volts applied to the armature, the armature current was found to be 3 amp. Find (*a*) the power output of the motor, in horsepower, under normal load conditions and (b) the over-all efficiency of the motor under this operating condition.

2. Referring to the motor of Prob. 1, determine the approximate load in amperes at which maximum efficiency occurs and the value of the efficiency at this point.

3. If the average daily cycle of operations of the motor described in Prob. 1 includes 5 hr at normal load, 2 hr at half-normal load, and 3 hr at no load (motor running idle), what will be its all-day efficiency?

4. A shunt motor operating at 115 volts, 1150 rpm, has a rotational loss of 350 watts. The field current is 2.5 amp and armature current 72.5 amp. Armature resistance is 0.09 ohm, not including brushes. Determine the conventional efficiency.

5. Referring to the motor of Prob. 4, (a) determine the approximate load at which maximum efficiency occurs and the value of the efficiency at this point. (b) If the average cycle of operations includes 3 hr at full load, 3 hr at half load, and 2 hr at no load, with motor idling, what will be its all-day efficiency?

6. Test results as listed below were obtained upon a compound-wound generator rated 450 kw, 500/550 volts, connected for long-shunt operation.

Amp in external circuit..................................	820
Amp in shunt field.....................................	5.8
Terminal volts...	550
Combined resistance, armature and series field, ohms.........	0.02
Brush drop, assumed, volts..............................	2
Core loss, watts.......................................	7770
Brush friction, watts...................................	1220
Bearing friction and windage, watts......................	2950

Summarize the various losses, and calculate the efficiency for rated output, one-half rated output, and three-fourths rated output.

7. A 150-kw 500-volt shunt generator has an armature-circuit resistance, including brushes, of 0.06 ohm. The normal field current is 6 amp. When run idle as a motor, at the correct voltage to obtain the rotational losses corresponding to rated-load operation, the armature current was found to be 7.5 amp. (a) At what voltage was the no-load test made? (b) Calculate the rated-load efficiency.

8. A dynamo running idle as a shunt motor at 1600 rpm requires 4 amp armature current. Assuming this current to be unchanged by variations in applied voltage, determine the rotational loss when the machine is operated as a flat-compound long-shunt generator with the following data:

$V = 120$ volts $I_{line} = 37$ amp $R_{arm.} = 0.08$ ohm $R_{ser.} = 0.04$ ohm
$R_{sh} = 40$ ohms   Speed $= 1600$ rpm

Compute its efficiency for this condition.

9. Determine the highest efficiency the generator of Prob. 8 is likely to attain and the corresponding armature current.

10. A 25-hp 110-volt shunt motor, with a rated current of 195 amp, is found by test to have a no-load input to the armature of 8.5 amp at 100 volts and rated speed. With the armature stationary and 193 amp flowing, the voltage registered at the terminals is 8.7 volts. With 110 volts applied to the field terminals, the current is 2 amp. Calculate the rotational and copper losses, and determine the output, in horsepower, and the efficiency, when operating at rated voltage, current, and speed. Calculate also the horsepower output and efficiency for a load requiring 100 amp input to the motor, stating what assumptions are made.

11. If the motor of Prob. 22, Chap. VII, has an armature resistance of 1.0 ohm, including brushes, and series-field resistance of 0.3 ohm, calculate the rotational and copper losses, and determine the rated-load efficiency, assuming long-shunt connection. Compare with the value obtained by brake test.

12. It is desired to determine the power required for driving a certain machine. A 20-hp 230-volt shunt motor is belted to the machine and the following observations made:

Driving motor			Driven machine
Volts	Armature amp	Field amp	
230	50	1.50	Normal load conditions
230	65	1.50	Maximum operating load, short duration
220	3	....	Belt removed; motor running light at same speed as when driving machine

Armature resistance, not including brushes, 0.2 ohm.

Determine the power required for the machine, by calculation of losses in the driving motor and determination of its output for each of the two operating conditions. What horsepower rating is most suitable for a permanent driving motor?

13. The following results were obtained from test of a self-excited d-c generator rated 50 kw, 250 volts, 1200 rpm by the separate-drive method:

Driving motor		Generator under test
Applied volts	Line amp	
120	41.3	250 volts, 1200 rpm, no load
120	26.75	Field switch open, 1200 rpm
120	24.7	All brushes raised, 1200 rpm
120	18.2	Belt off, motor running light

Armature and brush resistance, 0.03 ohm
Series-field resistance, 0.01 ohm
Shunt-field resistance, 56 ohms.

Calculate the various losses, listing each separately; than find the total losses and efficiency for the rated-load condition. Assume that the driving-motor losses are essentially constant and that long-shunt connection is used.

14. A crane type of series motor, rated 20 hp, 230 volts, shows upon test the following results: armature resistance, 0.2 ohm; series-field resistance, 0.15 ohm; interpole-field resistance, 0.05 ohm, all corrected to 75° C.

Amp	Speed, rpm	Rotational loss, watts
20	2750	1010
40	2275	990
60	1900	978
80	1605	960
100	1410	935
120	1230	905

Calculate the horsepower output and efficiency for each of the load conditions listed; and plot speed, horsepower output and efficiency against amperes input. Assume constant brush drop of 2 volts.

15. A shunt motor with interpoles, operated from 250-volt bus bars, runs at 1200 rpm when the line current is 205 amp. Armature resistance is 0.0625 ohm, interpole resistance 0.0125 ohm, field resistance 50 ohms. At no load, the current input to the motor is found to be 25 amp.

Determine the horsepower output of the motor under the above operating condition. What is its efficiency?

CHAPTER X

RATINGS, WEIGHTS, AND COSTS

103. Output Limitations.—The materials used in the construction of electrical machinery will not long withstand the effects of excessive temperatures. This is particularly true of the materials used for insulation of conductors from each other and from the frame of the machine. Research is constantly being applied to the development of insulating materials that will withstand higher temperatures without rapid deterioration, and the upper limits of permissible temperature have been extended appreciably for some special-purpose machines.

Since the rate of heat transfer from the interior of the core and coils to the exterior of the machine, thence to the surrounding air, depends upon a difference in heat potential, as indicated by temperature differences, the designer must aim at the maintenance of a rate of heat transfer that will keep the internal temperatures within safe limits when the machine is being operated under its rated-load conditions.

Ordinarily, therefore, the maximum load that may be imposed upon a given electrical machine is determined by the temperature of the windings. The development of heat, and consequent rise in temperature, requires time; therefore an overload may be placed upon a machine for a time without danger from the standpoint of overheating, assuming that the machine has not been in operation or has been operating at reduced load for a time previous to imposition of the overload. If the excess load is only slightly above rated load, the overload may safely be impressed for a longer time than if the temporary overload is considerably above rated-load value.

Sometimes the safe loading of d-c machines may be determined by the ability of the commutator to handle the current without excessive sparking, flashing, or heating at the brush contacts. This is especially likely to be true if excessive loads are applied suddenly or removed suddenly. A motor tends to flash at the commutator with sudden application of load, and a generator tends to flash when heavy loads are removed suddenly. In machines having interpoles commutation difficulty is less likely to be a limiting factor; but machines that are normally subject to sudden wide changes in loading may be further safeguarded through the use of compensating windings (Art. 42).

104. Temperature Effects.—The effect of abnormal temperatures upon commonly used insulating materials is to weaken them by stiffening or charring them. The damage may not be noticeable at once, but the dielectric strength of the material will be lowered and its useful life shortened. The effect of poor commutation—serious arcing at the commutator—is rapid wear upon both commutator and brush. The heat developed causes pitting and blackening of the commutator, which in turn causes the arcing to become worse, so that the result is cumulative in its action and harmful effect.

Experience and experimental data indicate the maximum safe operating temperatures for insulating materials ordinarily used to be as follows: [1]

Class *O*, cotton, silk, paper, and similar organic materials not impregnated or immersed in a liquid dielectric . . . .   90°C

Class *A*, organic materials as above but impregnated with insulating material or immersed in a liquid dielectric; molded and laminated materials with cellulose filler, phenolic resins and other resins of similar properties; films and sheets of cellulose acetate and other cellulose derivatives of similar properties; and varnishes (enamel) as applied to conductors . . . .   105°C

Class *B*, insulation composed principally of mica, asbestos, fiber glass, and similar inorganic materials in built-up form with organic materials as binders . . . .   130°C

Class *C*, insulation consisting entirely of mica, porcelain, glass, quartz, and similar inorganic materials for which no temperature limit has yet been selected

The above temperatures apply to the hottest spot in the winding, which is generally not accessible for direct measurement by thermometer. A certain difference should therefore be allowed between the temperature taken by thermometer and the so-called

[1] A.I.E.E. standards, 1940.

hottest spot temperature. A.I.E.E. standards recommend that a difference of 15°C be allowed for classes O and A material and a difference of 20°C be allowed for class B material. Thus, for class O material, the surface temperature, measured by a thermometer, should not be allowed to exceed 75°C; for Class A, it should not be allowed to exceed 90°C; and, for class B, it should not be allowed to exceed 110°C. Where the temperature determinations are made by resistance measurements or by the use of embedded detectors, a difference of 5°C is recommended for classes O and A materials and 10°C for class B material.

105. Temperature Rise.—Since a certain difference in temperature is required between the inside and the outside of coils and other parts of the machine, in order that heat may be carried away as rapidly as it is generated, the actual temperature of the windings during normal operation will depend upon the ambient temperature, or temperature of the surrounding air. If a machine under normal load conditions has a temperature rise of 40°C, the actual temperature will be 65°C for an ambient temperature of 25°C or 80°C for an ambient temperature of 40°C. When operating outside, therefore, especially in the winter season, a given motor could reasonably be expected to carry a somewhat greater load than when operating inside a warm room. For operation in furnace rooms and other abnormally warm locations, the materials used for insulation should be composed principally of mica or asbestos or should be provided with a forced-ventilation system whereby cooling air, from sources other than the room in which the machine is located, may pass through and around the parts of the machine that require cooling.

The guarantees on electrical equipment are made upon the basis of temperature rise. The usual temperature guarantee for motors is made upon the basis of 40°C rise except for enclosed motors, whose guarantee basis may be as high as 55°C. The temperature rises chosen as a guarantee basis for other types of electrical equipment are selected through mutual agreement among manufacturers or through recommendations of the A.I.E.E. and vary from 30°C for certain types of switches and circuit breakers to 55°C for transformers.

106. Ratings.—Since the power rating of a given machine is dependent upon the rise in temperature of the windings, it is necessary for the manufacturer to take account of the conditions under which the machine is to operate before deciding upon the rating that should be applied. This includes consideration of the time the machine will be operated continuously, the load conditions during this period, the freedom with which air may circulate around and through the windings, and the temperature of the surrounding air. Since it is not possible always to foretell these conditions for each individual machine, the standard name-plate rating assumes, unless otherwise specified, that the machine will be operated continuously, 8 hr or more, at full load, with free circulation of surrounding air that does not exceed 40°C in temperature. The manufacturer, in effect, guarantees that the windings will not reach an injurious temperature so long as name-plate ratings and conditions of operation—stated or implied—are not exceeded.

For motors to be used on applications known to require relatively short periods under load, such as crane service, the rating may be based on 30-min operating periods instead of 8-hr, or continuous, periods, the presumption being that the machine will be idle, and therefore cooling downward toward room temperature, for a larger proportion of the total time than it will be in operation. Under such conditions, a somewhat higher temperature rise—during operating periods—is permissible. It would not be proper, therefore, to operate a motor continuously, under full load, if its rating is upon the half-hour basis, since it would be practically certain to overheat and suffer damage to its windings. The name plate should make clear the conditions of operation upon which the rating is based, as well as the temperature rise to be expected when operating at full load under these conditions.

Any electrical equipment may be operated under an overload for a short time, without having the windings exceed their normal full-load operating temperature, provided (*a*) that the machine has not been operated at or near full load for some time prior to application of the overload and (*b*) that the load is reduced to normal, or less, before the internal temperatures have mounted to values exceeding those due to normal operation. Usually, when starting "cold," a motor or generator can carry 25 to 50 per cent overload for an hour or so without having normal temperatures exceeded. Temporary overloads of 50 to 100 per cent do no particular harm, provided that there is not excessive sparking at the commutator. Modern machines can usually commutate excess loads of this degree without serious sparking.

Fig. 136.—General purpose sleeve-bearing motor, 75 to 100-hp ratings. (*Century Electric Company.*)

It is not usually possible to maintain exactly rated conditions upon electrical equipment in service, the principal variant being the supply voltage. Fortunately some variation is permissible. For lighting, the extreme variations should not exceed 5 per cent above or below rated voltage; and, for motors, a 10 per cent variation can usually be allowed before the operation begins to be noticeably affected.

107. Standard Ratings.—In order to simplify manufacturing processes and reduce costs, electrical machinery within the usual range of demand is made in certain standard sizes and ratings. For the average installation, the available range of standard equipment is sufficiently varied so that there is little need for purchase of equipment made on special order. Exceptions to this will be found in very large motors and generators or in control equipment for operations not within the usual range of demand.

Standard d-c motor voltages are 115, 230, and 550 volts. For average industrial applications, 230 volts is the most common, the 550-volt rating being confined largely to street-railway applications and the 115-volt rating to small applications where lighting and motor circuits are furnished from a common supply. The corresponding generator voltages are 125, 250, and 600 volts, in order to allow for line drops.

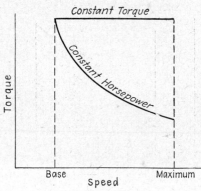

Fig. 137.—Speed-torque relations for adjustable-speed motors having the same ratings at their base speeds.

Rated speeds of generators driven by prime movers are largely determined by the speeds at which the prime movers operate most efficiently; but motor speeds may be fixed, independently of the source of supply, at values best suited to the loads to be driven by the motors. Motors may be rated for a single speed—at rated output—or they may be rated for a range of speeds such as 2:1, 3:1, or 4:1, the base speed being that attained by the motor, with rated voltage applied, with no external resistance in either the armature or the field circuit. Such adjustable-speed motors may be rated upon a constant-torque or a constant-horsepower basis. The constant-torque rating is applied to a motor capable of operating at constant torque throughout its speed range—its horsepower output rising with speed—and the constant-horsepower rating is applied to a motor capable of maintaining constant horsepower output at all speeds within its range—the torque decreasing with rise in speed.

A motor operating from a variable-voltage supply, with constant field excitation, is representative of the constant-torque type, and a motor having its speed controlled through variations in shunt-field current is representative of the constant-horsepower type. Figures 137 and 138 represent the relations of torque, power, and speed for two motors having the same rating at the base or minimum speed—one having a constant-torque rating and the other a

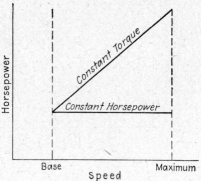

Fig. 138.—Speed-horsepower relations for adjustable-speed motors having the same ratings at their base speeds.

constant-horsepower rating. Such motors would have the same physical dimensions, but two motors having the same ratings of torque and horsepower at their *maximum* speed would differ materially in their physical dimensions, the constant-horsepower motor being considerably larger than the other because torque requirement is greatly increased at the lower speeds.[1]

The power rating of a generator is given in kilowatts and is the product of volts and amperes output under rated operating conditions. The power rating of a motor, on the other hand, is given in horsepower output, whereas the ampere and voltage ratings apply

[1] Shoults, Rife, and Johnson, "Electric Motors in Industry," John Wiley & Sons, Inc., 1942.

to the input side. Thus the *name-plate efficiency* of a motor may be determined by reducing the horsepower rating to watts and dividing by the product of rated volts and rated amperes.

108. Standard Classifications.[1]—With regard to *speed*, motors are classified as:

a. Constant-speed motors, referring to motors having very nearly constant speeds, such as the shunt motor.

Fig. 139.—7.5-hp, 1750-rpm, 115-volt, open, d-c motor. (*Crocker-Wheeler Electric Manufacturing Company.*)

b. Multispeed motors, referring to motors that can be operated at any one of several distinct speeds but cannot be operated at intermediate speeds.

c. Adjustable-speed motors, referring to motors that can be adjusted for operation at any speed over a wide range, with good regulation, such as the shunt motor with field control.

d. Varying-speed motors, referring to motors whose speed decreases markedly with increase in load, such as the series motor.

e. Adjustable varying-speed motors, referring to motors whose speed can be adjusted over a considerable range but will neverthe-

[1] A.I.E.E. standards.

less vary with changes in load from that at which the adjustment was made, such as the compound motor with field control.

With regard to *enclosure,* motors or generators are classified as

a. Open, where the construction is such as to give no appreciable restriction to ventilation.

b. Semienclosed, where the ventilating openings are protected by screens that present only a moderate interference with the ventilating air.

Fig. 140.—General-purpose ball-bearing motor, with top covers and screening. (*Century Electric Co.*)

c. Totally enclosed, where the circulation of air for ventilating purposes is entirely cut off, but not sufficiently that the machine might be termed airtight.

With regard to *operating duty,* motors are classified as

a. Continuous duty, referring to operation at practically constant load for unlimited periods.

b. Short-time duty, referring to operation at practically constant load for specified limited periods, such as $\frac{1}{2}$ hr, 1 hr, or 2 hr.

c. Intermittent duty, referring to operation under conditions of alternate load and rest periods.

d. Periodic duty, referring to operation under conditions in which the load and rest periods alternate in a well-defined cycle.

e Varying duty, referring to operation under widely varying conditions of load and periods of time.

109. Effects of Enclosure of Motors.—For use in very dusty or dirty locations, especially where flying chips or particles may collect and interfere with operation, it is necessary to enclose the

Fig. 141.—A 15-kw, 125-volt generator, semienclosed. (*Fairbanks, Morse & Co.*)

motor, partly or wholly. Semienclosure may be accomplished by the use of gratings or screens across the openings; whereas total enclosure requires the use of metal plates, closely fitted, which stop off the flow of air entirely. For industrial sizes of motor, the end bells are usually so designed that the motor may be adapted for semienclosed or enclosed operation by bolting on standard screens or plates.

When purchasing a motor for a specific purpose, it is well to give the manufacturer, or sales agency, full information as to the conditions under which it is to be operated, since this will permit the recommendation of the motor best adapted to these conditions. When adapting for use a motor already on hand, the conditions should be carefully checked and every precaution taken to avoid damage from overload or other misapplication.

If the motor was originally designed and rated for open operation, with free access to the surrounding air, any obstruction, such

Fig. 142.—A 200-hp, 230-volt motor, arranged for pipe ventilation. (*Crocker-Wheeler Electric Manufacturing Company.*)

as protective screens or plates, will cause the temperature of the machine interior to rise. If normal operation is at or near rated value, the temperature may be forced upward to a point that will materially shorten the life of the insulation. A motor rated for open operation may usually be operated totally enclosed at one-half to two-thirds its former rating without having the windings attain unsafe temperatures, the exact value depending upon various conditions, such as shape of the frame, the distribution of losses, and the speed. Semienclosure, with protecting screens, will frequently serve to provide needed protection without cutting down the safe loading of the motor to so great an extent as total enclosure.

Practically all modern power-station generators, and some of the larger industrial motors, are totally enclosed but have forced circulation of air[1] through large ducts. This air is fanned out through the stator iron and windings and subsequently used in heating the room or for fire-box supply of preheated air in the boiler room.

Fig. 143.—A 7.5-hp, 230-volt, totally-enclosed motor designed for 55° C temperature rise, for full-load continuous duty. (*Crocker-Wheeler Electric Manufacturing Company.*)

110. Speed vs. Weight and Cost.—With constant field flux, the power output of a given d-c generator or motor may be considered proportional to the generated emf, which is directly proportional to the speed. Thus, by increasing the operating speed, a smaller, lighter, and less expensive machine can be built for a given output. This is upon the assumption that the armature current is limited

[1] Many power-station generators are now designed for the use of hydrogen as a cooling medium, it having a number of advantages over air for this purpose.

by temperature rise to a certain value regardless of speed. Actually the ventilation of the armature is improved with rise in speed, thereby enabling the armature conductors to carry somewhat greater currents without appreciable increase in temperature. On the other hand, core losses increase with the high speeds, tending to raise temperatures. Also high speeds call for more secure bracing of armature coils in the slots and heavier insulation to withstand the higher voltages, thus reducing the conductor cross section and raising the current density.

Because of the lighter weights of rotating parts and shorter radii of armature conductors with reference to the central shaft, small machines may be more readily built for high-speed operation than large, heavy machines. For some applications, such as aircraft auxiliary motors and generators for various purposes, the weight and space factors are of such importance that other considerations are largely disregarded, and the smallest, lightest possible machine is produced for a given output. For industrial motors, however, where efficiency and maintenance costs are of greater importance, there is less tendency toward high speeds except as they may be desirable for direct drives of high-speed tools. For industrial applications, the motor speed is usually limited by the application rather than by design factors, but the tendency is toward higher speeds for production equipment as improvement in materials and design methods are effected that raise the critical speed limit for machines of a given capacity. In general, however, the greater the capacity the lower the speed limit for which the machine may be safely and economically designed. But, within a certain rather definite speed range for a given capacity, the highest speed machine that is suited to the task at hand will be the lightest and cheapest machine.

The shortage of certain critical materials during the war gave impetus to the use of higher speed machinery, because of the material savings it was possible to make. The chief causes of the trend toward higher speeds, however, are the demands for better efficiency and lower production costs. But progress in materials and designs was necessary before higher speeds were practicable. Actual savings in material vary with types and sizes, but doubling the speed of a motor may reasonably be expected to result in a saving of one-fourth to one-half the motor weight.

Better operating characteristics, particularly better efficiencies, are usually associated with higher speeds in motors, an increase in efficiency of 3 to 4 per cent frequently being obtainable by doubling the speed, the gain being particularly noticeable at loads below the rated load.

Higher speeds necessitate closer attention to maintenance of bearings, commutators, and brushes, but this is not likely to prove difficult or expensive. Where direct drives are not feasible, the use of speed-reduction devices may offset the gains to some extent in floor space and efficiency.

111. Unit Cost vs. Capacity.—The size and weight of motors and generators will, in general, increase with capacity. The number of parts in a large machine may not differ greatly from the number in a small machine, but the weight of each part will be greater in proportion to the increased capacity. The larger parts are likely to be handled more efficiently; and, since approximately the same number of parts are being machined, assembled, and tested, the cost of the finished machine will not increase directly with the capacity. Thus the cost per horsepower or per kilowatt will usually decrease as the capacity increases.

Manufacturing costs are greatly influenced by the number of units of a given capacity being produced at a given time. With small motors, the quantity-production methods that are frequently applicable result in marked reduction in unit costs. Thus the cost of a ¼-hp motor, produced in quantity, might be less than the cost of a ⅛-hp motor not produced on a quantity basis, the reason being that, in small motors, the cost of material is low in comparison with the labor cost and would not differ greatly between the two sizes above cited. But the larger production of ¼-hp motors would justify the maximum use of labor-saving devices and methods, resulting in a lower unit cost for the larger motor. This opposition to the usual trend is exceptional; but it should be noted that the cost of standard motors and generators of particular ratings will be appreciably less than the cost of machines especially designed for a given application, because all design work has been done for the standard machine, there is no uncertainty as to the characteristics of the finished product, and the production of the machine can proceed without the necessity for checks and special tests.

Problems

1. A d-c generator is rated 75 kw, 250 volts, 1200 rpm. Specify a suitable driving motor for direct connection.

2. A motor is found to have its horsepower rating omitted from its name plate. The current rating is 150 amp and the voltage 220. What should be the horsepower rating?

3. The motor of Prob. 2 is rated 1500 rpm. It is to be used, however, on a drive requiring that it be operated at 1200 rpm. If the reduction is effected by insertion of resistance in the armature circuit, what horsepower load can it carry safely at the reduced speed? How will the losses, the efficiency, and the operating temperature be affected?

4. A 15-hp motor is applied to a machine in a planing mill, tests of which have indicated a continuous demand of approximately 13 hp. In order to protect the motor from dust, it is completely enclosed in a metal box. Later, the motor is found to be operating at an objectionably high temperature. Diagnose the trouble, and suggest a remedy.

5. A 20-hp 230-volt motor, rated on a 30-min operation basis, is available for a certain drive requiring 15-hp input for periods of 6 to 8 hr continuously. Is it likely that this motor will prove satisfactory? Give reasons for your conclusion.

6. Given a 40-hp 230-volt 1700-rpm shunt motor, so located that 115 volts is the only available d-c power supply. Could this motor, as an emergency measure, be operated from the 115-volt supply at reduced output? If so, what should be its new horsepower, current, and speed ratings?

7. Repeat Prob. 6, assuming the motor to be rated 115 volts and the available power supply to be 230 volts.

8. What would be the effect, or effects, upon operating characteristics of operating a 115-volt shunt motor from a 125-volt supply? from a 105-volt supply?

CHAPTER XI

SPECIAL TYPES AND APPLICATIONS

112. Variable-speed Generators.—For application to automobile and train service, where storage batteries are employed and where the speed at which the generator is driven varies between wide limits, it is necessary to use a type of generator that will maintain its load current practically constant, regardless of speed variations. Two types of generator having such characteristics are illustrated in Figs. 144 and 145. Each of these depends for its

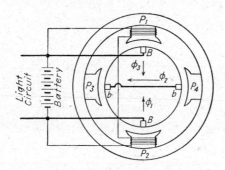

Fig. 144.—The Rosenberg generator.

successful operation upon a battery continuously connected to its terminals when operating at a speed higher than that which generates a voltage equal to the emf of the battery. An automatic cutout is utilized for closing the circuit when the generator voltage reaches a point slightly above the value of the battery cmf and for opening it when, because of decrease in speed, the generator voltage falls below the battery emf. When lights are in use, they are supplied from the generator when this is in operation, with the cutout closed, or from the battery when the cutout is open and the generator disconnected.

The Rosenberg generator (Fig. 144) has its shunt-field winding connected across the battery, causing the poles P_1 and P_2 to main-

tain a flux ϕ_1, which produces voltage at the brushes *bb* but not at
the brushes *BB*. The brushes *bb* are short-circuited, and current
flows in the armature which sets up a cross field ϕ_2. This field is
cut by the armature inductors and produces voltage at the brushes
BB which is applied to the battery and lighting circuit. The
resulting current flow sets up a flux ϕ_3 which opposes ϕ_1, the original field flux. Thus the current in the external circuit exerts a
controlling influence over the flux cut by the armature inductors,
which maintains the load current at or near its rated value. A
similar effect is produced by the *third-brush generator* illustrated

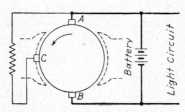

FIG. 145.—The third-brush generator.

in Fig. 145. Here the shunt-field
current depends upon the voltage
between the brushes *A* and *C*, the
latter being adjustable in position relative to *A* in order to permit adjustments in the value of the
charging current. Since the flux
due to armature reaction produces
a distorting effect that results in

a weakening of the field near the leading pole tip, the voltage generated by the inductors between brushes *A* and *C* will be reduced
by an increase in armature current; and, with proper setting of
brush *C*, the current supplied the battery and lamps will be maintained very near a constant value.

Generators of this type may be short-circuited without having
the current reach an unsafe value; and, since the regulating action
is dependent upon armature current, the generator should never be
operated with the battery disconnected unless the generator has
previously been short-circuited—or grounded, in systems using
the frame of the car as one side of the electric circuit.

For a constant-resistance load, the current would increase with
the speed but at a decreasing rate; whereas, for a storage-battery
load, the current characteristic rises rapidly with increase in speed
until a maximum is reached, after which a further increase in speed
results in a current decrease, as shown by Fig. 146. This effect is
produced partly by the reduction in field current caused by the
strong armature-reaction effect for which this type of generator is

designed and partly by the load characteristic of a charging storage battery. This characteristic of the third-brush generator is ideal for automobile use, since moderate speeds, as in city driving, permits the battery to charge at a relatively high rate and the higher speeds of distance driving result in a decreased charging rate. The charging rate may be adjusted to a limited extent by shifting the position of the third brush C. Also, it should be noted, an automatic cutout —not shown in Fig. 145— must be provided between the generator and the battery. This cutout serves to disconnect the battery from the generator when the generator voltage falls below that of the battery, thus preventing discharge of the battery back through the armature circuit at low or zero engine speeds.

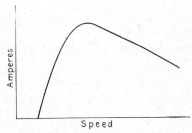

Fig. 146.—Typical battery-charging curve for a third-brush automobile generator.

113. Arc-welding Generators.—Special arc-welding generators are required when welding is to be done with precision and in quantity production, construction, extensive repair work, etc. Since there is considerable variation in the circuit resistance with different lengths of arc and short circuits are produced when striking the arc, it is necessary to have the supply voltage decrease in value quickly with increase in arc current but recover immediately when the resistance of the circuit is restored. The differential-compound generator would appear to approximate the voltage characteristic desired for such an application but actually would be likely to be too unstable and too slow in recovering its voltage, since it would have to undergo the voltage-build-up process of a self-excited shunt generator, which is not usually a rapid process and may at times need the encouragement of overspeeding or other helps. This being the case, it is obvious that some form of separate excitation rather than self-excitation might be desirable. The desired characteristic may be obtained in a satisfactory degree by a modified form of the third-brush generator, similar to that employed in automobile generators; or a dual excitation system may be employed, using a separately excited shunt-field winding

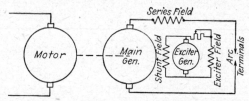

Fig. 147.—Circuit diagram for an arc-welding generator.

in combination with a series field connected to give a differential excitation effect, as illustrated in Fig. 147. A coil is usually inserted in series with the arc circuit also for stabilizing purposes, its presence tending to damp out rapid fluctuations in current.

Fig. 148.—Portable arc-welding motor-generator set. (*The Hobart Brothers Co.*)

Where separate excitation is required, small exciter generators are mounted for direct drive by the same motor that drives the arc-welding generator. Arc-welding sets may be designed for stationary or portable service, depending upon the nature of the work to be done. Figure 148 illustrates a typical form of portable set, with an exciter mounted at the end, for welding work where the work is large or located at various points such that it is more convenient to carry the welding equipment to the work than to bring the work to the welding equipment.

114. The Diverter-pole Generator.—To meet requirements for a more constant voltage at all points between no load and rated load than can be supplied by the flat-compound generator, the diverter-pole generator has been developed, the desired characteristic being obtained by a magnetic shunt of special design.

As shown by the section view of the magnetic circuit (Fig. 149), the diverter-pole generator has the same number of interpoles as main poles but differs from the conventional design in that a magnetic shunt bridges the gap between each interpole and the adjacent main pole of the same polarity. Thus the mmfs of the two poles oppose each other across the magnetic bridge connecting them. The main poles and interpoles are wound and connected into the circuit in the usual

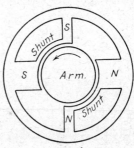

Fig. 149.—Magnetic circuits of the diverter-pole type generator.

manner, the cross section of the connecting shunt being made of the proper value to bring about certain saturation and leakage effects essential to the operation of the generator.

When the generator is not carrying load, there is no current through the interpole coils, and a portion of the main-pole flux follows the magnetic shunt and completes its circuit through the yoke, without crossing the air gap. As the load upon the generator rises, however, the current through the interpole winding increases, producing an opposing mmf and bringing about an increase in the flux crossing the air gap and entering the armature. By careful design, the increase in flux entering the armature with load increase upon the generator may be made to counteract exactly the effects of armature reaction, IR drop in the armature circuit, and decrease in speed, if any, of the driving motor, thus maintaining constant voltage over the usual range of generator loads. At rated load, sufficient flux should cross the air gap beneath the interpoles to provide good commutation; and, under overload conditions, the mmf of the interpole winding exceeds that due to the shunt winding and, acting along the shunt path and main-pole core, reduces the flux from the main pole which enters the armature, causing the terminal voltage to drop rapidly, as indicated by the curve (Fig. 150).

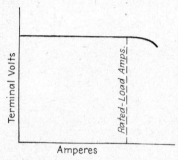

The diverter-pole generator is especially useful for operation in parallel with storage batteries, since, with its constant-voltage characteristic, it charges at a high rate when the battery voltage is low, tapering off as the battery voltage rises. Also, under overload conditions upon the system, the generator voltage drops and allows the battery to carry the major portion of the excess load.

Fig. 150.—Voltage characteristic of the diverter-pole generator.

115. Applications of Generators.—D-c generators are no longer used to any extent in central-station service, except for auxiliary services such as exciters for a-c generators. These may be either shunt or compound, the voltage in either case being controlled by automatic regulators operating on the exciter field but controlling the output voltage of the a-c generators.

Many industrial applications require the use of d-c motors because of their preferred speed and torque characteristics; but, since the main source of power is almost universally alternating current, it is necessary to use conversion equipment of some kind to make the change from alternating to direct current. This conversion may be done by means of motor-generator sets, using a-c motors; or it may be done by the use of synchronous converters, a combination of a-c motor and d-c generator in a common frame; or it may be done by electronic devices such as the mercury-vapor converter. In some manufacturing processes, it is necessary to use elaborate control systems, such as the Ward Leonard system, which requires a separate motor-generator set for each motor or set of motors; whereas, for other processes, a single motor-generator set may supply d-c power at constant voltage for many motors.

For supplying direct current to street and interurban trolley systems, it is standard practice to generate and transmit alternating current, converting this to direct current at various points along the line. Some railway systems follow this practice also but in other cases are finding it advantageous to operate self-contained

Fig. 151.—A large motor-generator set for direct-current supply in electrolytic processes. (*Westinghouse Electric Corporation.*)

electric cars or locomotives, making use of a d-c generator driven by a gasoline or oil engine, for supplying power to driving motors geared to the axles. The same system is also being applied to large busses and trucks for highway service.

Some of the largest motor-generator and synchronous-converter equipment manufactured is in use for supplying the direct currents required in the electrolytic deposition of metals and similar processes. Many thousands of tons of copper alone are produced annually by electrolytic methods. The manufacture of storage batteries, and the electroplating processes used in many industries, also require large amounts of electrical energy in the form of direct currents at relatively low voltages.

The d-c generator in small capacities is used for various special purposes, such as arc-welding sets, automobile generators, train-lighting systems and aircraft.

116. The Voltage Booster.—Since d-c distribution must usually be handled at a comparatively low voltage, the matter of line drop is likely to prove a serious handicap as loads increase upon a given system. One way to prevent excessive drop in pressure is to provide extra feeders, paralleling the existing circuits, but this method is likely to prove expensive because of the large cross sections of

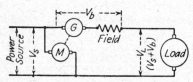

FIG. 152.—The series booster.

conductor required. Another method, less expensive but fully as satisfactory in many cases, lies in the installation of a low-voltage motor-driven generator, with its armature in series with the feeder circuit, operated as a voltage "booster." It may be placed at the station end of the line or at the load end and arranged for either manual or automatic operation. Also, if conditions require it, the polarity of the booster may be reversed and its voltage used to "buck" the line voltage.

Boosters are frequently used in connection with storage batteries for raising the voltage to the value necessary to charge the battery completely and, by reversal of the booster voltage, to assist the battery in discharging.

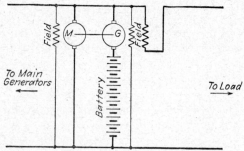

FIG. 153.—One form of differential-booster control of a floating battery.

In floating batteries intended to carry peak loads on a system with rapidly fluctuating demands, such as steel-mill operations, it is frequently necessary to magnify the changes in voltage at the battery terminals in order to accelerate the action of the battery. Booster generators may be applied in a number of ways to effect this magnification. In Fig. 153 is shown a simple form of differential booster, in which the flux set up by the shunt field acts in opposition to the flux set up by the series field. Under normal-load conditions, the two fluxes are equal, resulting in zero emf at the booster terminals, and the battery neither charges nor discharges. Under light-load conditions, the shunt field is stronger than the series field, resulting in addition of the booster emf to the line emf and causing a charging current to flow. Under heavy-load conditions, the series field becomes the stronger, resulting in addition of the booster emf to the battery emf and causing the battery to discharge.

Other more complicated types of differential booster depend upon relays of one form or another to control the direction and

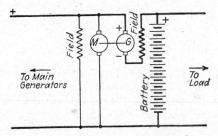

Fig. 154.—A series-booster battery-control system.

strength of the booster field. Boosters may also be arranged for shunt, separate, series, or compound excitation according to the requirements of a particular application and the ideas of the engineer in charge.

Where batteries are located at the end of a line having poor voltage regulation, the variations in voltage due to changes in load may be sufficient to cause the battery to charge and discharge without the aid of a booster. If the same effect is desired on a line having good regulation, a series booster may be applied in the manner indicated in Fig. 154. Under normal conditions, the booster voltage is low and has no appreciable effect; but, under conditions of heavy demand, the voltage of the booster rises and, being opposed to the main supply voltage, reduces the voltage at the battery terminals to a point that allows the battery to discharge rapidly.

117. The Edison Three-wire System.—This system is used in order to provide 110 to 120 volts for lamps[1] while at the same time securing the advantages of higher voltage distribution and providing 220 to 240 volts for motors.

If an arrangement as shown in Fig. 155 is used, there is a perfect balance and the proper voltage is applied to each bank of lamps as long as there is exactly the same capacity in lamps on each side of

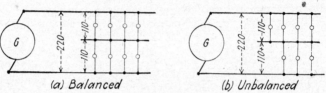

FIG. 155.—A three-wire system without provision for maintaining voltage balance.

the neutral wire, and no current will flow in the neutral wire. If the system becomes unbalanced, as in diagram *b*, however, the voltage rises above normal on one side—that of the higher resistance—and sinks below normal on the other side. In the extreme case when only one lamp is burning on one side, as contrasted with a large number burning on the other side, this lamp will have nearly double voltage impressed upon it while the others will have very little voltage applied to them. This arrangement would therefore not operate satisfactorily; and, in order to maintain a proper voltage upon the two sides of the system, certain auxiliary apparatus is required, as described below.

The Two-generator System.—With this arrangement, two generators of equal capacity are required, each capable of handling half the total load. No special equipment is necessary, the connections being as shown in Fig. 156.

The Balancer System.—In this system, a single standard generator is used, with a small motor-generator set connected as shown in Fig. 157 to maintain the voltage balance. When the load is per-

---

[1] The 220- to 240-volt lamps may be procured but are more expensive and less satisfactory than those designed for 110 to 120 volts. Because of the greater fragility of their filaments, their life is likely to be shorter than that of the lower voltage lamps.

fectly balanced, the two machines of the balancer set operate as
two motors in series across a 220-volt line, taking only enough
power to supply their own losses. The neutral line under this condition carries no current. If the load becomes unbalanced, as
shown in the diagram, however, the un-
balanced current flows back through the
neutral line and divides, part going through
the lower machine, which is now operating
as a motor,[1] and part through the upper
machine, which now acts as a generator.
If the losses in the balancer set are neglected, the neutral current may be considered to divide equally between motor
and generator, as in the condition assumed

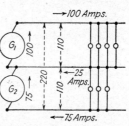

FIG. 156.—The two-genera-
tor three-wire system.

in Fig. 157. The following example illustrates the method to be
followed in determining the division of the neutral current when
the balancer losses are to be taken into account.

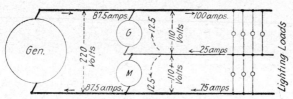

FIG. 157.—The balancer system

Example.—A 125/250-volt three-wire system has a load on the positive
side of 500 amp, on the negative side of 450 amp, the neutral current therefore being 50 amp. If each machine of the balancer set has an efficiency of
86 per cent, calculate the current for each of these machines and for the main
generator.

Solution:

$$\text{Efficiency of balancer set} = \frac{\text{output of generator}}{\text{input of motor}} = \frac{I_g \times 125}{I_m \times 125}$$

$$= \frac{I_g}{I_m} = \frac{I_g}{50 - I_g} = 0.86 \times 0.86 = 0.74$$

Therefore

$$I_g = 0.74(50 - I_g)$$

[1] The machine upon which the voltage is rising becomes the motor, the other
a generator.

from which

$$I_g = 21.26 \text{ amp}$$
$$I_m = 50 - I_g = 28.74 \text{ amp}$$

I of main generator $= 500 - 21.26 = 450 + 28.74 = 478.74$ amp

The Three-wire Generator System.—This system requires the use of a generator with special slip rings, to which are attached leads connected to opposite points on the armature. The brushes that bear on these rings are connected to opposite terminals of an inductance coil (Fig. 158) to the mid-point of which the neutral wire

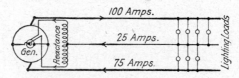

Fig. 158.—The three-wire generator system.

is attached. This coil will allow very little passage of current from one side of the armature to the other—this current being alternating in character—but, the resistance being low, very little hindrance is offered the direct current flowing in from the neutral wire.

In order to obtain better distribution of current in the armature, two or even three coils may be employed, the former arrangement requiring four slip rings and the latter three slip rings, corresponding to two-phase and three-phase (star) arrangements, as used on a-c circuits. Also the inductance is sometimes built into the armature of the machine, in which case only one slip ring is required.

The three-wire generator is naturally somewhat more expensive than the standard type, and for a particular system this additional cost must be balanced against the costs, or disadvantages, incident to the use of a balancer set.

118. Applications of Motors.—D-c motors are preferred for many industrial and railway applications even though the only power immediately available is alternating current, making necessary the use of conversion equipment in order to secure a d-c power supply. Formerly it was necessary to use rotating equipment in the form of motor-generator sets or synchronous converters, but much of this conversion is now accomplished with static devices, such as the mercury-vapor converter.

The chief reason for preference of the d-c motor lies in the wide and economical ranges of speed control possible, with the excellent

FIG. 159.—A 7.5-hp vertical ball-bearing motor, with ring base and louvered covers. (*Century Electric Co.*)

speed regulation of the shunt motor and the high starting-torque capabilities, combined with wide ranges of speed control, of the series and compound types.

In selecting a motor for a given drive, careful consideration should be given to the following points:

a. Starting Conditions.—Starting torque required, in terms of normal load torque; effect of starting currents upon other apparatus in the shop or locality; probable time interval between starts, etc.

b. Running Conditions.—Average and maximum operating loads; probable overloads; frequency of occurrence, extent, and duration. Speed regulation, range of speed control. Nature of connections between motor and load, type of load, etc.

Fig. 160.—Standard mill-type motor, 25 hp, 230 volts. (*Crocker-Wheeler Electric Manufacturing Company.*)

c. General Surroundings.—Presence of dust, grit, moisture, gases, or fumes in objectionable quantities. Proximity to explosives, extent of air circulation, range of room temperature, etc.

Particular attention should be given, of course, to the horsepower rating required. Allowance should be made for all probable overloads, but "overmotoring" should be avoided.

119. Industrial Motor Applications.—The d-c motor is preferred for many industrial applications because of its ability to operate over a wide range of speeds economically and with good regulation. For constant-speed service, however, the advantages of the d-c motor are not so marked, and the a-c motor may even be preferable because of its greater ruggedness and its lower first cost.

Machine Tools.—Except in the smaller sizes, such machines as lathes, drills, planers, etc., are usually equipped with individual motors, the present practice being to have special provision made by the manufacturer of the machine tool for accommodation of the motor, rather than to mount the motor separately. The motor may also be supplied by the tool manufacturer, in which case he assumes responsibility for the rating and characteristics of the motor. For machines such as lathes and drills, the shunt motor is the best type of motor because of its wide range of speed control and good speed regulation. For planers, a compound motor is preferable because of the more variable load and heavier torque requirements. A reversing motor is available for drives of this sort and is more satisfactory than the belt-shift arrangement, especially for the larger machines. Small lathes, drill presses, shapers, automatic screw machines, etc., are sometimes arranged for group drive by a single motor. No provision need be made in this case for speed variation, and a shunt motor without speed control is entirely satisfactory. Where group drive is employed, the individual machines that require variation in speed must be provided with a cone pulley or gear box. In very large planers, boring mills, etc., the use of auxiliary motors, independent of the main drive, for the feed mechanisms may sometimes be justified because of the simpler design and the more flexible control that is thus made possible.

Special controllers of the drum type (Fig. 105) are generally used for machine-tool motors, except in the larger sizes of machines, such as planers, where automatic control equipment is used.

Certain types of machines, such as punch presses, have periodic power demands and are usually equipped with flywheels to equalize the load upon the motor. In order that the flywheel may be effective in doing this, however, the motor must have poor speed regulation. This may be provided through the use of a compound motor or of a shunt motor with extra resistance in the armature circuit. The use of the compound motor is preferable, other things being equal, because of its better torque characteristic and higher efficiency. The series motor is not suitable for this or other machine-tool applications because of its tendency to overspeed under light-load conditions.

Elevators.—Passenger elevators fo. m a special type of application upon which a great deal of work has been done. A motor for this service must have high starting torque in order to accelerate the car rapidly and must run at practically constant speed, regardless of load. A special motor and control is sometimes used—the

Fig. 161.—Motor room of a steel mill, showing 4500-hp mill motors and 6000-kw motor-generator sets. (*Allis-Chalmers Manufacturing Company.*)

motor operating compound during the starting and acceleration period but having the series field short-circuited after normal operating speed has been attained.

The most satisfactory arrangement, especially for high-speed service, appears to lie in the variable voltage control obtained through the use of a separate motor-generator set for each elevator motor—the Ward Leonard system (Art. 85). The armature of the elevator motor being the only load upon the generator, a wide range of control is available, through variation in the generator voltage. The use of this system also provides the advantages of d-c motors and control even though the available supply is alternating current. In order to provide effective braking, a regenerative system is used, the motors being made to act as generators for braking purposes. The operator is provided with a master controller having start, stop, and reverse positions, the remainder of the control operations being automatic, including such special means as may be provided for ensuring accurate stoppage at the desired floor levels.

Freight elevators and hoists require motors having high starting torque characteristics and also allowing some speed variation at the discretion of the operator. Compound-wound motors are commonly used, except that, in large mine hoists, special control features are sometimes found necessary in the form of Ward Leonard or similar systems involving the use of motor-generator sets. Dynamic braking systems are usually employed in such installations.

120. Railway Service.—Railway service forms another special application for which the d-c motor is particularly well adapted. Since this service requires a motor with the ability to start very heavy loads and since the motor is always under the control of an operator, the series motor has little competition in this field. For street-railway service, 600 volts is the standard voltage and two motors are generally used—the controller being arranged to connect them in series for low speeds and in parallel for high speeds, as previously described. Motors of 600, 1200, 2400, and 3000 volts are in use on different systems; but, for the higher voltages, two motors are operated in series, as a unit, thus holding the voltage per motor to 1500 as a maximum.

Drum controllers are used for street car motors; but, for interurban cars and passenger locomotives, on trunk-line systems, some form of remote control is usually preferred.

Diesel-electric locomotives are replacing steam locomotives on many railroads for high-speed passenger and freight service as well as for switching service because of their superior operating characteristics. For switching service, a single unit is generally used;

and, for regular road service, two or more units are coupled in series, and the controls are centered in the cab of the head locomotive.

The Diesel-electric locomotive is a self-contained power plant with an output capacity determined by the capacity of the Diesel engine. The generator therefore cannot be designed for constant voltage output, as are ordinary generators, but must be designed for poor voltage regulation in order to avoid overloading the engine under heavy-torque-load operation of the locomotive, the ideal setup being one that keeps the engine fully loaded under all conditions of operation, with the generator furnishing a constant product of volts and amperes—high amperes at low voltage for heavy torque demands at low locomotive speeds, when starting heavy trains, and low amperes at high voltage for high locomotive speeds, with automatic adjustment to meet all intermediate operating conditions. To approximate this ideal operating characteristic, the generator is designed for poor regulation, either inherently or through use of a separate exciter with the necessary characteristics. Also the driving motors are arranged for automatic shift from series connection at low speeds, through series-parallel at intermediate speeds, to parallel at high speeds if the motors are designed to operate individually on full generator voltage, or to reduced-field operation if two motors are permanently connected in series. Thus maximum tractive effort is applied to moving the train at low speeds, without danger of overloading the Diesel engine, and full power output from the engine continues available at the higher locomotive speeds. Manual control of locomotive operation is provided in the form of an engine throttle, which operates through a governor to control fuel supply to the engine.

It is necessary of course for the Diesel-electric locomotive to carry a storage battery—for auxiliary lighting and for engine starting. Because of the main generator voltage and characteristics, it is not feasible to charge the battery from the main generator, and an auxiliary generator must be provided for this purpose. The main generator, however, is converted to motor action for cranking the engine, being provided with an auxiliary series winding for securing high-torque series-motor action, with the battery as power source. All shifts in traction motor connections, reversals in direction, etc., are handled by relays suitable for control of the compressed air or electric solenoids that furnish the actual motivating power. Numerous safety features are also provided for protection of the equipment.

Fig. 162.—Auxiliary marine-type motor, 250 hp, 240 volts, 1200 rpm. (*Crocker-Wheeler Electric Manufacturing Company.*)

Storage-battery locomotives find extensive application for light switching service around industrial plants and in coal mines. Their use removes objectionable hazards always present when the trolley or third rail is used for power supply.

121. Marine Service.—Marine service is divided into two general classes, the main propulsion equipment and the auxiliary equipment, such as winches and other cargo-handling apparatus, anchor windlasses, and ventilating fans.

Insofar as the main propulsion equipment is concerned, distinct advantages are incident to the use of direct currents, particularly when the Diesel engine is used as prime mover, the operation of both generators and motors being carried on more effectively and efficiently. For steam turbine drives, the a-c system competes with the direct current on a more equal basis, and several recent installations have utilized a-c equipment. For the auxiliary equipment, however, the advantages of the d-c motor are so marked that few a-c systems have been installed for this class of service, the power being supplied by auxiliary d-c generators.

For the main propulsion equipment, there are recognized advantages in operating the generators in series rather than in parallel, since with this system the Ward Leonard method of control can be utilized and furthermore a greater reserve capacity is available if one or more of the main generators is out of commission. Generators and motors are of the shunt type, with separately excited fields, and speed control is effected by varying the excitation of the generator field. By this means, a simple and efficient control is obtained from full speed ahead to full speed astern without the necessity for changes in engine speeds.

122. Aircraft Applications.—The first applications of electricity to aircraft followed the automobile pattern, using a storage battery and small d-c generator, first of 12-volt rating, later of 24-volt rating, with the ampere ratings growing from 50 to 200 amp. At present, the larger aircraft employ generators of 30-volt 300-amp rating. In the largest four-engine craft, however, four such generators, one driven by each engine, do not provide sufficient electrical energy for the many tasks for which electrical motors have been found to be the most flexible, dependable, and convenient methods of applying power. Consequently, the trend for the larger aircraft is away from d-c generation and toward the use of alternating current as a primary power source, this being converted to direct current at such points and for such applications as can best be handled by direct current—forming a miniature power station, transmission system, and substations for both direct and alternating current, such as exists in connection with large stationary power systems.

The requirements for aircraft d-c generators and motors are essentially different from those for industrial service. The fact that the plane flies through varying altitudes and changing atmospheric conditions imposes problems not confronting the designer of industrial equipment. Since the generator is driven direct from the main engines in practically all cases, mechanical forces caused by engine vibration must be dealt with as well as electrical problems caused by high altitudes and low temperatures. One such problem arises from the fact that ordinary carbon brushes wear at greatly accelerated rates under conditions of high-altitude flying; another arises from the lowered breakdown voltage of the air and accompanying ionization effects at high altitudes, causing arcs to be established and spread more readily than at sea level. These conditions necessitate unusual care in design to provide

FIG. 163.—Aircraft dynamotor. (*Pioneer Gen-E-Motor Corp.*)

perfect commutation and to guard against vibration effects upon brushes. Greater creepage distances should be provided than would be necessary for sea-level generators of the same voltage rating.

The best design of d-c generator, in order to meet the foregoing requirements, must include interpoles and compensating windings, together with relatively high spring pressures for ensuring continuous contact between brushes and commutator. By this combination of design features, it has been found possible to eliminate entirely any tendency to spark at the commutator and to reduce losses to a minimum. Efficiencies of 75 to 80 per cent are attainable despite the relatively low kilowatt capacities and the light weight of these generator units.

The weight of aircraft motors and generators has been reduced markedly over those of industrial machines of corresponding output, partly by operating at high speeds and partly through the tolerance of much higher operating temperatures. By utilizing insulation composed chiefly of glass and mica, it has been found possible to operate these machines with a temperature rise of 100°C, as contrasted with 40°C for industrial equipment using cotton-base insulation. The generators are designed for air-blast cooling, by scooping in the outside air and forcing it through the generator parts. Special brush materials and treatments have been evolved to compensate for the tendency of ordinary brushes to disintegrate rapidly at high altitudes.

123. Servo Motors.—The substitution of automatic control for human control of measurable and controllable operations is made possible by the development of suitable "servo mechanisms." Examples of such devices are to be found in the speed control of steam turbines and water wheels by governors, the automatic steering of ships, the stabilization of ships by gyroscopes, the automatic control of aircraft in flight, as well as the automatic control of many industrial and military operations. The servo mechanism is essentially a power-amplifying device but has functions other than that of power amplification, since the power input of the mechanism must be actuated by the difference between its input, from the controlling device, and its output to the device or part that is being controlled. There must be no overdrive and no appreciable oscillation or hunting.

Servo mechanisms may be operated by compressed air, by liquids, by electrical devices, or by a combination of these. The wholly electrical means, employing vacuum-tube or equivalent circuits for the control and amplification functions and motors for the actual operation of the controlled part, provides the most sensitive and flexible arrangement and is rapidly superseding other methods.

The motors employed in such devices are called *servo motors* and may be of either the d-c or the a-c type, though the d-c motor has certain advantages for many such applications. The motor may be of standard design but usually requires certain special features, making a specially designed motor necessary. Usually these are of fairly low power rating; but, because their operation is limited to a few revolutions at a time—as in a governor motor, when responding to a call for more steam to handle an increased load upon a turbine—their output rating may be set much higher than would be possible if operation were continuous. On the other hand, the limited operation of the motor supplies little ventilation for cooling and it may be mounted in a location of high ambient temperature.

An important requirement of many servo motors is high starting torque, in order that positive movement may take place upon first closure of the control circuit. This gives the series motor a decided advantage for such applications. A double field winding is generally used for securing rotation in either direction, only one field winding being in use at a time. When it is necessary to control the speed of the motor, this may be accomplished by variable resistors or other means of changing the voltage applied to the motor terminals.

In other types of mechanism, where torque is not a major factor, control may best be effected by varying the current supply to an armature in a constant-flux field, requiring a motor of the shunt type with the field coils separately excited.

For some applications, special features of motor design may be necessary in order to provide low inertia for the moving parts. This requirement may be met by providing that the armature core of the motor be stationary, with armature coils operating in the air gap between poles and armature core—as in the D'Arsonval type of d-c ammeter or voltmeter. Low inertia for moving parts may also be achieved by using a small motor of conventional design in series with a mechanical torque amplifier, or a high torque-inertia ratio may be obtained through the use of a short armature radius.

124. Dynamotors.—The dynamotor is a combination of motor and generator within a simple frame and utilizing a single rotor. The yoke and pole structure are those of a standard shunt motor or generator, but the rotor contains a double armature winding, sandwiched into adjacent slots, each half of the winding being complete in itself and terminating in the bars of separate commutators, located at opposite ends of the armature. Voltage and current relations between the two windings are determined by the relative number of inductors making up the coils, the nominal power ratings of the two windings being the same. Either winding, when supplied with its proper voltage and field excitation, will act as the motor element while the other winding generates a voltage and may be used as a voltage source for an appropriate circuit. Since the same field coils and magnetic circuit serve both windings, there is a fixed ratio between the voltages of the motor and generator elements, and neither voltage can be varied independently of the other.   This limits the usefulness of this type of voltage converter to a considerable extent.

The dynamotor is finding extensive application in connection with radio transmitters on police cars, in aircraft, and on marine vessels, where the d-c supply of power is limited to relatively low voltages, the dynamotor serving as a voltage step-up device.   For such purposes, they are built in capacities ranging from about 20 to 1000 watts, with input voltages from 6 to 115 volts and output voltages from 200 to 1800 volts.   The efficiencies are quite high,

Fig. 164.—Dual-voltage dynamotor.   Input, 13 or 26 volts, 13 or 6.5 amp, d-c. Output, 300 volts, 0.355 amp, d-c.   Speed 4800 rpm.   (*Pioneer Gen-E-Motor Corp.*)

when the relatively low capacity of the units is considered, ranging from about 50 per cent in the lower capacity units to about 70 per cent for the largest size units, at their rated outputs.   For loads below rated, however, the efficiency is inclined to drop off somewhat faster than with industrial sizes of generators and motors. The units are sturdily constructed, usually made completely enclosed, and are capable of giving dependable service under difficult operating conditions.

Figure 164 shows the general appearance of the small dynamotor, as described, and its circuit diagram.   Figure 165 shows a typical set of characteristic curves for such a machine.

125. Automotive Equipment.—D-c motors and generators of low capacity are used in conjunction with storage batteries for lighting, ignition, and starting service on automobiles, and for other types of automotive equipment. The generators for this service, usually of the third-brush type, are designed for approximately constant current output, as shown in Art. 112, because of the vary-

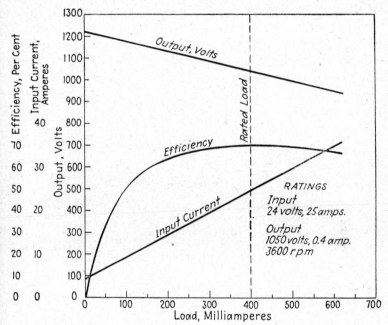

FIG. 165.—Typical dynamotor-performance curves.

ing engine speeds and the charging requirements of the storage battery.

On some car generators, a special heat-actuated relay is used to insert extra resistance into the field circuit of the generator when the generator temperature has reached a preset value. Thus, for short trips, the battery will be charged at relatively high current values; while driving at high speeds for long periods will result in higher temperatures, causing the charging current to be reduced, thus avoiding continued overcharging of the battery.

The starting motor must develop a heavy torque, and consequently the series motor is the accepted standard for this service. It is possible to utilize the same machine for both starting and generation, but in general two units have been found more satisfactory.

The gas-electric bus is designed upon the same principles and for the same reasons of economy and flexibility as the gas-electric railway car but requires compactness in the design and location of its equipment. The better designs build the engine and generator as a compact unit. The use of series-motor driving units provides the same advantages in torque characteristics and speed-control features as exist in connection with electric-railway cars. In addition, some designs make effective use of electric braking. Because of the absence of rigid mechanical transmissions, the engine-generator units can be so located as to provide maximum accessibility for inspection and repair, and less mechanical strain is placed upon the equipment during operation.

Problems

1. Given a three-wire system, with connected load of 11.5 kw in 115-volt lamps and 23 kw in 230-volt motors, making use of a three-wire generator for maintaining voltage balance: (a) Sketch a diagram of connections, and indicate the value and direction of current at all points, assuming the total load to be in operation. (b) Repeat (a) with the same conditions except one-fifth the lighting load turned off on one side, giving a 20 per cent unbalance.

2. Repeat (b) of Prob. 1 assuming the use of a booster or balancer set for maintaining voltage balance, the efficiency of each machine of this set being estimated at 70.7 per cent.

3. A 125/250-volt three-wire system has a load on the positive side of 250 amp and on the negative side of 100 amp. Of the current in the neutral wire, 60 per cent goes to the motor of the balancer set. (a) Show by sketch the current distribution in the system. (b) Calculate the power delivered by the main generator, and show that this includes the losses in the balancer set. (c) Calculate the efficiency of the balancer set.

4. Prove that, for a given amount of power to be transmitted, at a given percentage line drop, the weight of copper required in a transmission line is inversely proportional to the square of the transmission voltage. Illustrate by a numerical example.

5. Determine the saving in copper effected by using the three-wire instead of the two-wire system (a) where the middle wire is one-fourth the size of the outer wires, (b) where the middle wire is the same size as the outer wires, and (c) where the middle wire is double the size of the outer wires.

6. A three-wire system has three load-distribution centers designated A, B, and C. The loads for the condition under consideration are as follows:

Load	Amp	
	Positive	Negative
A (nearest generator).............................	25	35
B..	65	40
C..	15	25

Indicate on a sketch the value and direction of current flow in each part of the circuit.

7. It is desired to supply a 250-kw load at 600 volts, from 550-volt d-c supply lines. (a) Suggest two practicable means for accomplishing this, and specify the equipment needed in each case. State which method would in your estimation be preferable and why. (b) Suppose the situation reversed and the load at 550 volts to be supplied from 600-volt lines. How would this affect the solution of the problem?

8. The voltage drop in a d-c feeder supplying a 50-kw load is too great for satisfactory operation, the voltage falling from 240 volts at the generator to 200 volts at the load 1000 ft distant. Suggest two practicable means for supplying the load with normal voltage—230—and specify the equipment needed. Which method would you advise using, and why?

9. A load of 32.5 kw, at 250 volts, is to be connected to a 125-volt line. Specify the ratings of motor and generator required to raise the voltage for this load from 125 to 250 volts (a) by means of a motor-generator set and (b) by means of a booster.

10. A motor is direct-connected to a machine operating at 1500 rpm and requiring 20-lb torque at a radius of 3.5 ft. After installation, it was found necessary to enclose the motor, and this resulted in such unsatisfactory operation that it was decided to buy a new motor. What horsepower motor should be purchased?

11. A motor for use in hoisting service will be required to raise 2 tons at a rate of 250 fpm, the efficiency of the hoist being 75 per cent. What horsepower motor should be used (a) if rating is based on ½-hr operating periods, (b) if rating is based on 1-hr operating periods, and (c) if rating is based on 8-hr operating periods.

12. A motor is to drive a boiler-feed pump of the centrifugal type, the normal boiler pressure being 400 lb. per sq. in. The pump is required to deliver a maximum of 150 gpm continuously. Assuming a pump efficiency of 60 per cent, specify the kind and size of d-c motor that should be used.

13. A town of 3000 population is considering the replacement of its waterworks steam pumps with motor-driven pumps. By means of a stroke counter operated by the steam pumps, the water consumption for the past year is found to be 80 million gal. A standpipe is already in use and is 16 ft diameter by 110 ft high, with its base 30 ft above the level of the pumps. Water stands at such level in the wells that suction lift is negligible. It is decided to use an automatic, part-time-operation system, the control to be by relay set to start the pump at 45 lb pressure and shut it down at 60 lb pressure, 2 hr being required under average conditions to raise the pressure from lower to upper limit. (a) Specify the motor and pump (centrifugal) required; 220-volt d-c power is available. (b) Estimate the annual power bill if energy costs 3 cents per kw-hr.

14. A town is considering the installation of a water-supply system and wishes estimates for each of two systems: (a) pumping to mains with elevated tank storage and (b) pumping to mains with no storage. The average pressure decided upon is 60 psi at the pumps. The average suction lift will be about 15 ft. Estimated demand is as follows:

6 to 8 A.M. . . . . 250 gpm	5 to 7 P.M. . . . . 500 gpm
8 to 10 A.M. . . . . 125 gpm	7 P.M. to 12 M. . . . . 100 gpm
10 A.M. to 1 P.M. . . . . 200 gpm	12 M. to 6 A.M. . . . . 50 gpm
1 to 5 P.M. . . . . 125 gpm	

Specify the size and type of pump and driving motor (direct current) for each application, and the capacity of storage tank necessary for the first case. Estimate the annual power bill, with energy at 3.5 cents per kw-hr.

15. Analyze the operational requirements of the following machines upon the basis of (a) torque at starting as compared with normal running torque; (b) permissible speed change with variations in load; (c) type of load, continuous, variable, or intermittent; and (d) necessary or desirable range of operating speeds. Assume average operating conditions, or note such special conditions as may be assured. Upon the basis of this analysis, choose the type of d-c motor—hoisting, trolley, or bridge—best suited to drive each machine.

1. Engine lathe.	12. Yard locomotive.
2. Metal planer.	13. Heavy shaft grinder.
3. Milling machine.	14. Ventilating fan.
4. Drill press.	15. Pile driver.
5. Line shaft.	16. Stone crusher.
6. Passenger elevator.	17. Air compressor.
7. Freight elevator.	18. Concrete mixer.
8. Punch press, with flywheel.	19. Electric generator.
9. Circular saw.	20. Coal hoist.
10. Waterworks pump, reciprocating type.	21. Boring mill.
	22. Locomotive turntable.
11. Waterworks pump, centrifugal type.	23. Wood planer.
	24. Overhead crane.

CHAPTER XII

TESTING AND MAINTENANCE

126. Indicating Instruments.—The permanent-magnet type, also known as the D'Arsonval type, is one of the most satisfactory types of d-c instrument and is widely used in connection with laboratory and other work involving d-c measurements. Its operation is based upon the principle that a current-carrying conductor in a magnetic field is acted on by a force tending to move it to one side and out of the field, the basis of d-c motor action.

The construction of this type of instrument may be seen by reference to Fig. 166. The permanent magnet furnishes a relatively strong field in order that outside fields may not easily affect the indications, the magnetic circuit being completed through soft-iron pole pieces, a short air gap, and a cylindrical soft-iron core. A coil of fine enameled-copper wire is wound upon a frame of light material, usually aluminum, which is supported by delicate bearings and to which is attached the pointer. Control of the coil movement is effected by light spiral springs above and below, these springs serving also as conductors for the current entering and leaving the coil.

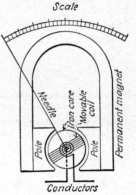

Fɪɢ. 166.—Construction of the permanent-magnet type of d-c instrument.

Damping is produced by the braking action of eddy currents set up in the metal frame upon which the coil is wound, the direction of these currents being, in accordance with Lenz's law, such as to react against the causative force.

Since the moving element must be very lightly constructed in order to reduce the inertia of the moving parts to a minimum, its use as a series instrument is limited to circuits involving very small currents. However, by the use of *shunts* and *multipliers*, the instrument may be adapted to use as an ammeter or voltmeter of practically any range. Instruments of this type are nonreversible, *i.e.*, since the magnetic field is fixed in direction, the current must always pass through the coil in a certain direction in order to produce a positive indication. The torque being proportional to the first power of the current passing through the coil, the scale divisions are more evenly spaced than would be the case with an instrument whose torque varied otherwise.

127. Shunts and Multipliers.—Since, by Ohm's law, $V = IR$ or $I = V/R$, the instrument described in the preceding paragraph may be used, in conjunction with proper shunts and multipliers, as either ammeter or voltmeter.

A shunt is a low-resistance conductor designed to carry the bulk of the line current while setting up a potential difference across the terminals sufficient to cause the proper value of current to flow through the instrument. The instrument scale may be, and usually is, graduated and marked in terms of the line current to which its indications are proportional. The instrument and shunt must be properly suited to one another, and shunts are not interchangeable without due consideration being given to their resistance values and multiplying factors. For capacities up to 25 amp, the shunt is usually made an integral part of the instrument and placed inside the case. Above this value, the shunt is usually separate and external to the case. It should still, however, be considered a part of the instrument.

A multiplier is a resistor of high resistance and low current capacity designed for connection in series with the instrument element previously described. When so connected, the scale may be graduated and marked in terms of the voltage across the combination of instrument and multiplier, the current through the instrument being proportional to this voltage. For portable service, the multiplier is usually made an integral part of the instrument and placed within the case. For switchboard service, the multiplier is frequently external and mounted back of the switchboard. The range of any voltmeter may be doubled by placing in series with it a resistance equal to that of the instrument, including its multiplier. The scalar divisions should then be multiplied by two. By using a resistance equal to twice that of the instrument and its multiplier, the range of the combination is three times that of the original instrument and multiplier, etc.

Example.—A certain d-c instrument has 100-mv drop across its terminals with full-scale deflection. Its resistance is 1 ohm. (*a*) Specify the shunt necessary for adapting this instrument to use as an ammeter of 100 amp capacity. (*b*) Specify the resistance necessary for adapting it to use as a voltmeter of 100 volts capacity.

Solution:

(*a*)
$$I = \frac{V}{R} = \frac{0.1}{1} = 0.1 \text{ amp for full deflection}$$

$$100 - 0.1 = 99.9 \text{ amp} = \text{current through shunt}$$

$$R = \frac{V}{I} \quad \frac{0.1}{99.9} = 0.001 + \text{ohm, resistance of shunt}$$

(*b*)
$$\text{Total } R = \frac{V}{I} = \frac{100}{0.1} = 1000 \text{ ohms}$$

Resistance to be added $= 1000 - 1 = 999$ ohms
Current-carrying capacity of multiplier $= 0.1$ amp

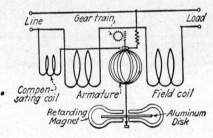

Fig. 167.—Construction of the commutator-type, d-c watt-hour meter.

128. Watt-hour Meters.—The watt-hour meter, for integrating the energy used in a given circuit over a period of time, consists essentially of a small motor, which supplies the driving force for a spindle and gear train, the torque developed being proportional to the power required by the circuit; a braking arrangement such that the retarding force is proportional to the speed of the spindle; and a system of gears and dials for registering the revolutions of the spindle.

In the commutator type of d-c watt-hour meter (see Figs. 167 and 168), the driving force is supplied by a small commutator motor with armature windings placed directly on the meter spindle, differing from the ordinary type of motor by the absence of iron in the magnetic circuit and by having the armature connected *across* the load circuit and the field coil in series with this circuit.

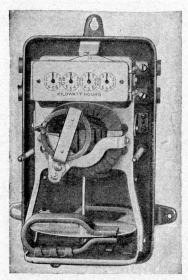

FIG. 168.—The direct-current watt-hour meter. (*Duncan Electric Manufacturing Company.*)

Extra resistance is added to the armature circuit in order to reduce its current to a small value.

Since there is no metal in the path of the magnetic flux produced by the field coils, the magnetic field is proportional to the load current. And since the armature, in series with considerable resistance, is across the load circuit and develops a very low counter emf, the current in the armature may be considered proportional to the circuit voltage, without appreciable error. The torque will therefore be very closely proportional to the product of load current and load voltage, or to the power being transmitted to the load.

If the angular velocity of the armature is to be proportional to the power supplied to the load, so that the revolutions of the armature within a given time interval are proportional to the energy supplied to the load during that interval, a retarding torque proportional to angular velocity of the armature must be provided.[1] This is supplied by an aluminum disk, attached to the spindle and made to rotate between the poles, or under the influence, of a permanent magnet. The eddy currents set up in the disk result in a drag upon the moving parts, including the armature, directly proportional to the speed. The drag due to the permanent magnets may be adjusted, usually by shifting the position of the

[1] For mathematical proof, see Frank A. Laws, "Electrical Measurements," 2d ed., McGraw-Hill Book Company, Inc., 1938.

magnets, in order to provide means of correcting the meter to maximum accuracy after manufacture or from time to time when it is in use.

The friction in meters of this type is reduced to a small value by use of very light parts, supported on jewel bearings, but nevertheless it is necessary to supply a friction-compensating device. This is usually done by placing a small coil in series with the potential circuit and so locating it that a weak field is provided—just sufficient to create a friction-balancing torque. The strength of this compensating field can be adjusted by changing the position of

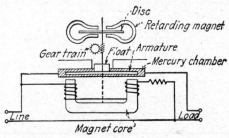

Fig. 169.—Construction of the mercury-flotation-type watt-hour meter.

the coil or by shunting some of the current around it and should be so adjusted that rotation begins with the least addition of load but causes no creepage without load.

The mercury-flotation type of meter is designed upon a somewhat different principle, the action being known as that of *Barlow's wheel*. The field coil (Fig. 169) is connected across the circuit, its current being therefore proportional to line voltage. The armature consists of a slotted copper disk floating in mercury—the mercury serving to carry the weight of the moving parts as well as to conduct current to and from the armature. The armature circuit carries the line current—or a definite proportion of it— through use of a shunt. Braking action is provided by a disk rotating between poles of a permanent magnet in the same manner as with the commutator type of meter.

129. Calibration of Instruments and Meters.—For accurate testing, it is essential that properly adjusted and carefully calibrated instruments be used. Most test departments maintain, or have access to, more or less elaborately equipped calibration laboratories in which secondary standards are kept for use in checking from time to time the calibration of the instruments used upon the test floor. These instruments are more delicately constructed than the usual grade of instruments and are frequently much larger in physical dimensions, with longer indicators and more finely divided scales. They should not be used for purposes other than calibration and should themselves be checked from time to time by comparison with other standards.

Standardization of ammeters and voltmeters is usually based upon resistance and emf standards because of the practical difficulty of duplicating the international standard volt and the international standard ampere. Certification of such resistance and emf standards may be obtained from the U.S. Bureau of Standards. So-called *standard cells* (Art. 150) are utilized as emf standards.

In checking the accuracy of watt-hour meters, the use of a "rotating standard" is the preferable method, although reasonably accurate checks may be made with indicating instruments and a stop watch, if the supply voltage can be held at a steady value during the test. The accuracy of the rotating standard is not affected by changes in load or voltage, since any change affects alike the meter under test and the standard.

Since it would require several hours to determine the accuracy of a watt-hour meter by means of the dial registration, recourse is had to the revolutions of the meter spindle and their relation to the power recorded. If the gear ratio between the meter spindle and the lowest index hand is known, the accuracy may be determined by counting the revolutions of the spindle over a short interval. The "meter constant" may have any one of several meanings but is most generally understood to mean watt-hours recorded on the lowest dial per revolution of the meter spindle. This constant is usually stamped upon the name plate or marked upon the metal disk of the meter.

When using a rotating standard, the percentage registration of the meter under test in relation to the standard may be determined from the following formula.

Percentage registration

$$= \frac{100 \times \text{revolutions of test meter} \times \text{its constant}}{\text{revolutions of rotating standard} \times \text{its constant}} \quad (71)$$

If the percentage registration is below 100, the meter is slow; if above 100, it is fast by the percentage that the registration differs from 100.

When using indicating instruments and timing revolutions of the spindle with a stop watch, the following formulas may be employed, assuming the watts load to be known and the revolutions to be counted for 1 min:

$$\text{Correct rpm} = \frac{\text{watts load}}{\text{watt-hour per revolution} \times 60} \quad (72)$$

$$\text{Percentage registration} = \frac{100 \times \text{rpm observed}}{\text{correct rpm}} \quad (73)$$

130. Selection and Application of Instruments.—In selecting instruments for test measurements, it is important that instruments of proper range for the particular test be chosen—that proper consideration be given to the point upon the scale at which the indications are likely to occur. If an instrument of insufficient range is selected, it may be overloaded and damaged, the needle bent if the overload is slight and quickly removed, and the shunt or the operating coil damaged by overheating if the current is excessive or if the overload is not quickly removed. If an instrument of too high range is selected, the readings may have to be made at such low points upon the scale that considerable error is introduced. The best selection will provide instruments of such ranges that the majority of the test readings will occur over the central 50 percent of the scale—few if any in the lowest or the highest quarter.

In order that an instrument of proper range may be selected, the voltages and currents to be utilized must be known with a fair degree of accuracy. The maximum voltage of the circuit will usually be that of the voltage source, and the current values will be determined by the emfs and resistances of the circuit—one or both of which will usually be under the control of the operator. In case of doubt, of course, an instrument may be selected for the initial readings of larger capacity than will prove desirable for later use

If an instrument proves upon trial to have an excessive range for the values to be measured, it should, if possible, be exchanged for one of lower range.

Many instruments, especially voltmeters, have multiple ranges, the shift from one to another of the ranges being effected by turning a rotary switch or by shifting leads from one terminal to another. When using such instruments, it is wise to start with the highest range—shifting to a lower range only after a positive indication has shown that the shift may safely be made.

Several meter functions, with a wide varitey of ranges, are sometimes incorporated into a single case, with a single moving-coil unit that may be connected across shunts of various resistances or in series with multipliers of various resistances to give indications of amperes, volts, and possibly ohms as well upon one of several scales. Such instruments are valuable to the experienced test man, since a single instrument performs the duties of many single-function single-range instruments; but they are usually rather complicated for the beginner, the chances being considerably greater than with the simpler instrum.nts that errors will be made in connection, scale range, and scale readings.

After the choice of instrument has been made, its location in the circuit must be such that it correctly measures the quantity to be observed and is not affected appreciably in its accuracy by the magnetic fields (stray fields) set up by currents through adjacent conductors. The proximity of magnetic materials, such as steel panels, should be avoided, especially with instruments not protected against such outside influences by magnetic shielding. Also the presence of conductors carrying heavy currents is likely to affect the accuracy of unshielded instruments. Two unshielded instruments placed immediately adjacent to one another may have both their readings affected through interaction of the two magnetic fields. For such unshielded instruments, a spacing of 6 to 8 in. is desirable, whereas instruments having built-in magnetic shields may usually be set up with their outer cases in contact without appreciable loss in accuracy.

Unshielded instruments should be placed at an appreciable distance from current-carrying conductors. Shielded instruments are less likely to be affected by near-by currents but may have their readings affected if the currents are heavy. In general, straight conductors carrying 50 amp or less should be not less than 6 in. from unshielded instruments, this spacing being doubled for currents of 100 amp, etc.[1] For shielded instruments, appreciably less distance is necessary, but some precaution is still desirable.

131. Resistance Measurements.— The "drop-of-potential" method offers the simplest means of determining the resistance of armature and field circuits. It is a commonly used method and is sufficiently accurate except for very heavy low-resistance windings. For these, the more accurate "bridge" methods should be used.[2]

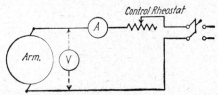

Fig. 170.—Determination of armature-circuit resistance by the drop-of-potential method.

In making determinations by the drop-of-potential method, a circuit is established as indicated in Fig. 170 from a convenient source (a storage battery may be used if no other d-c source is available) with a rheostat of sufficient capacity to control the current flow. For armature and series-field circuits, current values up to rated values as given on the name plate may be used, though it is not essential insofar as accuracy of determination is concerned. For shunt-field circuits, the maximum current is not likely to exceed 4 per cent of the name-plate value and may be considerably less. The maximum drop across the shunt field will be equal to the supply voltage but the drop across the armature and the series field, with rated current flowing, will be only a small percentage of this value. Consequently, a low-reading voltmeter will be required for accurate determinations of armature and series-field resistance.

[1] Electrical Instruments, Circular B2209a, Westinghouse Electric Corporation.

[2] See any standard work on electrical measurements.

Care should be taken to avoid error due to the instruments themselves when measurements are made of low-resistance circuits, such as armatures and series fields, by connecting the voltmeter directly to the terminals of the resistance circuit under consideration—not including the voltage drop through the ammeter or connecting leads and junctions. For low-resistance circuits, the error due to inclusion of the voltmeter current in the ammeter reading will be negligible. For relatively high resistance measurements, the error thus introduced may not be negligible but may be avoided, if the supply voltage is steady, by reading the two instruments separately; or a correction may be applied by calculating the voltmeter current and subtracting it from the reading of the ammeter. The voltmeter reads its own IR drop, and the resistance of the voltmeter is usually stated upon its rating plate.

Resistance measurements may be made after the machine has been in operation for several hours and the windings have attained normal operating temperature, but it is frequently more convenient and sufficiently accurate to make the determinations at room temperature and calculate the working resistance at an assumed operating temperature, 75°C being the generally accepted standard reference temperature. If, however, it is desired to calculate the temperature rise from resistance measurements, two sets of determinations must be made, one when the windings are at room temperature and another when they are at normal operating temperature.

In making cold-resistance determinations, low values of current should be used and the current left on the circuit only while readings are being made, in order to avoid heating the windings and thereby increasing their resistance. Some account should usually be taken of field-rheostat resistance if a field rheostat is in circuit during normal operation of the machine, since its losses are chargeable to operation of the machine.

The brush-contact resistance is found to vary with current flow, decreasing in value as the current rises. This being the case, a curve may be plotted between armature-circuit resistance and current values that will be concave upward; whereas resistance of the armature itself will not vary if the temperature does not vary.

The standards of the A.I.E.E. (Art. 146) recommend determination of the armature resistance alone and assumption of 2 volts total brush drop for determination of brush-contact loss when carbon

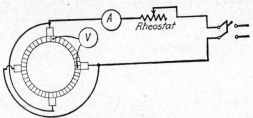

FIG. 171.—Determination of armature resistance exclusive of brushes and brush contacts.

or graphite brushes with shunts, or pigtails, are used, and assumption of 3-volts drop where shunts are not used. The armature resistance alone can be determined by placing the voltmeter leads in contact with the commutator bar nearest the center of two adjacent brushes, as shown in Fig. 171.

For determination of the insulation resistance between the conducting parts of a machine and its frame, a direct-reading instrument known as the *megger* (Fig. 172) is available. It is made upon the permanent-magnet, moving-coil principle and contains a small hand-driven d-c generator for supplying the test voltage. It is built in various ranges from 10,000 megohms to as low as 5 ohms and is of value for checking the condition of the insulation of electrical equipment during its manufacture as well as after installation.

FIG. 172.—The megger. (*James G. Biddle.*)

132. Speed Measurements.—In testing electrical machines, or in checking their performance, it is frequently necessary to determine speeds of rotation. The simplest device for determining such speeds is the *revolution counter*, used in conjunction with a watch or other timing device. When it is held in contact with the end of the shaft whose speed is to be determined, for a measured interval, the number of revolutions may be read from a scale and the rpm calculated—unless the interval has been exactly 1 min, when the rpm are read directly from the scale. The presumption of constant speed during the interval is necessary, of course, for determinations with the revolution counter. Otherwise the result is the average speed for the interval.

Fig. 173.—Hand tachometer in correct position for use. (*James G. Biddle Co.*)

Tachometers indicate the speed directly upon a scale and thus include the time element. They may be of the mechanical or the electrical type. The mechanical tachometer has its operation based upon the movement of weights by centrifugal action—similar to the centrifugal or fly-ball types of steam-engine governor —the speed being read from the position of a pointer upon a circular scale. The electrical tachometer is usually made in the form of a small magneto or d-c generator—the voltage being directly proportional to speed. The speed may therefore be read from the scale of a millivoltmeter and converted to rpm by use of a constant; or the millivoltmeter may be calibrated and marked directly in terms of rpm.

Reed tachometers are made up of a series of light reeds, varying in weight and length by carefully determined amounts, such that a suitable range of vibration frequencies is covered. Each reed is set in vibration as its resonant frequency is approached by vibrations from the machine whose speed is being determined, these vibrations being attuned to the speed of the machine. In its simplest form, the tachometer is held against the frame of the

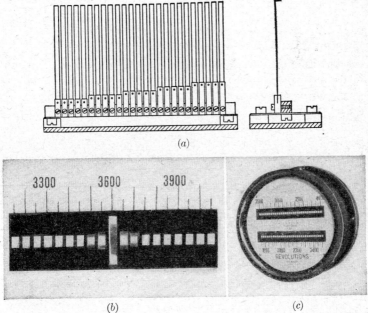

FIG. 174.—The vibrating-reed type of tachometer. (a) Tuned reeds. (b) Resonant vibration of reed at 3600 rpm. (c) One form of mounting. (*James G. Biddle Co.*)

rotating machine, and the speed is noted upon a scale opposite the reed having the widest amplitude of vibration. Since there are no rotating parts, there is little maintenance expense connected with this type of measuring device. It may be permanently bolted to the machine frame if desired.

Other and more expensive types of speed-indicating devices combine a chronometer element with a speed-counter element, the two being synchronized for automatic operation when the instrument shaft is brought into contact with the machine shaft and a release button pressed to initiate the timing movement. At the end of a very brief timing period, the pointer has rotated and stopped at the point corresponding to the speed, and the instrument may be withdrawn and read at leisure. Another button provides for returning the pointer to zero, thus resetting the mechanism for another observation.

A stroboscopic type consists of a neon lamp, with vacuum tubes and other equipment for forming an oscillator circuit for controlling the rate at which the lamp is flashed when connected to an a-c power supply of proper voltage and frequency. Since the flash rate of the lamp is controllable by simple means, it is only necessary to place the device in a position to illuminate the commutator, pulley, or shaft end of the machine whose speed is to be measured and then to adjust the flash rate until the moving part appears stationary, when the speed may be read from a dial. One advantage of this device lies in the fact that no physical contact with the machine under observation is necessary.

133. Motor Tests.—From the standpoint of the owner and operator of d-c motors, the tests of particular importance are those which reveal the following performance characteristics:

a. Efficiency, particularly at the normal load point.

b. Speed regulation.

c. Torque.

d. Temperature rise, for normal and overload conditions.

The efficiency for any load may be determined by direct measurement, loading the motor to the desired point by brake or dynamometer and measuring input and output, or by calculation of losses. The method of determining efficiency by calculation of losses is usually preferable because of steadier test conditions, the lesser effect of errors in making readings, and, in large machines, the difficulty of providing means to absorb the output. However, it is sometimes necessary or desirable to make direct determinations, and the methods employed are discussed in succeeding paragraphs. The method of determining efficiency by measurement or calculation of losses has been discussed and exemplified in Chap. IX.

The determination of speed regulation requires that the motor be loaded, although not necessarily in such a manner that the output can be measured. It may be loaded through connection to a generator, brake, machine tool, or by any other convenient means; and the speed may be measured at a sufficient number of points to permit a curve to be plotted between speeds as ordinates and amperes input as abscissas. If the result is to be thoroughly fair to the motor, the applied voltage should be held at, or very near, the rated, or name-plate, value, and the tests should be made when all parts are at normal operating temperature. Speeds may be determined by means of speed counters, which register the revolutions over a timed interval, or by a tachometer, which gives the rpm at any given instant. Any type of tachometer should be recalibrated at intervals and, if necessary, have corrections applied to its indications.

Torque may be determined directly from scale readings at the end of a brake arm or may be calculated from the horsepower formula (Art. 67) if horsepower and speed are known. Values of torque at various loads may be plotted as ordinates, against current input as abscissas; and the resulting curve may be utilized to study the performance of the motor under all load conditions within its range.

The temperature rise of field and armature windings, commutator, frame, bearings, etc., may be determined directly by thermometer measurements upon these points immediately following a run under any particular load condition for a duration of time sufficient to bring all parts of the machine to a constant temperature, *i.e.*, to such a point that heat is being dissipated at the same rate at which it is being generated. Care should be taken that the windings are not heated to a point that will prove injurious. If the motor appears to be heating unduly, the test should be terminated prior to the attainment of constant temperature, and the load should be reduced to a point that will result in attainment of a constant but safe operating temperature. This value of load should then not be exceeded for continuous operation. If the normal operation is for relatively short periods, however, a sufficiently increased load may be carried that will result in a maximum temperature not exceeding the safe value for the windings.

In all load tests, the commutation should be observed to see that such sparking as may occur is not sufficiently serious to prove injurious to the commutator. The brushes should be adjusted to the position that will give minimum sparking under average load conditions. For interpole machines, this position is the exact no-load neutral plane.

134. Motor Tests by Prony Brake —Prony brakes are made in various forms and styles, but the principle involved is as illustrated

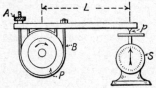

Fig. 175.—The Prony brake.

in Fig. 175. The brake pulley P is usually arranged for water cooling, sometimes with provision for continued circulation of water, in other types for insertion of water only in sufficient quantity to provide for evaporation. The brake band B should be lined with brake lining of the automobile type. The hand wheel A permits adjustment of the pressure and thereby of the load upon the motor.

The horsepower output of the motor is given by Eq. (45), Art. 67, as

$$\text{Hp} = \frac{2\pi ST}{33,000}$$

where S is the speed of the motor in rpm and T is the torque in pound-feet, equal to the product of net weight on the scale and length of brake arm in feet. The tare, or weight of the brake arm, must be subtracted from the gross weight indicated by the scale. The relative heights of brake pulley and scale top should be such that the brake arm is kept horizontal, and the pivot p should be placed near the center of the scale top or platform.

Small motors may sometimes be conveniently tested by the use of two spring dynamometers and a length of belt or brake lining, as indicated in Fig. 176, the dynamometers being held in place by hand if only approximate results are wanted, or supported by a framework if the results are to be more accurately checked. If

Fig. 176.— Brake test by use of spring dynamometers.

supported from a rigid framework, some means must be provided for adjusting the tension on the belt.

If F_1 and F_2 are the readings, in pounds, on the two dynamometers and D is the diameter of the pulley, then the torque output is equal to $(D/2)(F_1-F_2)$ lb-ft.

As previously indicated, brake tests are not usually considered to yield such accurate results as do certain other methods involving calculation of losses, the inaccuracy in the case of direct tests being due to the difficulty of maintaining steady load conditions during the test and to the fact that errors made on such tests have a more direct bearing upon the result than do errors of the same sort made in obtaining data for calculation of losses. For very large motors, it is impracticable to provide brakes of sufficient capacity to absorb the output.

Where it is desired to load a motor without means for determining its output, it may be belted to a generator, if one of sufficient capacity is available; and the generator may be loaded by means of a rheostat or lamp bank.[1]

135. Generator Tests.—The operating characteristics of d-c generators most likely to be of interest and importance are the following:

   a. Efficiency.

   b. Voltage regulation.

   c. Temperature rise.

The efficiency may be determined by direct measurement if means are available for determining the input, such as a motor whose efficiency is known for various values of input current, but the determination-of-losses method, as discussed and illustrated in Chap. IX, is usually the most accurate and convenient method.

The determination of voltage regulation requires that the generator be loaded and the output measured in amperes. The speed should be held at rated value and the voltage adjusted to rated value at full-load current output. Values of voltage may then be observed at various other loads, and a curve may be plotted between voltages as ordinates and current output as abscissas. The

[1] See Art. 17, p. 83.

machine should be at, or near, normal operating temperature when these tests are made.

The temperature-rise determinations should be made in the same manner as suggested for the motor. If desired in either motor or generator, the test may be shortened by operating the machine for a time under overload conditions, in order to bring the temperature more quickly to its normal operating value. Care should be observed, however, to reduce the load to its normal value in time to avoid having the temperature run past the desired point.

The same observations and precautions as to commutation should be observed as in a motor. If appreciable sparking occurs, the setting and spacing of the brushes should be carefully checked.

136. Efficiency by the Losses Method.—As noted under Art. 95, the mechanical and core losses, commonly referred to as the *rotational losses,* for a given generator or motor may be determined by operating the machine as a shunt motor at rated speed and excitation, measuring the input to the armature, and subtracting, or neglecting, the small no-load armature copper loss. Rated-load excitation may be assured by calculating the value of the generated emf—counter emf in a motor—and operating it at the correct applied voltage for obtaining the calculated voltage as counter emf during the running-light test. The basis for this lies in the fact that counter emf, or generated voltage, varies directly with speed and air-gap flux. With speed at rated value, by direct measurement, the flux should be at the same value in the air gap during the running-light test as in the motor or generator when operating at rated load, if the mechanical and core losses present during the no-load run are to duplicate mechanical and core losses present under rated-load operating conditions. This will be true if the counter emf during the running-light test has the same value as the counter emf or the generated voltage when operating at rated load and rated speed.

With motors or generators that are operated at or near constant speed and excitation, the mechanical and core losses determined by the running-light method may be considered, without serious error, to be constant for all loads. This applies generally to shunt motors and to shunt or separately excited generators, operated at constant speed. When the machine in question is a compound or series motor or generator, however, considerable error would be likely to be introduced by neglecting variations in the above losses with variations in load, speed, and excitation. For the compound generator, it would be necessary to determine, by the running-light method, the rotational losses for a range of generated emf covering the range from no-load to rated-load operation of the generator, perhaps plotting a curve of losses from which the value could be read for each load for which losses were to be calculated.

With the compound or series motor, it would be necessary to have the speed curve to current input, in order that the machine might be operated at the correct speed corresponding to each given load or for a series of loads covering the range for which losses were to be tabulated. The speed curve may be calculated if the proper data are available (Art. 76), or it could be determined from actual test if the machine could be conveniently loaded. With the series motor, the series field should be separately excited and the motor operated at the speed, read from the speed curve, corresponding to the load condition for which the armature and series-field current would have this value. The no-load input to the armature then gives the mechanical and core losses with reasonable accuracy for the assumed load condition (note that the effect of armature reaction upon the field flux is here being ignored). A series of such no-load readings, at the values of field current and speed consistent with their values when the motor is operated under load, will yield data from which a curve of rotational losses against current input may be plotted. From this curve, the proper value of these losses may be read for each load condition for which the losses are being tabulated.

The computed values of copper loss will naturally include the armature, series-field, shunt-field, interpole-field, or such other field windings as may be upon the particular machine, all resistance values being corrected to a standard reference temperature of 75°C. The brush-contact losses are calculated upon an assumed standard drop for loads within the usual operating range of the machine (Art. 93).

137. Separate-drive Test.—As stated in Art. 95, certain losses in large generators and motors may be determined by separately exciting the shunt-field coils and driving the machine at rated speed by means of a small motor whose losses or efficiencies are known over the range of input values necessary for the test. It is preferable to have the two machines direct-connected, since a driving belt would introduce additional losses rather difficult of determination—and belt slippage may sometimes introduce error.

With the brushes lifted from contact with the commutator on the machine under test and zero field current, the residual magnetism in the field cores having been reduced to zero or as near thereto as practical, the machine should be driven at its rated speed. The output of the driving motor then represents the bearing friction and windage loss in the driven machine. With the brushes in contact with the commutator, and the machine operated until the brushes are well seated, the added power will be that due to brush friction. Next, the field may be excited to its normal value, and the added power required for driving the machine will be that due to the armature-core losses—hysteresis and eddy current.

If the machine under test is a motor, the values of the rotational losses will vary with speed of operation; and it may be desirable to determine them at more than one speed, since speed will vary more or less with load and changes in field excitation when the machine is in actual operation. Care should of course be exercised to see that the field excitation for a given speed corresponds, under test conditions, with that which would obtain under actual operating conditions. The method of determining the correct exciting current for a given speed will vary with circumstances. For small machines, it may be determined by direct test; and, for large machines, it may be necessary to resort to calculations based upon design specifications and data.

A reasonable approximation of the loss determinations by the separate-drive test, using a motor whose losses are unknown, may be obtained by simply taking the differences in input to the driving motor for the different test conditions previously noted— assuming the losses of the driving motor to be essentially constant. This may best be accomplished through the use of a driving motor of such rating that it is loaded, under the various test conditions, over a range not less than one-half rated load and not exceeding one and one-quarter rated load, thus maintaining operation upon the flat portion of its efficiency curve. Also the rated speed of the driving motor should correspond closely with that of the driven machine; or, if belted, the pulley sizes should be such as to enable the driving motor to be operated at or near its rated speed.

138. Tests by Use of Dynamometer.—One of the principal objections to the prony-brake test lies in the difficulty of holding the load steady while readings are being made. An electric-generator load usually results in much steadier indications on the instruments; and, if an efficiency curve has previously been determined for the generator, this means of loading and testing the motor is preferable to that of the prony brake. Calibrated machines of this sort are frequently used on test floors, the efficiency having been determined at all the loads and speeds for which tests are likely to be required. Certain inaccuracies are involved, however, because of variations in temperature and friction; and, for this reason, a dynamometer of the type described below forms a better loading device.

The electromagnetic dynamometer (Fig. 177) is an electric machine—which may act as either generator or motor—equipped with a movable stator having a lever arm that may bear upon a scale platform. This makes it necessary that the stator be well balanced and be provided with an auxiliary set of bearings. With the field energized and current flowing in the armature conductors, a torque is exerted upon the rotor conductors that reacts against the stator, tending to turn it in the opposite direction. With the lever arm against the scale platform, the stator cannot turn but registers the torque exerted upon the rotor. However, when operating as a motor, at constant speed and with no external load, no torque will be indicated upon the scale, although a torque sufficient to overcome brush friction, bearing friction, and windage is being developed, with a corresponding reaction between armature and field structure. The reason is that the drag due to friction and windage is balanced by the torque reaction between armature and field structure that produces the rotation. If, however, the armature of the dynamometer is rotated mechanically, with no armature current flowing and no magnetic interaction between armature and field, the scale will then indicate the torque effect of the brush and bearing friction. With proper corrections, therefore, the dynamometer may be operated as a motor for determining the input to generators or as a generator to determine the output of motors.

A motor under test is made to operate the dynamometer as a generator, which may be loaded in the usual way with resistors or

Fig. 177.—Direct-current torque dynamometer. (*Westinghouse Electric Corporation.*)

made to pump back power to the motor supply circuit. The torque output of the motor is determined from the dynamometer net-scale reading multipled by the lever arm, and the horsepower output is calculated in the same manner as with the prony brake (Art. 134). A generator may be similarly tested by having the dynamometer act as a motor, taking power from the line and utilizing it to determine the input to the generator.

139. Opposition Tests.—For direct tests upon larger machines than can be handled effectively as individual units, the opposition,

"load-back" or "pump-back," type of test may be used. This
method has the advantage that a relatively small amount of energy
is wasted in carrying out the tests, but it becomes rather complicated and requires a considerable amount of equipment if individual machine efficiencies are to be determined. For determinations of voltage regulation (of a generator) and speed regulation
(of a motor) and for temperature tests, the requirements are
somewhat simpler. In general, the methods involving calculation of losses are preferable where efficiency determinations are to
be made.

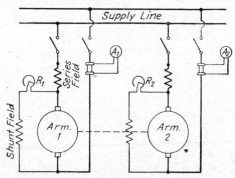

Fig. 178.—General plan for an opposition test.

In tests by opposition methods, two machines of equal capacity
are connected together mechanically and electrically and so
operated that one machine acts as a generator and the other as a
motor. The machine operating as motor drives the second machine as generator, the output from this machine then being returned to the input side of the motor. If both machines were
without losses of any kind, thus operating at 100 per cent efficiency,
the outfit would be self-contained; but, since there are losses to be
supplied, it is necessary that these be supplied, either electrically
or mechanically, from an outside source.

The simplest method is that illustrated in Fig. 179, known as
Kapp's method. Assuming that machine 1 is to be tested as a
motor, using machine 2 for loading, machine 1 would be started
in the usual way, using a starting resistor for reducing the starting
current and bringing the motor up to speed. The voltage on ma-

chine 2 is then caused to build up, and this machine is paralleled
with the supply line by adjusting its voltage to equal that of the
supply line and closing the switch, having first ascertained that the
voltage of the generator is opposed to that of the supply line.
Since the voltage of the generator (machine 2) is equal and opposite
to that of the supply line, no current will flow when the switch is
closed. In order to cause the generator to begin supplying power,
it is only necessary to increase its excitation, noting at the same
time the value of the current flowing from the generator to the
supply line as well as the value of the current flowing from the

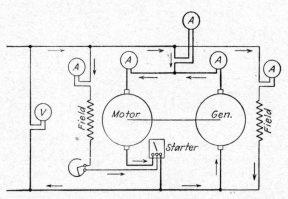

Fig. 179.—Motor-generator setup for an opposition test by Kapp's method.

supply line to the motor. Adjustment of the generator field
rheostat for amperes input to the motor, of the motor field rheostat
for speed, and of the supply-line voltage to rated value for the
motor will thus enable the proper test conditions to be attained.

Since the motor input must be greater than the generator output by the amount of the losses in the two machines, the excess of
motor input over generator output will be drawn from the supply
line. The energy wasted in conducting the test is thus kept to a
low figure as compared with that required for a brake test or
resistance-load generator test.

If the generator (machine 2) is to be tested instead of the motor,
the procedure is the same except that voltage, speed, and current

values are adjusted to rated conditions for the generator instead of the motor.

Kapp's method is frequently used for regulation and temperature tests and for determination of over-all efficiencies of motor-generator sets. Where it is desired to obtain accurately the individual machine efficiencies, this method alone is not to be depended upon, since both the copper losses and the core losses in the two machines are different. As an approximation, however, the total rotational-power loss may be divided between the two machines in proportion to their induced emfs. The copper losses may be calculated for each machine, since the currents and resistances are measurable.

Example—A 5½-kw shunt generator is direct-connected to a 7.5-hp motor and the generator is brought up to speed and connected in parallel with the supply line, as in Fig. 179, with suitable instruments for measuring input to the motor armature and output of the generator armature. Under this condition, after suitable adjustments to rated operating conditions have been made, the generator armature current is found to be 42.5 amp and the motor armature current 55.5 amp, the supply line consequently furnishing the difference, or 13 amp, in addition to the excitation current for the two fields. The armature-circuit resistances of the two machines were determined at rated current and normal operating temperature. For the motor, this was found to be 0.15 ohm, for the generator 0.12 ohm. To find the approximate values of rotational power loss for each machine, the procedure is as follows:
  Solution:

Power supplied by the line

$$120 \times 13 = 1560 \text{ watts}$$

Armature-circuit copper loss in the motor

$$\overline{55.5}^2 \times 0.15 = 462 \text{ watts}$$

Armature-circuit copper loss in the generator

$$\overline{42.5}^2 \times 0.12 = 217 \text{ watts}$$

Total rotational power loss

$$1560 - (462 + 217) = 881 \text{ watts}$$

Generated voltage of the motor

$$120 - (55.5 \times 0.15) = 111.7 \text{ volts}$$

Generated voltage of the generator

$$120 + (42.5 \times 0.12) = 125.1 \text{ volts}$$

$$\text{Motor rotational power loss} = \frac{111.7}{111.7 + 125.1} \times 881 = 416 \text{ watts}$$

and

$$\text{Generator rotational power loss} = \frac{125.1}{111.7 + 125.1} \times 881 = 465 \text{ watts}$$

140. Temperature Tests.—The object of heat tests is to determine whether the rise in temperature is below the value guaranteed by the manufacturer of the machine and whether the actual temperatures are below the maximum safe operating values assigned to the various classes of insulation (Art. 104).

Since it is impracticable to measure directly the "hottest-spot" temperature with thermometers, the use of either of the following methods is advocated by A.I.E.E. standards, with allowances for the difference between the temperatures arrived at by these methods and the actual hot-spot temperature.

a. Thermometer methods, by which thermometers are applied to the hottest part of the machine that is accessible to such application.

b. Resistance method, by which the hot resistance is measured and the average temperature of the winding calculated by reference to a known or "cold" resistance and temperature.

c. Embedded detector method, by which thermocouples or resistance temperature detectors are built into the machine in the regions calculated to reach the highest operating temperatures.

The recommended "conventional allowance," or marginal value to be added to the observed value in order to determine the estimated hottest-spot temperature, is

15°C for values determined by the thermometer method.

10°C for values determined by the resistance method.

5°C for values determined by the embedded detector method.

Before a temperature test is started, the machine to be tested should stand idle for a sufficient time to allow all its parts to reach the temperature of the surrounding air. Then the cold resistance of its armature and field circuits should be determined and the ambient temperature, or temperature of the surrounding air, noted. Thermometers should be attached to field coils, frame, and bearings with the bulb shielded from contact with the air. Normal load may then be applied and readings made of all thermometers at intervals of 10 or 15 min until no further rise is indicated. This usually requires 6 to 8 hr. When the temperature as indicated by the thermometers shows no further rise, the machine should be shut down and thermometers applied quickly to armature coils and commutator bars, the bulbs being shielded as before. Readings of all thermometers should then be made at 2-min intervals until the temperatures begin to fall. The hot resistance of all circuits should also be taken as quickly as possible after the shut down. The temperature rise of the stationary parts may then be calculated from the steady temperature near the end of the test and that of the rotating parts from the temperature immediately after shutdown. In addition, the temperature rise of the armature and field circuits may be calculated by the resistance method. The hottest-spot temperatures may then be estimated by adding the conventional allowance value, for the method used, to the external or average temperatures determined by the test.

Where it is impossible or inconvenient to take the necessary time for a temperature test as outlined above, the machine may be brought to steady operating temperature more quickly by overloading during the first hour or two and then reducing the load to its rated value. It is particularly important that rated conditions be closely adhered to during the final hour of the test run.

The machine under test should be shielded as far as possible from currents of air. The ambient temperature used in calculations should be the average of the readings of several thermometers located about the machine at distances of a few feet and on the same general level as the machine itself.

141. Acceptance Tests.—Contracts for the purchase of electrical machinery usually include guarantees, definitely stated or implied, as to its performance in operation; and, in order that the purchaser may feel assured that the terms of the contract are being met, some form of test is necessary. In large machinery, very complete tests are usually specified, as well as the manner in which they are to be made. Such tests may be made on the test floor of the manufacturing company, in the presence of the purchaser or his representatives as witnesses, or they may be made after installation if proper control of test conditions can be had.

For acceptance tests on the usual run of industrial equipment, such as motors, it is generally sufficient to operate the machine after installation under all load conditions to which it is likely to be subjected, noting the current input, supply voltage, speed, commutation, temperature (after its normal period of operation), and such other points as may be pertinent to the particular installation. A check-up of this kind should reveal any defects of sufficient consequence to justify refusal of the equipment. No equipment of any consequence should be accepted without a check test of some kind, and there is much less likelihood of misunderstanding and dissatisfaction if contracts include definite statements as to performance of the equipment under the working conditions for which it is intended.

142. Commutator Maintenance.—There are many causes of poor commutation; but, assuming reasonably good design and normal loading of the machine, the more likely ones may be listed as follows:

a. Brushes in wrong position.

b. Rough or unequally worn commutator.

c. Unequal brush spacing.

d. Insufficient brush tension.

e. Dirty commutator.

f. Open- or short-circuited armature coil.

On machines equipped with interpoles, it is particularly important that the brushes be located exactly in the neutral plane, and bad sparking may result from a slight shift. On machines without interpoles, the position of best commutation for a given average load can be determined only by trial and will vary as the load changes. It is not always possible, therefore, to obtain thoroughly satisfactory commutation on machines of this type.

Commutators may be roughened because of uneven wear or because the copper wears down faster than the mica insulating strips. In either case, the commutator should be trued up, either by use of a special tool applied while the armature is being driven under no-load conditions or by having it removed from the frame and placed in a lathe for a light cutting operation. Undercutting the mica—slotting it to a level slightly below that of the copper bars—is practical insurance against recurrence of trouble due to roughening.

Unequal brush spacing may be corrected by first checking accurately the distances between brushes and then rocking the brushes upon the studs as may be necessary to give equal spacings. The brushes that are changed should be refitted to give a proper bearing surface upon the commutator.

A brush pressure of 1 to $1\frac{1}{2}$ lb per sq. in. of contact area should cause the brush to hold to the commutator closely without heating by reason of excessive friction.

A dirty commutator results from the use of brushes that are too soft and oily. It may be cleaned by fine sandpaper pressed against it and slowly worked from side to side as it is driven at its usual speed. To prevent recurrence of the difficulty, slightly harder brushes may be substituted.

An open- or short-circuited armature coil may be suspected if bad sparking appears in a machine that has not previously given trouble from this cause. Checks described in Art. 144 should be applied to determine the exact nature and location of the difficulty. An open-circuited coil, if operation is allowed to continue, is likely to cause serious burning of the commutator bars to which it is attached, and a short-circuited coil may overheat to an extent that will necessitate its replacement.

A spare set of brushes should be kept on hand for each motor and generator. In selecting these, it is important that brushes of the proper degree of hardness be chosen, the preferable method being to purchase them through the firm supplying the machine.

In applying new brushes to the machine, each brush must be ground to a perfect fit by the use of fine sandpaper placed underneath the brush, as in Fig. 180. The strip of sandpaper is placed rough side up beneath the brush, held firmly against the commutator on either side of the brush in order to avoid rounding off the toe and heel, and drawn back and forth a sufficient number of times to insure a proper curvature to fit the commutator. For the final strokes, the sandpaper should be drawn only in the direction to be traveled by the commutator when the machine is in operation. Emery cloth should never be used on a brush or commutator, since the abrasive material is likely to become embedded in the brush and cut or groove the commutator. It may also become embedded between bars and result in the short-circuiting of a coil.

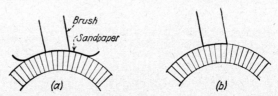

Fig. 180.—Fitting a new brush, with sandpaper.

When brushes properly adapted to a commutator are used, it is unnecessary and undesirable to have other lubricants applied to the commutator. The brush will contain sufficient graphite for lubrication, and further lubrication results only in undesirable softening of the brushes and gumming of the commutator. However, with a new commutator, it is sometimes necessary to furnish additional lubrication by an occasional touching up with a clean cotton rag upon which a few drops of machine oil have been placed, until a hard surface or glaze has been formed. A commutator in perfect condition may be recognized by the mirror-like sheen of its finely polished surface.

143. Bearings.—All bearings should be supplied with a good grade of oil, which should be renewed often enough to insure that the bearings are supplied with clean oil. When the oil wells are drained, they should be carefully flushed and cleaned before fresh oil is supplied.

When starting up a new machine, the bearings should be given close attention for several hours to see that their temperature does not become excessive. When a bearing does become seriously overheated, fresh oil should be supplied in liberal quantities, and the shaft should be kept turning slowly as the bearing cools in order to avoid "freezing" and sticking. Failure of oil rings to revolve and supply the bearing with oil is an occasional cause of overheating.

The wear of bearings should be checked occasionally. When evidence of sufficient wear to cause appreciable differences in air-gap width above and below an armature is discovered, the bearing shells should be replaced or rebabbitted. If wear of this kind is allowed to go unchecked, it may result in undesirable changes in the operating characteristics of the machine or may cause the armature to rub against the lower pole faces and result in breakage of band wires or other damage.

144. Winding Faults.—Faults likely to occur in armature or field windings are short circuits, open circuits, and grounds. These may or may not be obvious at once in the operation of the machine, but they are likely to manifest themselves eventually in the form of excessive heating, sparking at the commutator, or loss of voltage.

An open field circuit may be a cause for the failure of a generator to build up its voltage, or for the excessive speed of a motor, or its refusal to start. An ammeter may be inserted in the circuit to test the flow of current, or a "magneto," as used in old-style telephone sets, may be used to "ring out" the circuit. The actual location of the break may be determined by the use of a voltmeter, since, with the field switch closed, full voltage will appear across the gap in the circuit. Thus the voltmeter may be applied successively to the terminals of each field spool and of the field rheostat, and a reading will be secured only when the voltmeter is bridging the break in a circuit. A test lamp may be used instead of the volt-meter, provided that the current taken by the lamp is small in comparison with the normal field current.

A short circuit, by which one field spool or a fraction thereof is shunted, may be made evident through increased current and heating in the remainder of the circuit. A single "ground" to the framework of the machine may produce no visible effect, but volt-age will be found to exist between portions of the field circuit and the frame, resulting in a dangerous situation for operators or others touching the circuit when in contact with the framework of the machine. Two grounds will result in a portion of the field circuit being short-circuited. As a protection to operators, the framework of electrical machinery, switchboards, etc., should be definitely maintained at earth potential by means of a conductor connection to a copper plate buried in permanently moist earth, or to water piping that passes through damp earth.

Armature faults are frequently accompanied by excessive sparking at the commutator and should be remedied at once in order to prevent more serious damage. In order to locate the fault, the

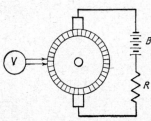

Fig. 181.—Test for open or short circuit.

machine should be shut down and the commutator and windings examined. Sometimes the fault can be located by direct examination, as when a short-circuited coil is made manifest by its excessive heating, or an open circuit by burns on the commutator bars connected to the coil that is open. When the trouble is not so manifested, however, the fault can usually be located with the aid of a battery and voltmeter, as in Fig. 181. When there is neither open circuit nor short circuit, the voltage drop should be the same between each pair of commutator bars for a particular path. But if a coil is short-circuited, there will be zero voltage drop across the bars to which its terminals are connected.[1] If there is an open-circuited coil in one of the paths, no current will flow through this path, and there will be zero voltage drop between each pair of commutator bars except the pair between which the open circuit is located, where the full battery voltage will appear.

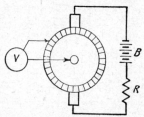

Fig. 182.—Test for grounds.

A grounded coil may be located by the method illustrated in Fig. 182, the voltmeter readings in this case being between each commutator bar and the armature shaft. If there is no ground, the voltage will be zero at all points; but, if a ground exists, the voltage readings will vary from point to point along the commuta-

---

[1] The type of winding on the armature will make some difference in the actual working out of these tests, but the same general method will be found to apply in all cases. Where there are more than two sets of brushes, all but two adjacent sets may be lifted from contact with the commutator.

tor and will be lowest at the segment nearest the grounded point. Continued search will probably reveal a second apparent ground in the other path, which is in parallel with the first. One of the two apparent grounds however, will prove to be a "phantom," made evident by the fact that there is an equipotential point in the second path corresponding to that in the first. The true ground may be distinguished from the apparent ground by marking the two points and then turning the armature through a part of a revolution and making another test. The true ground will appear at the same point for all positions of the armature, whereas the apparent ground will drift from point to point.

Repairs to armature windings should not be attempted by men not experienced in this line of work. Usually the wiser policy is to have repairs of this sort made by the manufacturer of the machine in question.

145. Electrical Codes.—The National Electrical Code [1] is a set of regulations for electrical wiring and apparatus as recommended by the National Fire Protection Association, in which are represented the various national electrical societies and insurance organizations interested in safety from fire hazard. It has no statutory force except in such cities as have ordinances providing that all electrical work done within their boundaries shall be done in accordance with the code. In many states and communities, however, the fire-insurance policies provide that all wiring and installation of equipment be done in strict accordance with the code, and its rules and regulations should therefore be considered to represent standard practice from the safety standpoint. Where local rules other than the national code are in effect, through ordinance or statute, they must of course be given precedence; but conflict between local requirements and the national code is unlikely. Where no legal or insurance requirement exists, the code should nevertheless be followed.

Cities having ordinances governing electrical installations re-

[1] The National Electrical Code is revised at two-year intervals, and a supplement and List of Approved Fittings is issued semiannually. Copies may be obtained from inspection bureaus, underwriters' association offices or direct from the National Board of Fire Underwriters, New York, N. Y.

quire that the work be inspected and passed by designated inspectors, to insure that local and code rules have been complied with. Where such inspection is not provided for, it is advisable in connection with installations of considerable magnitude to secure the service of an inspector from the nearest insurance underwriters' bureau to pass upon the work. Only qualified electricians, familiar with the requirements for safe wiring installations, should be employed.

The National Electrical Safety Code [1] is a set of rules similar to the National Electrical Code but broader in scope. It is published in the form of a handbook by the U.S. Bureau of Standards in cooperation with the American Engineering Standards Committee, representing the leading engineering societies, manufacturers' associations, state public service commissions, jobbers' associations, industrial accident commissions, etc., of the country, and has been approved by the American Engineering Standards Committee as an American standard. Its rules cover the installation and maintenance, from the safety standpoint, of stations and substations, with their equipment; of overhead and underground transmission and distribution lines, storage batteries, switchboards, fuses, circuit breakers, switches, and controllers; of hoists, elevators, communication apparatus where adjacent to electric power lines, etc.

146. A.I.E.E. Standards.—Since the year 1898, the American Institute of Electrical Engineers has, through a standards committee, guided the development of standards in the electrical field. The work of this committee on standards now covers a wide range, including standards for insulators, conductors, cables, measuring instruments, etc., in addition to the various types of motors and generators. The proposed nomenclature, test procedures, etc., embodied in some forty pamphlets, each devoted to a specific subject or type of equipment, are published by the institute and made available through its secretary for a nominal sum to cover cost of publication.

[1] Copies of the National Electrical Safety Code may be secured from the Superintendent of Documents, U.S. Government Printing Office, Washington, D. C.

CHAPTER XIII

BATTERIES

147. Classification.—Batteries may be divided into two general classes: (*a*) primary batteries, or batteries that are non-reversible in their action and (*b*) secondary batteries, or those which are completely reversible in that they can be restored to their original state after discharge by application of an external voltage sufficient to cause current flow through the battery against the emf of the battery. Primary batteries can be restored to their original condition after discharge only by addition of fresh materials; whereas secondary batteries, or storage batteries as they are more generally known, are reversible and can be put through a number of cycles of charge and discharge limited only by deterioration of the plates and wastage of the active material. They are essentially transformers of energy. The action on charge is the transformation of electrical energy into chemical energy, in which form it is retained until needed, when the reverse transformation is caused to take place, the stored chemical energy being transformed back into electrical energy. Each of these transformations is accompanied by certain losses, however, and the available energy from the battery is therefore always less than that put into it.

The battery unit is the *cell*, consisting of plates or electrodes, of material that has proved suitable for the purpose, partly immersed in a solution called the *electrolyte*; the result being an emf between the ends or terminals of the electrodes that project above the surface of the electrolyte. Current is considered to flow from the positive terminal when the cell is supplying energy to an external circuit. It is at a higher potential than is the negative terminal, by which current enters the cell. In the zinc-acid-copper cell, the copper forms the positive electrode, called the *cathode*, and the zinc forms the negative electrode, or *anode*.

As current flows from and through a cell, chemical reactions are taking place, resulting usually in the formation of gas at one or both plates. Thus, in the zinc-acid-copper cell, hydrogen appears at the copper plate when the cell is discharging. This by-product of discharge, accompanied usually by temporary changes in concentration of electrolyte adjacent to the plates, is called *polarization*. Polarization tends to reduce the useful voltage of the cell during discharge, especially in the primary types of cell, but its effects disappear and the voltage returns to normal when the cell is allowed to "recuperate" for a time on open circuit. Certain chemical agents, whose function is to minimize the polarization effects, are usually included in the makeup of primary cells.

The battery may consist of any number of cells in series or in parallel, according to the requirements of the circuit to which it is being applied. If similar cells are connected in series, the total emf will be the emf of one cell times the number of cells in series, and the permissible current rating of the battery will be the same as for a single cell. With similar cells in parallel connection, on the other hand, the emf of the battery will be the same as that of a single cell, and the permissible current rating will be that of a single cell times the number of cells in parallel. Series-parallel combinations will provide voltages and currents calculated by further application of the same basic principles, though the need for such combinations is rarely encountered.

148. Primary Batteries.—Primary cells in general may be classified as *wet* cells or *dry* cells, and wet cells may be divided into *single-fluid* and *two-fluid* cells. There are many combinations of metals and solutions, or electrolytes, that form satisfactory batteries; but only a few of these are used to any extent, many having failed to survive because of high cost, low efficiency, rapid deterioration, or other reasons.

The Daniell cell is an example of the two-fluid wet type. It is made up with copper (cathode) and zinc (anode) electrodes, the zinc electrode being immersed in a zinc sulfate solution, $ZnSO_4$, and the copper electrode in a copper sulfate solution, $CuSO_4$, the copper sulfate acting to prevent polarization, or formation of hydrogen gas at the copper electrode, which intereferes with the action of the battery. The two solutions may be kept separate by placing the zinc electrode and zinc sulfate inside an unglazed earthenware cup, which is in turn set into the solution of copper sulfate within which the copper electrode is placed; or, as in a modification known as the *gravity cell*, the copper electrode may be placed in a solution of copper sulfate at the bottom of a jar and the zinc in the solution of zinc sulfate at the top of the same jar, the difference in density of the two solutions serving to keep them separate (see Fig. 183). The voltage of the Daniell and gravity cells is slightly over 1 volt. The internal re-sistance is relatively high, and it is therefore suitable only for low-current applications.

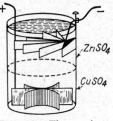

Fig. 183.—The gravity cell.

*Neither the Daniell nor the gravity cell is adapted to open-circuit applications because of the diffusion between the two liquids that takes place when the cell stands idle, the re-sult of such diffusion being the deposition of copper on the zinc plate. The gravity cell pictured here has been used extensively as a source of electrical energy on railway-telegraph systems.

The Bunsen cell develops a voltage of 1.9 to 2 volts and has low internal resistance. It consists of a zinc positive plate immersed in a sulfuric acid solution and a carbon negative plate, in the form of a rod, immersed in nitric acid, contained in a separate porous cup. Since it has low internal resistance, it is suited for high rates of discharge or heavy-current work. It cannot be allowed to stand on open circuit, however, but must be set up anew each time it is used. It also gives off the noxious vapors of nitric peroxide, which must be drawn off during operation of the cell.

Several other types of cell have been devised and are used to a limited extent, among them being the Grove cell; the chromic acid, or bichromate, cell; the Edison-Lalande cell; and the Leclanche cell.[1] Of these, the Leclanche cell finds the widest application, in a modified form known as the "dry" cell, described in the next article. In its earlier form, the Leclanche cell consisted of a carbon rod cathode contained in a porous cup, tightly packed in a mixture of crushed carbon and manganese dioxide—the depolarizing agent.

[1] Descriptions of these and other types of primary cell may be found in "Standard Handbook for Electrical Engineers," 7th ed., McGraw-Hill Book Company, Inc., 1941.

In more recent forms, the manganese dioxide and carbon are formed into a cylinder by molding, with a binding agent, in order to bring about a more intimate contact between the carbon and the manganese dioxide. A zinc anode, in the form of a rod, is suspended in a jar filled with ammonium chloride (sal ammoniac). The cell develops about 1.4 volts but, because of resistance drop and rapid polarization, is usually considered to furnish 1 volt per cell under conditions of use. It is best suited to circuits of intermittent duty, with frequent recuperation periods.

149. Dry Batteries.—The dry cell is a modification of the Leclanche cell, with the electrolyte kept from "slopping" by reason of its retention in absorbent blotting material and with the top of the cell permanently closed with a special sealing compound. The container is a zinc "can," which serves as the negative electrode. Its bottom and sides are lined with absorbent material, and a carbon rod is inserted in the center, packed about with a filler of finely crushed coke and powdered manganese dioxide, the absorbent material on the outer side as well as the filler being saturated with a solution of sal ammoniac and zinc chloride. Binding posts are attached to the top of the carbon rod and the zinc container; or, if the cells are to be connected in series, a projection may be left atop the carbon rod to make contact with the bottom of the next cell in series. The cells are usually covered with a cylindrical cardboard casing for protection against accidental circuit contacts.

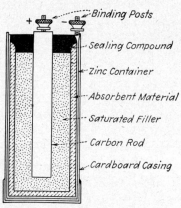

Binding Posts

Sealing Compound

Zinc Container

Absorbent Material

Saturated Filler

Carbon Rod

Cardboard Casing

Fig. 184.—The dry-cell, sectional view.

For use in flashlights, the cells are held in contact, the top of one to the bottom of another, by a spring in the end of the screw cap—the circuit being completed through a switch, the case at one end and the light bulb at the other. For high-voltage batteries, of low current capacity, a considerable number of the cells may be assembled for series addition of voltages and sealed in a block of insulating compound. For low-voltage batteries of current capacity higher than that which a single cell can furnish, the parallel connection arrangement may be used, either through the connection of individual cells or through permanent sealing into blocks.

The open-circuit voltage of a new dry cell may be as high as 1.6 volts, but, for the same reasons as mentioned in connection with the wet type of Leclanche cell, the voltage in service is usually about 1 volt per cell. This decreases somewhat with age because of increase in internal resistance.

Dry cells are subject to "shelf wear" or depreciation when not in use, and reputable manufacturers therefore date the cells for the protection of the purchaser. Most such cells become worthless within 12 to 15 months after manufacture, whether used or not. The rate of deterioration is greater with high temperatures. Cells not in use should therefore be stored in locations that are as cool as possible. Below-freezing temperatures do not affect them seriously except that, at excessively low temperatures, the voltage and service life are both decreased appreciably.

Dry cells are used for many applications of relatively low energy and current requirements, of intermittent or infrequent operational types. Among these are gas-engine-ignition applications, doorbells and other signal devices, some types of telephone equipment, portable lanterns, flashlights, and radio receivers. In general, there are three standard sizes of cell or battery available: the large cells, about 6 in. high by $2\frac{1}{2}$ in. diameter, the flashlight cells, and the block batteries of 15 or 30 cells for B batteries on radio-receiving sets.

150. Standard Cells.—Since instruments, such as voltmeters and ammeters, are subject to varying degrees of depreciation in practical use, with resulting variations in accuracy from time to time, it is essential that means be available for their calibration by comparison with more accurate standards. From Ohm's law, if two of the three quantities, volts, amperes, and ohms, are known, the third can be calculated. To be of value as standards, not only must the value of the quantities be accurately known but they must be known to yield the same values, under the same conditions, at different times and places; also the unit must be capable of reproduction, with other units yielding the same values, under the same conditions, as the original unit. It is easy to make reliable standard resistance units, but to produce reliable sources of emf or current for use as standards of reference is neither simple nor easy.

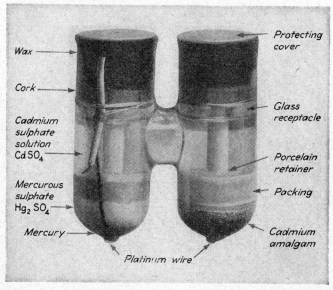

Fig. 185.—Weston standard cell. (*Weston Electrical Instrument Corporations*)

Experience indicates that a standard of voltage is easier to manufacture and maintain than a standard of current. Many attempts have been made by physicists to produce a thoroughly reliable *standard cell*, but very few have withstood the test of time and gained recognition for themselves as practical standards of voltage reference. An example of such a cell is the Weston cell, pictured in Fig. 185. It is claimed for the Weston cell that it is possible to reproduce them with emfs differing by only a few parts in 100,000. Its emf is affected only slightly by variations in temperature, and corrections can be accurately made.

In the Weston standard cell, the cathode is mercury, placed at the bottom of one leg of an H tube. Next is a layer of mercurous sulfate in paste form. A porcelain tube, expanded at the bottom and packed with cotton, serves both to hold materials in place and to vent such gases as may be formed. The anode, of cadmium amalgam, is placed at the bottom of the second leg of the H tube, and this also is held in place by a porcelain tube packed with cotton. Cadmium sulfate solution forms the electrolyte, and leads for attaching to binding posts are sealed into the bottom of the tubes. The upper part of the cell is sealed with cork and wax, and the completed cell is usually mounted in a case, with only the binding posts exposed.

The Weston cell is made in two forms, the "normal," or saturated, cell and the "standard," or unsaturated, cell. Cadmium sulfate crystals are left in the solution of the normal cell so that it is always saturated, and the solution of the unsaturated cell is saturated at 4°C, with no crystals left in the solution. The unsaturated cell has practically no temperature coefficient, whereas, in the normal cell, the emf changes slightly with temperature. The normal cell is considered to be more permanent and reliable as a standard and is the official standard. Its emf is accepted, by international agreement, as being 1.01830 volts at 20°C. However, the unsaturated cell is considered more satisfactory for general use and is the form furnished by the Weston Electrical Instrument Corporation, who certify the voltage, between 1.0185 and 1.0190 volts, for each cell supplied by them.

The standard cell is not to be used as a current source, it not being considered permissible to take more than 0.0001 amp from the cell at any time. Instead it is used in voltage-balance work, with potentiometers,[1] in which precise measurements are made by comparison methods, where, in making preliminary adjustments, the standard cell is protected by a resistance in series with it of not less than 10,000 ohms. For final checks, after a balance has been practically obtained, the resistance is removed.

If the cell is moved to a location where the temperature is per-

[1] See ROLAND B. MARSHALL, "Measurements in Electrical Engineering," John S. Swift Co., Inc., Cincinnati, Ohio, 1943.

ceptibly different, it should be allowed to stand for several hours
before using, in order that all parts of the cell may have reached
the same temperature. By this means, precise determinations
can be made without the necessity of current flow from the standard cell. It is thus used to compare secondary standards with
national standards and may also be used to compare national
standards with international standards. And, by the use of auxiliary equipment, it may also be used to measure current and
resistance. Thus the standard cell, with the potentiometer, is

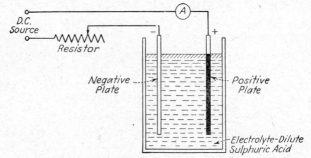

Fig. 186.—A simple form of storage cell.

the basis for accurate calibration of all current- and voltage-
measuring instruments.

151. Storage Batteries.—Certain of the so-called primary cells
are partly reversible and can be used to a limited extent as storage
batteries; but, since a certain amount of the material used in the
battery is wasted during each cycle of charge and discharge, the
life of such cells is short. Only two types of storage cell have
proved enduring enough to become generally accepted and widely
used, the lead-acid cell and the Edison, or nickel-iron alkaline cell.

A simple form of lead-acid cell may be made by immersing two
strips of lead sheet in a glass tumbler of dilute sulfuric acid (Fig.
186), the plates having previously been scored to increase their
surface area. When the plates are connected in series with a
suitable resistor and to a source of direct current, the circuit being
completed through the electrolyte, it will be observed that gas
bubbles are given off at each plate and that one plate gradually

changes color, becoming dark chocolate, while the other plate retains its original color. After charging for a time, the power may be disconnected and the cell found capable of supplying a small current, through suitable resistance, for a limited time. The chocolate-colored plate is the positive plate, or cathode, the other, having become more spongy than the original plate, the negative plate, or anode. When charging, hydrogen bubbles may be observed to come from the negative plate, while bubbles of oxygen come from the positive plate. Because of the presence of these gases, bare flames should never be allowed near a lead-acid battery while it is being charged.

Batteries for commercial and industrial applications vary greatly in size, shape, number of cells, method of manufacture, and assembly of plates. Batteries intended for stationary use and not subject to frequent or excessive overloads may be given heavier plates, with consequent lower deterioration and longer life than batteries intended for portable service where weight and the ability to discharge rapidly are of greater importance than long life.

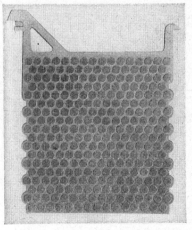

Fig. 187.—Manchester positive plate. (*The Electric Storage Battery Company.*)

152. Construction of the Lead-acid Battery.—The lead-acid cell has a positive plate of lead peroxide, PbO_2, and a negative plate of sponge lead, Pb, immersed in a dilute solution of sulfuric acid, H_2SO_4. The plate materials are not of this exact composition, however, when first inserted in or on the plate but are formed electrolytically on the plate as a part of the manufacturing process.

Various methods are used in the formation of battery plates. One of the oldest types of plate, the Planté type, has the active material formed electrochemically from the material of the plate itself, in a fashion similar to that described for the simple battery

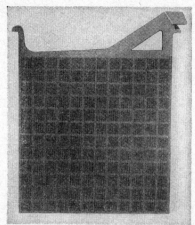

Fig. 188.—Box negative plate. (*The Electric Storage Battery Company.*)

of the preceding paragraph. The active material being thus an integral part of the plate, the loss of material in service is slow and is automatically replaced by fresh formation. The Manchester type (Fig. 187) has the active material for the positive plate rolled and inserted in holes in a hardened-lead frame. Other forms, known as *pasted-plate* types, have the material spread over a grid-work for holding it in place and at the same time pro-

viding a large, easily penetrable body of active material. By this method, lighter, lower resistance batteries, capable of discharging at high rates, can be produced, but at some sacrifice of durability. Batteries for automobile starting and ignition service have plates made in this manner. The iron-clad type of plate (Fig. 189) consists of cylindrical hard-rubber casings that hold the active material, these being supported by a hardened lead-alloy framework. Free access of electrolyte is provided by small holes or slots.

The positive plate has, inherently, a greater tendency to deterioration than the negative plate, and much greater care is

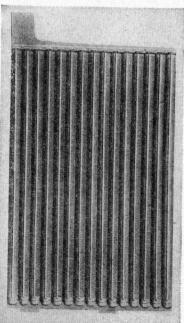

Fig. 189.—Positive plate of Exide iron-clad battery. (*The Electric Storage Battery Company.*)

usually expended in its design and manufacture. Hence, the positive and negative plates for a given battery may differ in design.

Groups of positive and negative plates are sandwiched together to form the completed battery, insulating separators being used to prevent the plates from coming into contact through expansion or buckling. Current capacity is a function of plate area; therefore

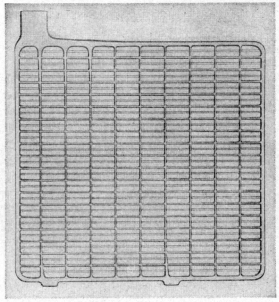

Fig. 190.—Grid for pasted-plate battery. (*Willard Storage Battery Co.*)

the greater the number of plates in parallel the greater will be the rated current output of the battery. For voltages greater than that given by a single cell, two or more separate cells must be connected in series.

Figures 190 to 192 illustrate the appearance of the components of a pasted-plate battery for starting and lighting purposes in an automobile, and Fig. 193 shows a cutaway view of the assembled battery. The grid forms the framework of the plate, and the active material is inserted upon and into the latticework of this grid to form the plate. The chief ingredient of the active material initially is lead oxide. This is mixed into a soft paste and spread evenly over and into the grid framework by special machines designed for the purpose. The plates are then dried in ovens having controlled temperature and humidity conditions. They are then assembled and placed in large tanks of dilute acid and given a forming charge, which changes the material of the positive plate

Fig. 191.—Groups of finished positive and negative plates—partly sheathed. (*Willard Storage Battery Co.*)

to lead peroxide, PbO_2, and the material of the negative plate to sponge lead, Pb. The color of the positive plate is then a chocolate brown and that of the negative plate is a slate gray. The plates are then dried and assembled into containers of hard rubber. The three-cell battery, having a nominal 6-volt rating, is generally used for passenger automobiles; and the 6-cell battery, with a nominal rating of 12 volts, is used for motor busses, trucks, and larger vehicles.

In assembling the plates into positive and negative groups, special separators of treated wood, porous rubber, or fiber glass are used. One more negative than positive plate is used in the assembly in order to provide for the uniform working of all the positive plates. The lugs at the plate tops are welded to a connecting strap that places all the positive plates in parallel and connects them to the positive cell post and places all the negative plates in

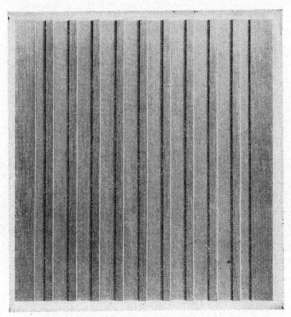

FIG. 192.—A wood separator. (*Willard Storage Battery Co.*)

parallel and connects them to the negative cell post. The several cells are then connected in series by connecting positive to negative by suitable connectors, the end posts being left for connection to the external circuit.

153. Chemical Reactions.—The complete chemical reaction in the lead-acid cell is rather complicated, but the fully charged state finds the material on the positive plate converted into lead peroxide, PbO_2, while that on the negative plate has become metallic lead of a rather soft, spongy texture. During discharge, lead sulfate, $PbSO_4$, is formed upon both plates, and water, H_2O, is released and goes into solution to dilute the electrolyte. Thus the specific gravity of the electrolyte is lowered with discharge and raised again during charge, becoming thus a ready means for determining the state of charge of the battery.

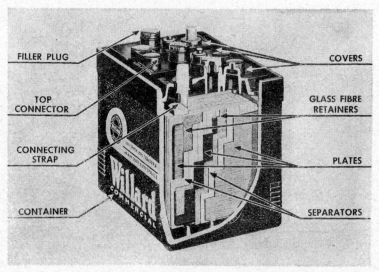

FILLER PLUG

TOP CONNECTOR

CONNECTING STRAP

CONTAINER

COVERS

GLASS FIBRE RETAINERS

PLATES

SEPARATORS

Fig. 193.—Cutaway view of the automobile-type battery. (*Willard Storage Battery Co.*)

The principal chemical reactions involved may be indicated by the following equation:

$$PbO_2 + Pb + 2H_2SO_4 \underset{\text{Charge}}{\overset{\text{Discharge}}{\rightleftarrows}} 2PbSO_4 + 2H_2O \qquad (74)$$

When a cell is being charged at a high rate, or is being "overcharged," an electrolysis action, known as *gassing*, takes place and results in the liberation of hydrogen at the negative plate and oxygen at the positive plate. A mixture of gases that is highly explosive thus results, and great care should be exercised to prevent accumulations of these gases about the battery. This action results in a loss of water in the electrolyte, which must be replaced at intervals. The gassing may also result in loss of small quantities of electrolyte in the form of spray. This, however, is usually of little consequence as far as its effect upon the operation of the battery is concerned.

If a cell is discharged to a very low value or if it is allowed to remain in a partly discharged condition for a considerable period of time, the lead sulfate on the plates tends to pass into an insoluble form that renders restoration to the original state of full charge a matter of considerable difficulty. Unless care is exercised, therefore, to keep the battery reasonably well charged at all times or to recharge promptly following an extensive discharge, the plates are likely to be permanently damaged.

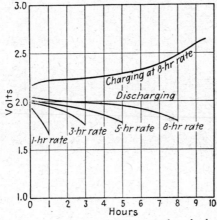

FIG. 194.—Typical charge and discharge curves for a lead-acid battery.

Storage batteries, like primary cells, discharge slowly when not in use and will eventually become seriously sulfated and damaged if left in storage, without recharging, for long periods of time. If not in normal use, with alternate charge and discharge periods, the battery should be given an occasional freshening charge if it is to be kept in proper condition. During winter storage of cars, boats, etc., the battery should be removed and placed in the care of a battery station where the necessary replenishing charges will be applied at suitable intervals.

154. Operating Characteristics.—A typical voltage curve for the lead-acid battery is shown in Fig. 194. This shows the average voltage on discharge to be near 2 volts. Near the end of discharge, the voltage begins to drop rapidly; and, to avoid possible damage to the plates, the discharge should not be carried beyond 1.8 volts, measured with rated current flowing.

On discharge, the terminal voltage of the cell is less than its actual emf but, on charge, a voltage greater than the emf must be applied. Near the end of the charging period, the voltage that must be applied rises rapidly, making it necessary to provide a maximum voltage of about 2.5 volts per cell in order to insure proper charging of a battery, at a reduced charging rate.

The efficiency of a battery may be determined as the ratio of ampere-hours obtained on discharge to ampere-hours necessary for restoration of the charge, called the *ampere-hour efficiency*; but the true efficiency is the ratio of watt-hours output to watt-hours input, for the complete discharge and charge of the battery.[1]

Batteries for stationary service are commonly rated on an 8-hr normal discharge basis. Thus a 200 amp-hr battery would be a battery capable of furnishing 25 amp for 8 hr. Batteries intended for portable service, however, are given ratings based on shorter discharge periods, such as 5 or 6 hr. For the combined lighting and starting service to which automotive batteries are applied, it is considered necessary to have two ratings—the first indicating the lighting ability of the battery and being the capacity in ampere-hours when discharged continuously at a rate of 5 amp, to a final voltage of not less than 1.8 per cell; and the second indicating the engine-starting ability of the battery and being the rate in amperes at which the battery will discharge for 20 min continuousy, to a final voltage of not less than 1.5 per cell, the starting temperature in each case being 80°F.

In practice, it is not usually possible so to control conditions that the normal rate of discharge from a battery can be closely adhered to, nor is it particularly desirable that this be done, since such limitation would frequently defeat the purpose for which the

---

[1] The term *volt efficiency* is also sometimes used, this being taken to mean the ratio of average volts on discharge to average volts on charge. The watt-hour efficiency then becomes the product of ampere-hour efficiency and volt efficiency.

battery was installed. An excessive discharge rate for a short period of time is not likely to damage the plates, but the high discharge rate should not be maintained long enough to exhaust the battery or to cause excessive temperatures or buckling of the plate due to rapid formation and expansion of the active material. The chief danger lies in discharging below the lower working voltage limit, resulting in sulfation that will be difficult to remove. However, some makes of cells are designed to tolerate practical exhaustion at excessive discharge rates without permanent damage if the battery is promptly recharged.

The available capacity of a battery in ampere-hours is a function of the discharge rate, and therefore less energy can be taken from the battery at high rates of discharge. This is due to the fact that, at high discharge rates, sufficient time is not allowed for diffusion of the electrolyte. The solution in the pores of the plates therefore becomes more dilute than in the main body of the cell, and the cell is exhausted more quickly than when discharge is proceeding at a less rapid rate.

Fig. 195.—Lead-acid cell for stationary service. (*The Electric Storage Battery Company.*)

If allowed to stand for a time, however, the cell will recuperate, as the electrolyte diffuses, and may then be discharged still further.

A battery is less active at low temperatures, both the voltage and ampere-hour capacity being reduced while under this condition. When in use, however, batteries are self-warming to a considerable extent by reason of the conversion of resistance losses into heat. There is little danger of freezing as long as the battery is kept well charged, as indicated by the curve (Fig. 196) and the following chart.[1]

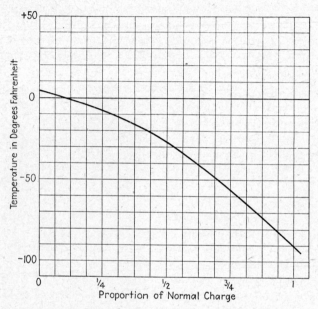

Fig. 196.—Curve showing the approximate freezing points of lead-acid cell electrolyte for various states of charge.

FREEZING TEMPERATURES OF ELECTROLYTE IN LEAD-ACID BATTERIES FOR VARIOUS DENSITIES WITHIN THE NORMAL WORKING RANGE

Specific Gravity	Freezing Point, °F
1.275	− 85
1.250	− 62
1.225	− 35
1.200	− 16
1.175	− 4
1.150	+ 5
1.125	+ 13
1.100	+ 19
1.000 (water)	+ 32

[1] From Electric Storage Battery Company Technical Manual for Automotive Batteries.

155. Care of Lead-acid Batteries.—Care must be taken to see that lead-acid batteries are not allowed to stand for long intervals in a wholly or partly discharged state. A freshening charge should be given about once a month to an idle battery if it is to be kept in the best of condition and ready for service when wanted. When, because of unexpected or emergency demands, the battery has been discharged to, or below, the established lower limit of voltage, or specific gravity, it should be recharged at once. When this is done, no permanent damage need be expected, but a delay in recharging may render complete recovery very difficult or even impossible.

With lead-acid cells, the hydrometer reading provides a satisfactory and reasonably accurate means of determining the state of charge. Such readings should not be taken immediately following the addition of water to the cell, but only after sufficient time has elapsed to insure a uniform density. The specific-gravity range varies somewhat with different makes of battery and with batteries designed for different purposes but in general runs from about 1.25 at full charge to about 1.15 when discharged to the lowest point to which the discharge can be carried without endangering the plates. Batteries for automobile service are commonly operated at somewhat higher densities than those designed for stationary service— a specific-gravity reading of 1.280 usually indicating full charge for the automobile type of battery. Regardless of its normal full-charge gravity reading, however, a battery should not be considered fully charged until its specific gravity shows no further rise with continued charging—the final measure of full charge always being the highest attainable density value.

Battery hydrometer readings do not indicate the true condition of the battery at all temperatures until corrections are applied. Most battery manufacturers adjust the acid content for maximum accuracy at 80°F, but a few use 60°F as a standard or reference temperature. The recommended correction in either case is 0.004 specific gravity per 10°F deviation from the standard reference temperature—to be added to the hydrometer reading for temperatures above the reference temperature and subtracted for temperatures below the reference temperature. Although no serious error

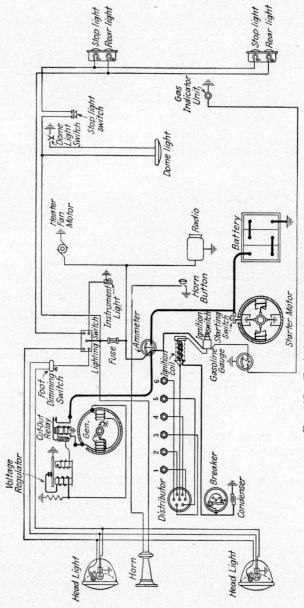

Fig. 197.—Typical wiring diagram for an automobile.

will result from failure to apply this correction at ordinary temperatures, it may be seen that erroneous conclusions may be reached if only the uncorrected hydrometer readings are considered at very high or very low temperatures of the electrolyte.

As an alternative device, the ampere-hour meter is available for measuring the output and input of the battery. In order to use this method satisfactorily, the approximate ampere-hour efficiency of the battery must be known and the required number of additional ampere-hours supplied to the battery over and above that taken from it during discharge. Determination of the state of charge of a battery by measurement of terminal voltage is not a dependable means unless conditions are such that the current can be closely controlled, since the curve values of discharge voltage apply only for specified discharge-current values.

Care should be observed that pure water is added to cells with sufficient frequency that no portion of the active plate surface is exposed to the air. The safest practice is to add only distilled water, since other waters are likely to have dissolved in them substances that react harmfully in the battery.

Batteries should be protected from too great changes in temperature, particularly during the winter season, since the capacity is considerably reduced at low temperatures. The battery should be protected from danger of freezing by keeping it well charged.

Proper charge and discharge rates for a given battery should be obtained from the manufacturer and these values adhered to within reasonable limits. It is usually permissible to exceed the normal charging rate for the first hour or two of recharging a completely discharged battery, provided that the excess is not sufficiently great or sufficiently prolonged to cause the plates to become overheated. Two very common sources of damage to plates are overheating due to excessive charge or discharge currents, and the tearing away of active material from the plates due to excessive gassing when the finish charging rate is too high or the charging period unnecessarily prolonged. An occasional overcharge at a low rate is advisable, however, in order to insure that no sulfate remains upon the plates.

Plates that have, through neglect or abuse, become badly sulfated may sometimes be brought back to normal by a prolonged "soaking" at a low rate or, in extreme cases, by charging with pure water as electrolyte—replacing the water with fresh electrolyte of the proper specific gravity when the charge has been completed and going through one or two cycles of discharge and charge, at somewhat less than normal rates, in order to insure that all active material has been restored to normal condition.

The useful life of batteries may be terminated by buckling of the plates due to overcharging and overheating, with resultant short-circuiting of the plates, or through gradual wasting away of the active material, thus reducing its possible chemical activity and ultimately causing a short circuit because of collection of debris in the bottom of the cell.

156. Construction of the Edison Battery.—The Edison, or nickel-iron-alkaline, battery is of very rugged construction. The active material of the positive plate is packed in perforated tubes made of steel and secured against expansion by steel bonds, these tubes being held in place upon a metal rack. The negative plate is made up of flat steel pockets for holding the active material and is likewise held in place upon a metal rack. The plates are kept separated by means of hard-rubber insulators, and the whole assembly is bolted securely together and placed in a pressed-steel container. Since there is little opportunity for wastage of active material, very little space is allowed for collection of debris underneath the plates, and the top is sealed tight except for a small vent and filler cap.

The construction of the Edison cell (see Fig. 198) allows for very rough usage as compared with the lead cell and insures a long life. The type of construction is, comparatively, an expensive one.

The initial material in the positive tubes consists of nickel hydrate $Ni(OH)_2$, and in the negative pockets of iron oxide, Fe_2O_3, these being reduced electrolytically to NiO_2 and Fe, respectively, in preparing the plates for service. To increase the conductivity of the material in the positive tube, the tubes are heavily nickel-plated, and flake nickel is mixed with the nickel hydrate. The electrolyte is a dilute solution of potassium hydrate, KOH.

Despite its rugged construction, as compared with the lead-acid battery, the Edison battery is distinctly lighter, its weight for an equivalent capacity being only about two-thirds that of the lead-acid battery. This sometimes gives it the preference for applications where weight is a major consideration.

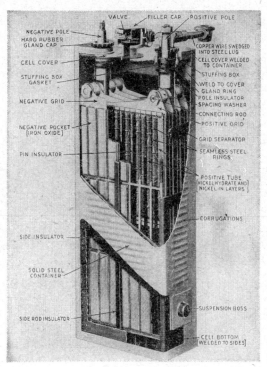

FIG. 198.—The Edison cell. (*The Edison Storage Battery Div., Thomas A. Edison, Inc.*)

157. Chemical Reactions in the Edison Cell.

—The exact chemical reactions involved in charge and discharge of the Edison cell are not thoroughly understood, and the chemical formulas representing the reactions are subject to somewhat more doubt than are those in lead-acid batteries. A considerable amount of research has been done upon the subject, and a number of equations to represent the reactions have been proposed, but general agreement has not been reached to such an extent that a single equation, representing the complete reactions, may be set down. It is agreed, however, that the over-all effects of the reactions that take place during charge and discharge are oxidation and reduction. During discharge, the nickel oxide that forms the positive active material is reduced to a lower oxide, and the metallic iron that forms the negative active material is oxidized to form an iron oxide. During

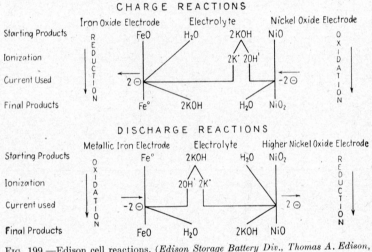

Fig. 199.—Edison cell reactions. (*Edison Storage Battery Div., Thomas A. Edison, Inc.*)

charge, reoxidation to the higher oxide of nickel and reduction of the iron oxide to metallic iron are the reactions, thus, in effect, bringing about a transfer of oxygen from positive to negative plates during discharge and from negative to positive plates during charge. These reactions do not sensibly change the density of the electrolyte, its function being that of a conductor and oxygen carrier. Since neither of the active materials is soluble in the electrolyte, no detrimental action takes place when the cell is left for extended periods in the discharged state.

The diagrams in Fig. 199 have been prepared and published by the Edison Storage Battery Company to represent the charge and discharge reactions, but authorities do not agree that they provide a complete explanation of what occurs at each of the plates.

During charge, hydrogen is liberated at the negative plate and plays a part in the operation of the battery by keeping the iron in an active state chemically. Near the end of the charging period, oxygen is also liberated, the relative amounts of hydrogen and oxygen approaching the two parts of hydrogen to one of oxygen representing electrolysis of water as the battery approaches full charge. The same precautions as with the lead-acid battery for ventilation of battery rooms and avoidance of bare flames near the battery are necessary to avoid the possibility of explosion.

The electrolyte in the Edison cell has a tendency to change its character through absorption of impurities from the air and from the water added to replace that lost through gassing and evaporation, the net result being a gradual decrease in specific gravity with use of the battery. It is recommended, therefore, that the old electrolyte be replaced occasionally by fresh solution, furnished by the manufacturer for this purpose. Since there is no harmful deposit upon the plates during discharge, there is less need for accurate information on the state of charge than with the lead-acid battery, the voltage of the battery being a sufficient indication in many cases; whereas in others an ampere-hour meter may be used to measure the amount of energy that has been taken from the battery. Storage of idle batteries is a simpler problem with the Edison battery than with the lead-acid battery, and another advantage of the Edison battery lies in its immunity to damage by freezing, regardless of its state of charge.

158. Operating Characteristics of the Edison Battery.—Typical charge and discharge voltage curves are shown in Fig. 200. These show a considerably lower discharge voltage than in the lead cell, the average value being about 1.2 volts. There is no fixed lower limit of discharge in the Edison cell, as with the lead cell, the only restriction being that imposed by the circuit to which it is connected. It is not usually advisable, however, to discharge it below 1 volt per cell.

The Edison cell has a much higher internal resistance than the lead cell, and the internal losses are correspondingly greater. For this reason, it is not well adapted to applications requiring high rates of discharge, such as are required in automobile batteries and other applications involving the cranking of gasoline or Diesel engines for starting purposes. Although this characteristic limits its field of application somewhat, there are many applications for which its other advantages give it a high or perhaps superior rating as compared with the lead-acid battery. Because of its rugged construction, with the active material held closely in place, it suffers

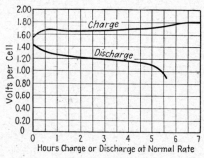

Fig. 200.—Charge and discharge voltage curves for the Edison cell.

less as a result of loss of material from the plates and consequently may be expected to have an appreciably longer useful life than the lead-acid battery. Thus the longer life expectancy may be considered to balance the greater first cost of the Edison battery, due to its more solid construction, for applications where the greater internal resistance does not work to the disadvantage of the Edison battery.

159. Battery Resistance Drop.—Since a storage battery has appreciable resistance to the flow of electric current through its electrolyte and plates, the terminal voltage will be lower when current is flowing than when the circuit is open. The open-circuit voltage is the true emf developed by the battery, but, when the circuit is closed through a resistance or other form of external circuit, a portion of the emf is used in overcoming the IR drop of the battery itself, the amount so used being proportional to the current flowing.

Data for determining the approximate resistance of a battery may be secured by first reading the terminal voltage on open circuit and then closing the circuit through a resistance and again noting the value of the terminal voltage and also reading the value of the current flowing through the circuit. The resistance drop in the battery will then be equal to the difference between the two voltage readings; and the internal resistance of the battery, or cell, may be found by dividing the resistance drop by the value of the current. Thus

$$R_b = \frac{E - V}{I} \tag{75}$$

where R_b is battery resistance, in ohms, E is open-circuit terminal volts, V is closed-circuit terminal volts, and I is the current in amperes. Battery resistance should not be considered constant for all conditions, however, since it varies appreciably with temperature and state of charge of the battery.

Example.—The terminal voltage of a battery was found to be 50 volts on open circuit and 45 volts with a current of 10 amp flowing. What is the internal resistance of the battery?

Solution:

$$E = 50 \text{ volts} \qquad V = 45 \text{ volts} \qquad I = 10 \text{ amp}$$

Therefore

$$R_b = \frac{50 - 45}{10} = \frac{5}{10} = 0.5 \text{ ohm}$$

It should be noted that, in the preceding discussion, it has been assumed that the effect of the current required by the voltmeter used in making the measurements is of negligible effect. This is not always the case, since, with small-capacity cells, the voltmeter current causes a considerable IR drop; and, for such cells, this method of determining the resistance will not yield correct results.

When discharging, the terminal voltage of a battery is appreciably less than the emf of the battery because of the IR drop. Since the IR drop varies with the current and the battery emf varies somewhat with the state of charge of the battery, the terminal voltage of the battery is likely to vary appreciably under varying load conditions. Also, in charging a battery, it is necessary to supply a *higher* voltage than the battery emf in order to cause a current to flow against the emf and to overcome the IR drop. When discharging, then, the terminal voltage is equa' to the emf of the battery *minus* the IR drop; and, during charge, the terminal voltage is equal to the emf of the battery *plus* the IR drop.

160. Temperature Effects.—Both the lead-acid and the Edison batteries are adversely affected by extremes in temperature, these effects for the lower temperatures being due to changes in the rate of diffusion of the electrolyte into the pores of the active material composing the plates. In general, the capacity in ampere-hours decreases with a decrease in temperature. The change per degree is more marked for temperatures below the standard 80°F temperature than above it. For the lead-acid battery, the capacity at 0°F is reduced to almost half its capacity at 80°F. Thus an automobile battery is doubly at a disadvantage in cold weather, first, because its capacity is markedly lowered and, second, because the starting load is much heavier by reason of stiffness of engine bearings, etc. The battery is also subject to damage by freezing if not well charged. It is therefore important for three reasons that the battery be kept well charged during the winter months.

EFFECT OF TEMPERATURE ON CAPACITY OF AUTOMOBILE BATTERIES[*]

Temperature		Proportion of Capacity Available	
° F	° C	20-hr rate (lighting ability), per cent	300 amp (cranking time), per cent
80	26	100	100
60	15	97	91
40	4	92	81
20	− 7	83	72
10	−12	74	65
0	−18	60	58

[*] From bulletin, "The Starting and Lighting Battery," by Willard Storage Battery Company.

At the other end of the temperature range, both the lead-acid and the Edison batteries are subject to damage by high temperatures. A limiting temperature of electrolyte recommended for the lead-acid battery is 110°F and for the Edison battery 115°F. Such temperatures are dependent not upon atmospheric temperatures alone but upon a combination of ambient temperature and the temperature created by the I^2R losses in the battery during charge or discharge. Such high temperatures are more likely to be created as a result of a high rate of charge, with high ambient temperature, over a considerable period of time. The remedy is, of course, to reduce the charging rate to a point at which the temperature will not be objectionably high.

Fig. 201.—High-capacity, lead-lined wood tank battery for emergency standby power supply. (*The Electric Storage Battery Company.*)

161. Care of Edison Batteries.—Since the Edison battery is not damaged by complete discharge, it may safely be discharged to the lower limit of useful voltage, usually about 1 volt per cell. It is not injured by standing idle in a partly discharged or completely discharged condition and may be short-circuited without injury. For storing it, the makers recommend that it be discharged to zero voltage and then short-circuited. Upon restoration to active service, it should be overcharged, or charged at the normal rate for a period of time in excess of the time required for a normal charge, the actual time varying with the type of cell, the temperature during such overcharge not being allowed to exceed 115°F.

The Edison battery is not damaged by freezing, and the absence of corrosive acid fumes permits it to be closely associated with delicate apparatus.

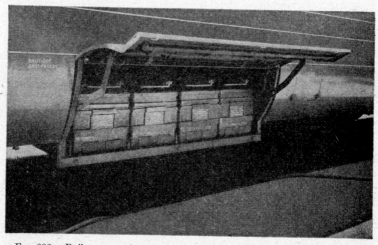

Fig. 202.—Railway car battery—for lighting and air-conditioning auxiliary power. A generator beneath the car supplies power and charges the battery when the train is in motion. (*The Electric Storage Battery Company.*)

Pure water, preferably distilled, should be added frequently to the electrolyte to replace that lost by evaporation and decomposition. During the working life of the battery, the electrolyte gradually loses in density and should be renewed when the density falls below 1.160 specific gravity. Before the old electrolyte is replaced, the battery should be discharged at its normal rate to zero voltage, then short-circuited for an hour or two. The jars may then be drained and refilled with fresh electrolyte. It should then be overcharged at its normal rate before being put back into service. Cells should not be allowed to stand empty, without electrolyte in contact with the plates.

Since there is no appreciable change in density of the electrolyte during a normal cycle of charge and discharge, specific-gravity readings are of no value in determining the state of charge of the Edison battery, their only value being to indicate when the electrolyte should be renewed. Charge and discharge are best regulated by ampere-hour meters; but, for proper use of this method, it is necessary to know the ampere-hour efficiency of the battery. It is usually necessary to add 20 to 30 per cent additional ampere-hours, over and above the ampere-hours obtained on discharge.

Voltage readings may be used to indicate the approximate state of charge if the current is under close control. Final check for full charge is failure of the voltage readings to show any change over half-hourly intervals while the charge is continued at normal rate.

Specific instructions are furnished by the manufacturers as to normal charge and discharge rates for the various types and capacities of cell. Low-rate, or trickle, charging is in general not recommended, since it is likely to cause the battery to become sluggish, requiring an overcharge to bring it back to normal activity.

162. Applications of Batteries.—There are many applications to which either the lead-acid or the Edison battery may be suited. The lead-acid battery is particularly well suited to applications where high discharge rates are required, as in automobile or other engine-starting services. The Edison battery may be preferred for applications where light weight or ruggedness and ability to stand abuse are major considerations.

Battery power is depended upon for such a wide variety of purposes that compilation of a complete list of applications would be likely to prove an impossible task. Many needs, where power demand is light, may be economically served by primary batteries —usually of the dry-cell type. For many others, however, the storage battery is the preferred source. Following are a few of the more outstanding applications:

a. As stand-by power supply for emergency lighting in theaters, hospitals, large stores, and other public buildings.

b. As a dependable, detached power supply for operating electrically controlled switches in power plants and substations.

   c. For operation of fire alarms, telephone, and telegraph systems.

   d. As a power source in commercial and industrial trucks and tractors.

Fig. 203.—Storage-battery mine locomotive. As a less spectacular, application, note also that the operator wears an electric cap-lamp, supplied by a small storage battery. (*Edison Storage Battery Div., Thomas A. Edison, Inc.*)

   e. As an auxiliary power supply for railway-car lighting and air-conditioning systems.

   f. As an auxiliary power supply for farm-lighting systems, passenger automobiles and busses, highway trucks. farm tractors, etc.

   g. As an auxiliary lighting and power supply in all types of airplanes.

   h. As a source of power for lighting and propulsion in mine and factory locomotives.

   i. As an auxiliary power source for carrying peak loads upon small power stations and for carrying the entire load when the station is too small to justify full-time operation of the generating equipment.

j. For operation of railway signals and switching equipment.

Fig. 204.—Much industrial transport and heavy lifting is done by storage battery trucks and tractors. (*Edison Storage Battery Div., Thomas A. Edison, Inc.*)

163. Regulating Equipment.—Since the voltage of a battery varies over a considerable range while discharging, it is frequently necessary to provide some means for controlling it to the end that the variation may be kept within reasonable limits, these limits being established by the requirements of the load that is supplied by the battery.

Voltage-control systems may be of the hand- or automatic-operation type. The simplest form of hand control consists of a rheostat with a sufficient number of steps, resistance being inserted when the battery is fully charged and gradually cut out as the discharge proceeds. A system of this kind may also be designed for automatic operation, as indicated in Fig. 205, where a rise in voltage relieves the pressure on the carbon block rheostat, increasing its resistance, and a drop in voltage has the opposite effect.

Example.—Determine the range of resistance values required in a rheostat for maintaining constant voltage at the terminals of a 2-kw 115-volt load, the battery consisting of 64 cells of the lead-acid type, with terminal voltage varying from 2.1 volts at full charge to 1.8 volts at the lower discharge limit.

Solution:

$$64 \times 2.1 = 134.5 \text{ volts at beginning of discharge}$$
$$64 \times 1.8 = 115 \text{ volts at end of discharge}$$
$$134.5 - 115 = 19.5 \text{ volts max drop across rheostat}$$

$$\frac{2 \times 1000}{115} = 17.4 \text{ amp load current}$$

$$\frac{19.5}{17.4} = 1.12 \text{ ohms}$$

A suitable rheostat must therefore have a resistance ranging from 1.12 ohms at beginning of discharge to 0 at end of discharge, with a current capacity of 17.4 amp.

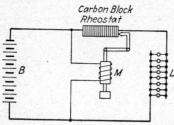

Fig. 205.—A simple form of automatic voltage regulator.

Rather elaborate voltage-control systems are used in connection with the electrical systems of railway coaches, pullmans, and dining cars in order to maintain constant voltage at the lamp terminals whether the car is stationary or in motion. The absence of such equipment would inevitably result in unsatisfactory lighting and reduced life of lamps, the voltage being appreciably higher at the battery terminals when the generator is operating and supplying current to both lamps and battery than when the generator is disconnected and the battery is supplying current to the lamps. The voltage is also affected by the number of lamps or other electrical devices that are being supplied at a given time; and, further, the voltage at the battery terminals, when under charge, varies with the state of charge and the temperature of the electrolyte. The same factors are in effect when the automobile-lighting system is being used, although it is generally somewhat less important here that constant voltage be maintained at the lamp terminals. Nevertheless a regulating system of some sort is desirable also for such applications. In short, the battery alone is seldom a satisfactory source of voltage. It must be supplemented with regulating devices of more or less elaborate design in order that the voltage regulation may be appreciably better than it would be with the battery alone or with the combination of battery and charging generator.

164. End-cell Control Systems.—The use of rheostats as a means of controlling the voltage from a battery source is objectionable in connection with the larger capacity installations because of the energy loss involved. Consequently, other systems have been developed and put into use. One such system consists of suitable switches for cutting one or more of a selected number of cells out of the circuit when the battery is well charged and into the circuit again as the discharge proceeds. In order to simplify the process of cutting cells in or out of the circuit, the group selected for this control is located on one end of the battery, hence the name end cells.

Fig. 206.—A simple form of end-cell switch.

In order that the end-cell switch may be operated without opening the circuit or short-circuiting the cells during its passage from one to the other, a form of switch similar to that in Fig. 206 must be used. The auxiliary contact C_2 serves to prevent the circuit from being opened entirely but has sufficient resistance r between it and the main contact C_1 to prevent an objectionably large current flow on short circuit. The mechanism should provide means for preventing stoppage of the switch in the short-circuit position.

Since the end cells are not so completely discharged as the main battery, they will become charged more quickly than the main group when the battery is on charge and must be cut out one by one as they become fully charged.

Operation of the end-cell controls may be by hand or automatic means. For very large battery systems, elaborate control systems are used, with motor drive for the end-cell switch.

Counter emf cells—simple cells with unformed plates—are sometimes used to absorb excess voltage at the beginning of discharge. When current flows through the cells, the main battery voltage is opposed by approximately 2.8 volts for each of the counter emf cells in series. They have the advantage over resistance control of providing a voltage drop that does not vary greatly with the current, but they represent a loss of energy to the total circuit, this waste energy resulting in considerable electrolysis action, making it necessary to add water to the cells frequently.

165. Charging Systems and Circuits.—In many installations, batteries are "floated on the line," *i.e.*, permanently connected to the system in such manner that they are being charged when the load demands are light and automatically discharged when the load grows heavy or when the ordinary power source is disconnected. In other installations, the battery is connected to the circuit when required, allowed to discharge to a certain point, then removed and recharged.

For batteries other than the "floating," or "system-governed," types, the methods of charging commonly advocated and used may be classified under the following headings:

    a. The constant-current system.

    b. The step, or taper-current, system.

    c. The constant-potential system.

    d. The modified constant-potential system.

In order to maintain a constant charging current, it is necessary that the voltage applied to the battery terminals be raised as the charging proceeds, since the back pressure from the cells rises with charge. Also, the value of charging current must be so chosen that there will not be excessive gassing at any stage of the charging period and that the temperature of the cells does not attain a value likely to prove injurious to the plates. The upper limit of safe temperature is usually considered to be 110°F for lead-acid cells and 115°F for Edison cells.

Since a discharged battery may be safely charged at a higher rate during the first portion of its charging period than during the later stages, considerable time may be gained by starting at a relatively high current value and tapering to a lower finishing value. With hand control, this may be accomplished by suitable variation of resistance in the circuit. The same result may be obtained automatically by applying a constant potential to the battery, this potential having a value calculated to result in completing the charge at relatively low current, the difference between the applied voltage and the countervoltage of the battery becoming gradually less as the charging proceeds. An objection to the use of this method lies in the fact that a slight change in the value of applied voltage may result in large variations in charging current, and it is usually considered advisable to use this system in the modified form resulting from insertion of a fixed value of resistance in series with the charging circuit. This resistance acts as a ballast to minimize the effects of variations in the supply voltage. The value of this resistance will depend upon the type and number of cells as well as the value of the supply voltage available. The same effect may be gained through the use of a separate charging generator for the battery circuit, provided that the generator has a drooping voltage characteristic. In general, automatic charging methods are to be preferred to hand-control methods.

The ampere-hour meter may be used for automatic control of the charging of a battery by using a type that runs more slowly when the battery is charging than when it is discharging, to an extent calculated to provide sufficient compensation for losses in the battery, and is provided with an electric trip for operating a circuit breaker when the required number of ampere-hours have been supplied to the battery. A reverse-current circuit breaker is a desirable accessory in any charging circuit, since it insures against discharge of the battery by reason of drops in the supply voltage or other happenings that would result in a reversal in direction of current flow.

The voltages necessary for battery charging may be obtained by three principal systems:

a. A special generator or current rectifier capable of supplying the required values of voltage without interference with other circuits.

b. A booster generator, to be operated in conjunction with a source of constant voltage, for boosting the voltage to the required values.

c. The battery may be divided into sections and the sections placed in parallel for charging from a constant voltage supply.

Example.—A certain storage battery requires 165 volts, 100 amp for charging. The available d-c supply is 125 volts. Specify the booster necessary to supply the extra voltage required. Compare this with the across-the-line motor-generator set required.

Solution:

$$165 - 125 = 40 \text{ volts additional required}$$

The booster armature must carry the 100-amp line current and raise the voltage from 125 to 165. Its rating will therefore be 4 kw, 40 volts, 100 amp.

A motor-generator set, having a generator capable of supplying 165 volts, 100 amp, and driven by a motor of corresponding rating, would require machines of approximately four times the capacity of those in the booster set.

Special high-rate chargers are frequently used to provide a quick freshening charge for automobile batteries. They do not bring the battery back to a fully charged condition but will bring it to a condition of charge that will enable it to continue in service under its usual operating condition, at least until time permits a more complete reconditioning charge to be made. Such charging equipment usually includes a constant-potential generator of high capacity, so that the initial charging rate may be as high as 100 amp. Such chargers are recommended by many battery manufacturers as a method supplementary to the slower, more thorough type of charger and are not likely to damage the battery if proper safeguards are applied to prevent the occurrence of damaging temperatures or excessive gassing. Without such safeguards, however, serious damage may be done to a battery, particularly if it is old and badly sulfated.

For complete charge of a lead-acid battery, the charge should be continued until, with a reduced charging current, all cells gas freely and the specific gravity shows no tendency toward further rise over a period of several hours of continued charging.

Problems

1. A storage cell has a rating of 360 amp-hr on the 8-hr basis. What is its normal discharge current? If its ampere-hour efficiency is 90 per cent, how many ampere-hours must be restored to the cell before it is fully charged?

2. If a uniform charging current equal to one-third its 8-hr discharge rate is maintained throughout the charging period, how many hours will be required for recharging the cell of Prob. 1?

3. Repeat Prob. 2, assuming that, for the first half of the charging period, the rate is the same as the 8-hr discharge rate and that, for the second half of the charging period, the rate is one-third this value.

4. If the average voltage on discharge of the cell referred to in Probs. 1 to 3 is 1.975 volts and the average voltage on charge is 2.2 volts, what will be the true efficiency of the cell?

5. A cell, discharged continuously at 62.5 amp, reaches its minimum permissible voltage limit in 8 hr; when discharged continuously at 250 amp, this limit is reached in 1 hr; and, if discharged continuously at 600 amp, this limit is reached in 5 min. Calculate the ampere-hour rating of the cell for each of these discharge rates, and account for the differences noted.

6. If the terminal voltage of a battery is 60 volts on open circuit and 56 volts when the circuit is closed, with 80 amp flowing, what is the internal resistance of the battery?

7. If the battery of Prob. 6 is applied to a circuit of 1.45 ohms resistance, what current will flow, and what will be the voltage at the battery terminals?

8. A battery has a resistance of 0.2 ohm. If its normal open-circuit voltage is 80, what will be its terminal voltage (a) when discharging at a 10-amp rate, (b) when discharging at a 50-amp rate, and (c) when charging at a 10-amp rate?

9. Specify the booster necessary for charging an 80-cell lead-acid battery at a maximum 25-amp rate from a 110-volt source. Include a connection diagram, with double-throw switch, for connecting the battery to the bus bars as desired for charge or discharge.

10. A small power plant has a daily load curve with the following approximate values:

7 A.M. to 5 P.M., motor load 60 hp
7 A.M. to 4 P.M., lighting load 3 kw
4 P.M. to 5 P.M., lighting load 20 kw
5 P.M. to 7 P.M., lighting load 7 kw
7 P.M. to 7 A.M., lighting load 2.5 kw

It is proposed to carry the night load by a storage battery. Specify (a) the battery required, (b) the hours for charging and the average charging current, and (c) the rheostat required for charging if the battery is to be cut in half and the two halves charged in parallel. Calculate the power loss in the rheostat. The normal station voltage is 125.

11. A garage desires provision for charging 200 lead storage cells simultaneously from a 115-volt d-c supply. The charging current is not to exceed 15 amp per cell. Specify (a) the apparatus necessary for charging if the cells are divided into four groups and (b) the apparatus necessary for charging if the cells are divided into five groups. (c) Give your conclusion, with reasons, as to the best method to use.

12. A department store requires a battery for an emergency lighting circuit totaling 3500 watts at 115 volts. Assuming a maximum usage of 1 hr, in event of trouble with the regular lighting system, specify the battery required (a) if lead-acid cells are to be used and (b) if Edison cells are to be used. (c) Suggest one or more means for charging the battery.

13. An electric switching locomotive carries an Edison battery of 120 cells, rated at 375 amp-hr, for operating its motors. The normal charge rate is 75 amp for 7 hr. Specify a suitable d-c generator for charging this battery.

14. A mining locomotive carries a lead-acid battery of 54 cells, rated at 340 amp-hr on a 6-hr basis. A source of direct current at 150 volts is available for charging. (a) Specify a suitable constant resistance for automatic charging, the finish current to be limited to 40 per cent of the normal discharge current. (b) What will be the starting current with the resistance determined in (a)? (c) What will be the approximate charging time required?

15. The voltage regulation on a 115-volt d-c feeder is found to be unsatisfactory, and tests are made that indicate that, between the hours of 4 and 10 P.M., the average load is 300 amp at 95 volts and that, for the remaining 18 hr of the day, the average load is 50 amp at 120 volts. It is proposed to install a battery that will supply 150 amp for the 6 hr of heavy load and will take such current from the line during the light-load period as will fully charge it during this period. Analyze this proposal as to its effect upon the voltage regulation, determining the voltages that will be available at the load after the battery is installed. Is the result likely to prove satisfactory? (Neglect the effect upon load currents of changes in load voltage brought about through addition of the battery.)

List of Visual Aids

The following list of visual aids may be used to supplement some of the material in this book. It is suggested that each film and filmstrip be previewed before using, since some may contain information that is too advanced while others may contain information that is too elementary.

These films and filmstrips can be obtained from the producer or distributor listed with each title. (The addresses of these producers and distributors are given at the end of this listing.) In many cases these visual materials can also be obtained from your local film library or local film distributor; many universities have large film libraries from which these films can be borrowed.

The running time (min), whether it is silent (si) or sound (sd), and whether it is a motion picture (MP) or filmstrip (FS) are listed with each title. All of the motion pictures are 16mm; filmstrips are 35mm.

Each film and filmstrip has been listed only once in connection with the chapter to which it is most applicable. However, in many cases it may be used advantageously in connection with other chapters.

The motion pictures produced by the U. S. Office of Education have coordinated silent filmstrips and instructor's manuals. In many cases, other films also have accompanying instructor's manuals.

Chapter I—Electromagnetic Induction

Induced Currents (EBF 15min si MP). Shows armatures, commutators, collector rings, mutual and self-induction.

Magnetism (GE FS). Explains concepts of magnetism and molecular theory of magnetism; the contributions of Faraday and Steinmetz to the study of the magnetic field.

Electromagnetism (JH FS). Construction and use of the electromagnet; effects of the electromagnetic field; Oersted's experiment; strength of fields; the polarity of a solenoid; the telegraph; Faraday's experiment.

Alternating Current (Army FS). An elementary introduction to principles of alternating current; demonstrates and explains Lenz's Law, simple wave alternator; discusses frequency, effective value, voltage-current time relationship, and power.

Alternating Current (JH FS). Inductance, capacitance and impedance in a circuit; transformers and rectifiers.

Chapter II—The Dynamo

Repulsion Motor Principles (USOE 18 min sd MP). Explains the construction of repulsion motor; rotor circuits and effects of brush position; short-circuiting and brush lifting mechanism; applications of repulsion motors.

Chapter III—Armature Windings

Field Coil Winding (Westinghouse 8min si MP). Shows operations of winding of motor and generator field coils for specified applications.

Multiple Field Coil Winding (Westinghouse 10min si MP). Shows winding operations in small motors and generators for five-field coils.

Stator Coil Winding by Machine (Westinghouse 8min si MP). Describes five methods of high-speed stator coil winding by machine.

Three-phase Stator Winding (Westinghouse 16min si MP). Describes three-phase motor stator winding operations.

Wound Rotor Controllers (USOE 18min sd MP). Illustrates wound rotor (slip-ring) motor principles; how a controller regulates resistance in secondary circuit; operation of face-plate controller; operation of drum-type, reversing controller; operation of automatic magnetic starter for a wound rotor motor.

Chapter IV—Commutation, Armature Reaction

Commutation of DC Machines (Westinghouse 11min sd MP). Theory and maintenance of commutation of direct-current motors and generators.

Chapter V—Operation of Generators
and
Chapter VI—Generator Characteristics

The Generator (JH FS). Principles of the generator; types; generating direct and alternating currents.

AC and DC Generators (SVE FS). Asks and answers questions about generators; shows hydroelectric plant.

Current Flashes (JH 10min sd MP). Explains the function of generator and battery.

Corebuilding Low and High Tension Winding (Westinghouse 10min si MP). Shows generator core building, low- and high-tension winding techniques; the operation of a small motor.

Current and Voltage Regulation (JH FS). Shows necessity for generator regulation; explains third-brush and external current regulation; external voltage regulation.

Chapter VII—Direct-current Motors

Motors (SVE FS). Principles of the electric motor; demonstrates parts and uses.

Electric Motors (JH FS). Principles of the motor; direct and alternating current motors; universal motors.

Principles of the Electric Motor (AMNH Slides). Magnets; electromagnets; commutator; electric motor; shunt-wound and series-wound motors; types of railway motors.

Chapter VIII—Motor Control

Across-the-line Starters (USOE 15min sd MP). Theory and operation of the manually operated thermal overload switch; the magnetically operated across-the-line starter; the drum reversing switch for a three-phase motor; the magnetic reversing switch.

Direct-current Controllers (USOE 15min sd MP). Illustrates shunt motors driving various types of equipment; direct-current controllers in operation; animation of a starting and speed-regulating direct-current faceplate controller connected to a shunt motor.

Reduced Voltage Starters (USOE 23min sd MP). Principles of the transformer; mechanical operation of the manual starting compensator; electrical operation of the manual starting compensator; operation of the thermal overload relay; mechanical and electrical operation of an automatic starting compensator.

Wound Rotor Controllers (USOE 17min sd MP). Explains wound rotor motor principles; shows the operation of a faceplate controller; drum-type nonreversing controller, drum-type reversing controller and automatic magnetic starter for a wound rotor motor.

Chapter XI—Special Types and Applications

Dynamotor Assembly and Inspection (Westinghouse 16min si MP). Detailed study of dynamotor; its assembly and inspection.

Chapter XII—Testing and Maintenance

D.C. Motor, Part 1: Mechanical Overhaul (USOE 20min sd MP). Shows how to test for electrical and mechanical faults; dismantle d-c motor; turn the commutator; repair and replace field coils; assemble the motor; adjust and make final tests.

D.C. Motor, Part 2: Rewinding (USOE 37min sd MP). Shows how to dismantle and clean an armature core; determine commutator pitch; reinsulate the core; how to insert coils; band an armature; shape coil ends; lay in and solder leads; balance the armature; impregnate the armature; turn a commutator.

Split-phase Motor: Rewinding (USOE 28min sd MP). Shows how to test a split-phase motor for electrical and mechanical faults.

Three-phase Motor, Part 1: Preparing to Rewind (USOE 17min sd PM). Shows how to interpret and record nameplate data of a three-phase motor; identify the line leads and finish leads; remove coils and determine coil span; use a coil-winding machine; and end-tape machine-wound coils.

Three-phase Motor, Part 2: Rewinding (USOE 17min sd MP). Shows how to insert mush coils; insert separators; fold, trim, and wedge slot insulation around windings; insert phase insulation; make a delta connection.

Repulsion-induction Motor: General Overhaul (USOE 25min sd MP). Shows how to check a repulsion-induction motor for electrical and mechanical faults; dismantle and assemble a repulsion-induction motor.

Chapter XIII—Batteries

Primary Cell (EBF 11min sd MP). Shows operation of dry cell in terms of electron action, including ionization of the electrolyte, polarization and depolarizer, batteries and cell in series and parallel wiring.

Chemical Effects of Electricity (EBF 15min si MP). Shows making of dry cells; storage batteries; electric batteries.

Electrochemistry (EBF 10min sd MP). Shows the chemical reactions as dynamic processes; electrolytic decomposition of hydrogen chloride; storage battery integrates both processes.

Storage Battery Power (Edison 20min si MP). Analytical study of storage batteries and the unique features of Edison's product.

The Story of a Storage Battery (USBM 30min si MP). Shows the historical development of the storage battery and the various steps in its manufacture; various ways in which battery is tested, sealed, and packed.

Electricity and the Storage Battery, Part 1 (JH FS). The most fundamental aspects of electricity; principles of simple primary and secondary cell, Ohm's law, series and parallel connections.

Electricity and the Storage Battery, Part 2 (JH FS). The storage battery of secondary cells; general construction and operation.

Sources of Films Listed Above

AMNH—American Museum of Natural History, 79th St. and Central Park West, New York 24.

Army—U. S. Army (Obtainable from Castle Films).

Castle Films Inc., 30 Rockefeller Plaza, New York 20.

EBF—Encyclopaedia Britannica Films, Inc., 20 N. Wacker Dr., Chicago 6.

Edison, Thomas A., Inc., West Orange, N. J.

GE—General Electric Co., Visual Instruction Section, 1 River Rd., Schenectady, N. Y.

JH—Jam Handy Organization, 2900 E. Grand Blvd., Detroit 11.

SVE—Society for Visual Education, 100 E. Ohio St., Chicago 11.

USBM—U. S. Bureau of Mines Experiment Station, 4800 Forbes St., Pittsburgh 13, Pa.

USOE—U. S. Office of Education (Obtainable from Castle Films Inc.).

Westinghouse Electric Corp., 306 Fourth Ave., Pittsburgh 30, Pa.

Index